Editors
Gisela Lee, M.A.
Lorin Klistoff, M.A.

Managing Editor
Karen J. Goldfluss, M.S. Ed.

Editor-in-Chief
Sharon Coan, M.S. Ed.

Cover Artist
Lee Aucoin

Art Coordinator
Denice Adorno

Imaging
James Edward Grace
Alfred Lau
Rosa C. See

Product Manager
Phil Garcia

Publishers
Rachelle Cracchiolo, M.S. Ed.
Mary Dupuy Smith, M.S. Ed.

Ages 9–11

skillbuilders

**Daily practice pages help kids build skills
in reading, writing, and math.**

Author

Mary Rosenberg

Teacher Created Materials, Inc.
6421 Industry Way
Westminster, CA 92683
www.teachercreated.com
ISBN-0-7439-8333-5
©2003 Teacher Created Materials, Inc.
Made in U.S.A.

Table of Contents

Table of Contents

Introduction

Skill Builders Ages 9-11 was designed to cover a wide range of skills your child will typically be exposed to during the school year. There are enough activity pages to provide children with a quick, fun way to practice skills frequently.

About This Book

The activity pages make excellent reinforcement exercises at home. With 300 pages from which to choose, your child is given an opportunity to review concepts and skills he or she already knows. For newly acquired skills, the pages provide additional reinforcement through practice. As pages are completed, parents and children can correct each page using the answer key on pages 305–354.

Each page has a five-box math section. Generally, there are four math problems and one word problem. To find the math topic or category your child may wish to complete, use the Table of Contents, which lists all topics and pages containing activities for that topic.

The bottom half of each page also provides your child with a language, reading, or writing opportunity. This section is an effective way for your child to quickly preview or review a skill or to provide practice with a newly acquired skill. Among the skills covered in this section are nouns, verbs, adjectives, adverbs, comma usage, homonyms, prefixes, suffixes, punctuation, pronouns, prepositions, analogies, abbreviations, spelling, and writing practices. For more specific skills and a listing of pages on which they are found, see the Table of Contents.

Although there is no specific order in which your child must complete the pages, keep in mind that the activities in this book (or within each topic or skill) begin on an easier level and become more difficult. Therefore, you should encourage your child to start with more familiar activities.

Make It Fun!

Use these helpful hints to make completion of each *Skill Builders* page fun:

- Set goals with your child, allowing him or her to choose how many activities or which pages to complete in a given time period.
- Encourage your child to verbalize how he or she chose to complete the exercises.
- Allow your child to correct his or her paper, assisting when necessary.
- Write a special note or place a sticker on pages of which your child is particularly proud.

Extras!

A reproducible award for effort or completion for some or all of the activities is provided on page 355. On page 356 you will find a multiplication table for use with some of the activity pages. A protractor template and geometric formulas chart are provided on page 357 for use with geometry activities. A metric conversion chart is provided on page 358 for reference use. On the last two pages, a writing journal cover and reproducible writing journal page have been provided so children can create their own journals as they complete the writing practice prompts at the bottoms of the activity pages.

Sets

Look at the following set of whole numbers through ten {0, 1, 2, 3, 4, 5, 6, 7, 8, 9, 10}. Using this set, list the sets below. Then solve problem 5.

1. even numbers	2. odd numbers	3. numbers divisible by 5
{ _____ }	{ _____ }	{ _____ }

4. numbers divisible by three	5. Bobbie is going to a party. He has to leave by 5:00. Before he can go, he has to finish his chores (15 min.), walk his sister to her friend's house (5 min.), get air put in his bike tire (10 min.), and finish his homework (25 min.). If he gets home from school at 3:30, how much time is left to get dressed?
{ _____ }	_____

Fact or Opinion

Write **F** if the statement is fact and **O** if the statement is opinion.

_____ 1. Piglets are cute baby pigs.

_____ 2. People may live in space someday.

_____ 3. An oyster has a shell.

_____ 4. There are aliens on Mars.

_____ 5. Libraries are fun to visit.

_____ 6. Water is necessary for humans to live.

_____ 7. Strawberries are delicious.

_____ 8. It is fun to play in the snow.

Writing Practice: Write a story using the sentence starter below.

It was so unfair . . .

Number Order

Solve the problems.

1. Write in order from least to greatest.	2. Write in order from least to greatest.	3. Write in order from greatest to least.
98,765 _____ 987.65 _____ 9,876.5 _____ 98.765 _____	104.235 _____ 10,423.5 _____ 1,042.35 _____ 10.4235 _____	989 _____ 898 _____ 999 _____ 899 _____

4. Write in order from greatest to least.	5. Noah brought 2 of most every kind of animal into the ark. If there were 189 kinds of animals, how many animals were in the ark?
2,003,005 _____ 200,300.5 _____ 20,030.05 _____ 2,003.005 _____	 _____

Interjections

Write an interjection before each sentence.

1. _____! Watch out for that car!

2. _____! That hurt!

3. _____! We won the game!

4. _____! I hate squash!

5. _____! The football team lost!

6. _____! I won the contest!

Ouch! Wow! Yuck! Stop! Yeah! Look!

Writing Practice: Write a story using the starter below.

We heard a noise and ran to the bush. There we saw . . .

Number Order

Write in order from least to greatest for problems 1–4. Then solve problem 5.

1.   13,765   13,705
     13,775   13,567
	2. 206 260
	    252 210
		3. 6,566 6,565
		     6,656 6,660

_____ , _____ ,   _____ , _____ ,   _____ , _____ ,

_____ , _____   _____ , _____   _____ , _____

4.   1,042   1,240
           1,402   1,024

_____ , _____ ,

_____ , _____

5. Margaret played basketball for the school's team. During the first six games, she scored 11 points, 8 points, 24 points, 16 points, 9 points, and 15 points. How many points did she score in all six games?

_____

Predicate (Verb)

Write the tenses of the following verbs:

	Past	Past Participle
Example: write	wrote	written
1. sing	_____	_____
2. go	_____	_____
3. blow	_____	_____
4. give	_____	_____
5. do	_____	_____

Writing Practice: Now choose one verb above and write a paragraph with all three tenses of the verb.

4 ————•————•————•————•————•————•————•————•————•————•————

Number Order and Writing Numbers

Follow the directions for each box.

1. Write in order from least to greatest. 47.03 4.037 470.3 47.30 4,730 _____ _____ _____	2. Write in order from greatest to least. 12.340 1,230 123.40 1,420 120.34 _____ _____ _____	3. Write the word name for this number. 4.037 _____ _____ _____

4. Write the word name for this number. 120.34 _____ _____ _____ _____	5. Read and solve the problem. The students in Mr. Randall's class are going on a field trip. Six parents will be driving mini-vans. How many students will be riding in each van if there are 36 students? _____

Proofreading

Circle all letters that should be capitalized and add commas and periods where they belong.

1. we went to the grocery store for butter eggs and cheese

2. i saw a big elephant at the st. louis zoo

3. i ate three pieces of sausage pepperoni and cheese pizza for lunch

4. sherry shouted "the house is on fire!"

5. when i get home i'll have to wash the dishes make up my bed and sweep the

   kitchen floor

 Writing Practice: You get to travel to a foreign country. Which country would you choose and why?

————•————•————•————•————•————•————•————•————•————•————

Number Order

Write the numbers in order from least to greatest and then solve probem 5.

1. 201,800   208,100
   202,788   202,877

   _____

   _____

   _____

   _____

2. 431,559   431.559
   4,315.59   43,155.9

   _____

   _____

   _____

   _____

3. 5,643   5,346
   5,436   5,634

   _____

   _____

   _____

   _____

4. 99,960   96,990   99,690   99,909

   _____

   _____

   _____

   _____

5. The Red Cross had a weekend blood drive. On Friday 120 people gave blood. On Saturday 191 gave blood, and on Sunday 85 people gave blood. By rounding each number to the nearest ten, estimate how many people gave blood during the weekend blood drive.

   _____

Pronouns

Read the first sentence. Write a pronoun in the second sentence that describes the first sentence.

1. Brook is my neighbor. _____ has two brothers.

2. Stephan likes to play baseball. _____ plays every week.

3. Ted and Jo made a volcano. _____ made it for science.

4. Sammy is Joella's brother. _____ is three years older than Joella.

5. The tiger is dangerous. Don't go near _____.

6. Most people don't like spiders or snakes. _____ are creepy animals.

Writing Practice: Write a paragraph describing how you feel about insects.

6

Standard Form

Write each in standard form for problems 1–4. Then solve problem 5.

1. 52 thousand 3 hundred _____	2. 4 thousand twenty-three _____	3. 1 hundred five _____
4. 4 hundred ninety-nine _____	5. There were 16 people in the gym, and seven were girls. How many were boys? _____	

Plurals

Write the plural of these nouns.

1. goose _____   4. city _____   7. cherry _____

2. ox _____   5. book _____   8. class _____

3. sheep _____   6. leaf _____

Now choose four plurals and write them in a complete sentence.

_____

_____

_____

_____

Writing Practice: Write a descriptive paragraph by finishing the story.

I was walking down the street when suddenly I saw a bright light.

Standard Form

For problems 1–2, write the standard form in expanded form. For problems 3–4, write the expanded form into standard form. Then solve problem 5.

1. 492 = _____ + _____ + _____	**2.** 1,021 = ____ + ____ + ____+ ____	**3.** 1,000 + 900 + 2 = _____
4. 20,000 + 8,000 + 300 + 10 + 9 = _____	**5.** Laurie earned $25.68 for helping clean the garage. Lewis earned $2.45 more than Laurie for also washing the car. How much money did Lewis earn? _____	

Abbreviations

Connect the titles of these names with the correct abbreviation.

Doctor	Jr.
Senator	Gov.
Governor	Dr.
Mister	Rev.
Reverend	Mr.
Junior	Sen.

 Writing Practice: Finish the sentence below. Then write a detailed description of how your costume would look. Then draw a picture of you in your costume.

On Halloween, I want to be a . . .

Writing Numbers

Write the following number words in numbers. Then solve problem 5.

1. eight million, two thousand, five hundred sixty-two	2. three million, four hundred thousand, seven hundred thirty	3. sixty-four million, four hundred twenty-one thousand, three hundred seven
_____	_____	_____

4. seventy-seven thousand, seven _____	5. We walked $\frac{1}{10}$ of a mile to see the giraffe, $\frac{2}{10}$ of a mile to see the elephants, $\frac{4}{10}$ of a mile to see the bears, and $\frac{1}{10}$ of a mile to see the tigers. How far did we walk? _____

Figurative Language

Write **L** if the statement is literal and **F** if the statement is figurative.

_____ 1. I'm so hungry I could eat a horse!

_____ 2. I'm exhausted!

_____ 3. Darkness swallowed the ghost town.

_____ 4. Boy, I'm late. Time surely does fly.

_____ 5. The flower floated on the water.

_____ 6. His eyes burned with fire.

 Writing Practice: Write a descriptive paragraph about spending the day at the zoo.

Writing Numbers

For problems 1 and 2, write the words in numbers. For problems 3 and 4, write the numbers in words. Then solve problem 5.

1. six million, one hundred four thousand, two hundred fifty-five _____	2. two hundred seventy-two thousand, six hundred ninety _____	3. 13,765 _____ _____ _____ _____
4. 1,206,400 _____ _____ _____		5. You and three friends are buying a present for your teacher and will need to pay equal amounts. The total is $20.44. How much will each pay? _____

Story Comprehension

Answer the questions about the story.

Amelia Earhart is known for being the first woman pilot to fly across the Atlantic Ocean. She made this famous flight in 1932. She received an award after this famous flight. The award was the Distinguished Flying Cross, and she was the first woman to have received the award. In 1937, she began a flight that would take her around the world. Her plane disappeared over the Pacific Ocean, and to this day, no one knows what happened to her.

1. What did Amelia Earhart do in 1932? _____

2. Name the award she received? _____

3. What did Amelia Earhart attempt to do in 1937?_____

4. How did she die? _____

Writing Practice: Write what you think the differences are in planes during Amelia Earhart's day and the jets that are used today.

Place Value

Look at the number **3,458**. Answer the questions about place value. Then solve number 5.

1. What place is the 5 in?	2. What place is the 3 in?	3. What place is the 4 in?
3,458	**3,458**	**3,458**
_____	_____	_____

4. What is the number value of the 5?	5. Joe had 32 marbles and gave Anita and Kim 8 each. How many did he have for himself?
3,458	
_____	_____

Predicate

Underline the predicate in each sentence.

1. The baseball team played on Saturday.

2. The students sang songs in choir.

3. Stars flicker and sparkle in the sky.

4. My favorite food is tacos.

5. Kim had to stay after school to finish her class work.

Writing Practice: Write a paragraph with the following beginning phrase.

People like me because . . .

Place Value

For problems 1–2, write the numeral in word form. For problems 3–4, write the numbers in the boxes. Then solve problem 5.

1. 305 _____ _____ _____	2. 2,295 _____ _____ _____	3. two hundred six ⬚⬚
4. eight thousand, one hundred forty-four ⬚⬚⬚	5. Mrs. Green and Ms. Ward bought school supplies for $13.42. If they paid with $20.00, what would their change be? _____	

Pronouns

Circle all pronouns in each sentence.

1. They asked if their teacher could give them some help.

2. The dog ate her hot dog after she dropped it on the floor.

3. Shoes were found in my locker, and they weren't mine.

4. My family likes to go shopping with our cousin.

5. We weren't sure if the present belonged to her.

Writing Practice: Write a paragraph about the best birthday party you ever had.

Place Value

For problems 1–4, find what number value is represented by the **7**. Then solve problem 5.

1. 76 _____	2. 927 _____	3. 7,253 _____

4. 6,745 _____	5. Sherwon had 38 baseball cards. He gave 10 to Antwone. How many cards does Sherwon have left? _____

Sentence Fragments

Finish each fragment to make complete sentences.

1. Jose came to_____.

2. Watch out for_____.

3. _____ finished the race.

4. _____ comes down the road.

5. An ugly bug_____.

6. _____ is pink with green stripes.

 Writing Practice: During holidays students get some extra days off from school. Write a paragraph about things you will do on your days off from school.

Place Value

Fill in the blanks. Then solve problem 5.

1. In the number 3,745, the digit in the hundreds place is _____.	2. In the number 3,745, the digit in the thousands place is _____.	3. In the number 583,564, the number value of the 8 is _____.
4. In the number 583,564, the number value of the 6 is _____.	5. Sherrie had 12 pairs of earrings. Her sister borrowed 3 pairs. How many pairs of earrings did she have left? _____	

Nouns

Circle all nouns in the following paragraph.

Thanksgiving

Thanksgiving is an American holiday. It is observed on the fourth Thursday in November. It all began many years ago when the Indians helped the Pilgrims who had come to America. The Indians helped them plant crops and showed them how to survive in their new land. They cele-brated by eating a feast together. This is how Thanksgiving began.

 Writing Practice: Write a paragraph using the starting sentence below.

If I were an animal, I would be . . .

Place Value

Look at the number **976,423** and answer the questions. Then solve problem 5.

1. What is the place value of 4?	2. What is the place value of 3?	3. What is the number value of 6?
976,423	**976,423**	**976,423**
_____	_____	_____

4. What is the number value of 2?	5. Frankie talked on the phone for 20 minutes. Jerry talked on the phone for $\frac{1}{2}$ of the time. How many minutes did Jerry talk on the phone?
976,423	
_____	_____

Commas

Write a **C** for correct or a **N** for not correct beside each sentence.

_____ 1. Lindsay turn off your, CD player.

_____ 2. "I like to play my video games," said Patrick.

_____ 3. How old are you, Laura?

_____ 4. Robert lives in Knoxville Tennessee.

_____ 5. Joey said "Kevin you are a good bowler."

_____ 6. Kimberly's cousins are Megan, Christen, and Katie.

_____ 7. "Before we eat, Stephen, you need to set the table," said Jenny.

_____ 8. Stephanie have you helped your sister Suzanne?

Writing Practice: Finish the statement below and write a paragraph on what makes you happy.

Happiness is . . .

Place Value

Circle the answer to each problem. Then solve problem 5.

1. Which number is five thousand, seven hundred eighty-six? a. 5,786 c. 50,768 b. 5,768 d. 50,786	2. Which is the number for ten thousand, five? a. 10,050 c. 10,005 b. 1,050 d. 1,005	3. Which number is 900 + 9? a. 9,909 c. 909 b. 9,009 d. 990
4. Which number is 20,000 + 5,000 + 70 + 3? a. 25,703 c. 20,573 b. 25,073 d. 25,730	5. Earth orbits the sun once in 365 days. How long would it take Earth to orbit the sun 25 times? _____	

Punctuation

Choose the correct punctuation mark (. ? !) for each sentence.

1. Do not pick the daisies____

2. Where are the shovels____

3. Can you hear the woodpecker____

4. Ouch, these thorns are very sharp____

5. She is planting seeds____

6. What a beautiful day to work in the garden____

Writing Practice: Write a paragraph about what you like or dislike about the month of November.

Place Value

For problems 1–4, name the place value in the following number: 1,876,321.
Then solve problem 5.

1. What is the place value of the 7? **1,876,321** _____	2. What is the place value of the 6? **1,876,321** _____	3. What is the place value of the 3? **1,876,321** _____
4. What is the place value of the 8? **1,876,321** _____	5. If three students paid $2.35 each for lunch and four students each paid $1.85 for lunch, how much did all the lunches cost? _____	

Prepositions

Fill in the blanks with a preposition from the box below. Use each word only once.

toward	before	to	into
with	down	around	from

1. I walked to school _____ my sister.

2. We went _____ the corner and _____ the street.

3. As we walked _____ the school, the bell rang.

4. My teacher walked _____ me and said, "Get a note _____ the office."

5. They gave me a note, and I went _____ my class _____ the second bell.

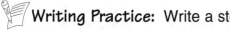 **Writing Practice:** Write a story using the sentence starter below.

The whole school could hear Matilda screaming . . .

Place Value

For problems 1–2, write the numbers in the boxes. For problems 3–4, write the numeral in word form. Then solve problem 5.

1. fifteen thousand, seventy-two	2. three hundred thirty thousand, one hundred two	3. 888

1. ☐☐ , ☐☐☐

2. ☐☐☐ , ☐☐☐

3. _____

_____

_____

4. 4.236

_____

_____

_____

5. Using the number of boys and girls in your class, write a number sentence showing how many students are in your class.

_____

Sentences

Rewrite the paragraph with complete sentences. Remember to add correct end marks and capital letters.

> During school today we had a test the test was in social studies we had to write the capital of each state I got two answers wrong the capital of Missouri is Jefferson City, not St. Louis, the capital of California is Sacramento, not Los Angeles.

_____

_____

_____

_____

 Writing Practice: Pretend you are a meteorologist for a television station. Write a weather forecast for the news by how it looks outside today.

18

Place Value

Answer the questions.

1. Write 3,456,100 in expanded form. _____ _____ _____	2. Write 672,008 in expanded form. _____ _____ _____	3. Write 20,000 + 8,000 + 300 + 9 in standard form. _____
4. Write 4,000,000 + 100,000 + 20,000 + 9,000 + 80 + 1 in standard form. _____	5. Teresa bought a cheeseburger for $1.50, French fries for $0.50, and a soda for $0.75. How much did she pay for her meal? _____	

Comprehension

Answer questions about the following facts.

Facts About Fish
• All fish live in water.　• Some are catfish.　• All fish are cold-blooded. • Most fish have scales.　• Some fish live in fresh water.　• Some fish live in salt water.

1. Is it true that all fish live in fresh water?_____

2. Is it true that all fish have scales? _____

3. Is it true that all catfish live in water? _____

4. Is it true that catfish are cold-blooded? _____

 Writing Practice: Write a paragraph using the sentence starter below.

Being a part of a family means . . .

Place Value

Write each number in standard form and then solve problem 5.

1. one thousand, four hundred three _____	2. two hundred thirty-seven thousand, nine hundred seventy _____	3. 2 thousands, 2 hundreds, 2 ones _____
4. 80 thousands, 9 hundreds, 1 ten, 8 ones _____	5. Kasey bought a present for her mother. She gave the cashier 4 tens and 7 ones. How much did it cost if she had the exact amount? _____	

Verbs

Write the correct form of the verb *see* in each sentence.

1. I looked out the window and _____ snow falling.

2. I hope I _____ _____ snow tomorrow.

3. Hey, I _____ the sun shining!

4. Last winter we _____ snow at Christmas time.

5. Maybe next winter we _____ _____ snow again.

 Writing Practice: Write a persuasive paragraph describing why everyone should like milk.

20

Place Value

Circle the correct place value of the underlined and boldfaced number. Then solve problem 5.

1. 2**5**,640 thousands tens ones	2. **2**,117,470 millions hundreds tens	3. 10,0**1**2 ten thousands tens ones
4. 936,**4**15 hundred thousands ten thousands hundreds	5. At the season's opening game, 34,523 people were present. The stadium held 45,000 people. How many empty seats were there? _____	

Main Idea

Write a category for each group.

1. lettuce   alien

   grass   emerald

   category _____

3. clock   telephone

   math book   keyboard

   category _____

2. carrot   scarf

   coal   sticks

   category _____

4. bowling ball   button

   cherry   moon

   category _____

 Writing Practice: Choose a list from above and write a paragraph.

Place Value

Write the correct value for the underlined, boldfaced number. Then solve problem 5.

1. 23,851,049.7**6** _____	2. **2**3,851,049.76 _____	3. 23,851,**0**49.76 _____

4. 23,**8**51,049.76 _____	5. Kyle loves bubble gum. He chews about 3 pieces a week. Estimate how many pieces of gum he'd chew in one month. How about in one year? month _____ year _____

Point of View

Write **F** for first person or **T** for third person.

_____ 1. We knew it was going to rain.

_____ 2. I said, "Go with me."

_____ 3. He replied, "Not today."

_____ 4. Their dog is a cocker spaniel.

_____ 5. Sue wondered if Cassie was sick.

_____ 6. My grandpa and I went fishing.

Writing Practice: What is your favorite cartoon on TV or in the comics section in your newspaper? Why?

Equivalent Numbers

For problems 1–4, write <, >, or = in the circle. Then solve problem 5.

1. 43 ◯ 63	2. 260 ◯ 206	3. 251 ◯ 215

4. 110 ◯ 101	5. Kayla brought 10 cookies for lunch. She shared 3 each with Shannon and Alyieh. How many cookies did Kayla end up eating? _____

Abbreviations

Match these street names with the correct abbreviation.

Avenue	Blvd.
Street	Cir.
Boulevard	Ave.
Drive	Hwy.
Circle	Dr.
Highway	St.

Writing Practice: Finish the sentence below and then write a paragraph telling what you really enjoy doing.

What I really enjoy doing is . . .

Equivalent Numbers

Fill in the blanks with <, >, or =. Be careful and follow each sign. Then solve problem 5.

1. 35 + 29 ◯ 42 + 21	2. 10 + (8 + 12) ◯ 45 – 10	3. 28 + 7 ◯ 7 x 5

4.

(20 + 3) + 12 ◯ 20 + (3 + 12)

5. A box holds 6 pencils. How many boxes are needed to hold 72 pencils?

_____

Homonyms

Circle the correct word in each sentence.

1. We bought a (fir, fur) tree for our Christmas tree.
2. She carried a (pail, pale) of water to wash her car.
3. May we have (some, sum) soda with our pizza?
4. They played volleyball on the (beech, beach).
5. Mr. Jones (tied, tide) the knot in the rope.
6. My sister asked for a (peace, piece) of my birthday cake.
7. The (led, lead) in my pencil just broke.
8. Have you (seen, scene) the new television show?
9. What did Joann give you (four, for) your birthday?
10. I think Joshua ate (to, too, two) much candy.

 Writing Practice: Think about something you've been studying in science. Write a paragraph about what you've learned.

Equivalent Numbers

Write < or > between each number for problems 1–4. Then solve problem 5.

1.

15,767 ◯ 157.67

2.

2,075 ◯ 20.75

3.

176.7 ◯ 1,767

4.

30,972 ◯ 309,720

5. Using the chart below, imagine that you have $8.00 to spend. List what you would buy. Make sure you have not spent more than $8.00.

SALE

Dolls $2.52 _____
Puzzles $1.25 _____
Books $1.75 _____
Cars $1.58 _____
Wagons $4.50 _____

Handwriting

Copy the poem below in your best cursive handwriting.

I Do Love Math

I do love math,

I think it is fun.

I like to do problems

And get them done.

When I do math,

I feel so good.

I do so well,

I think you could.

_____
                                    (title)
_____

_____

_____

_____

_____

_____

_____

_____

 Writing Practice: Who or what makes you laugh? Explain this person or thing in a paragraph, and tell why you laugh.

Comparing Numbers

Write < or > for each pair of numbers. Then solve problem 5.

1. 345 thousand ◯ 354,000	2. 12,878 ◯ 12,787	3. 49 billion ◯ 490,000,000

4. 62,357 ◯ 62,375	5. Todd ran in a 50-mile race. His first stop was 15 miles. His second stop was 10 miles before the end of the race. How many miles did he travel between both stops? _____

Plurals

Write the plural of these animals.

1. pony   _____

2. dog   _____

3. ox   _____

4. cow   _____

5. deer   _____

6. buffalo   _____

7. sheep   _____

8. fish   _____

 Writing Practice: In your opinion, what traits make a good friend? Write a descriptive paragraph.

Comparing Numbers

Which number is greater, **A** or **B**? Circle the correct answer. Then solve problem 5.

1. A. 625,834,222 B. 624,843,222	2. A. 354,827 B. 354,287	3. A. 9,268,925 B. 9,269,625
4. A. 800,000 x 3 B. 300,000 x 7	5. A toy company made 1,000,000 dolls in one year. They also made 10 times as many stuffed animals as dolls. How many stuffed animals did they make? _____	

Punctuation

Rewrite each sentence with correct capital letters and punctuation marks.

1. your letter is in the mail   _____

2. please do your homework tom   _____

3. i bought a hamburger at Mcdonald's _____

4. what a great game it was   _____

5. when will we go on our field trip   _____

6. the 4-h club meets every tuesday   _____

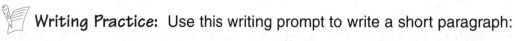 **Writing Practice:** Use this writing prompt to write a short paragraph:

Our school picnic was so much fun until . . .

Comparing Numbers

For problems 1–4, circle the correct answer (or answers). Then solve problem 5.

1. Which number is greater than 442,823?	2. Which number is less than 30,000?	3. Which number is between 195,000 and 305,000?
439,203 21,982 42,187 219,823 30,001 453,000 328,445 45,300	439,203 21,982 42,187 219,823 30,001 453,000 328,445 45,300	439,203 21,982 42,187 219,823 30,001 453,000 328,445 45,300

4. Which number is greater than 32,000 but lower than 54,850?	5. Manny has to read 91 pages in his novel before next week. How many pages must he read every day for 7 days to get it all read?
439,203 21,982 42,187 219,823 30,001 453,000 328,445 45,300	 _____

Verbs

Choose between *come* and *came*. Write the correct word in the space provided.

1. Yesterday, the rain _____ after the sunshine.

2. The sunshine had _____ and gone.

3. The mailman had _____ before noon yesterday.

4. He _____ after 1:00 P.M. today.

5. My brother _____ home late last night.

6. Have you _____ over to work on homework?

 Writing Practice: Everyone likes to get gifts, but how about giving them? What gift would you like to give someone? Write a paragraph describing your idea.

Comparing Numbers

Add <, >, or = between each pair of numbers. Then solve problem 5.

1. 45,697 ◯ 46,597	**2.** 1,520,019 ◯ 1,519,020	**3.** 43 hundreds ◯ 430 tens

4.

710 hundreds ◯ 71 thousands

5. Victor can run 3 miles in 32 minutes. Maurice can run it in 1,950 seconds. Who runs it faster and by how much?

Who runs faster? _____

By how much? _____

Abbreviations

Write each abbreviation.

1. number   _____

2. company   _____

3. postscript   _____

4. mountain   _____

5. ounce   _____

6. square   _____

7. Junior   _____

8. afternoon   _____

9. minute   _____

10. gallon   _____

Writing Practice: Invent a new type of currency or form of money. Describe how it is to be used and what it looks like, and what it is made of.

Rounding

Round to the nearest 10. Then solve problem 5.

1. 42 _____	2. 78 _____	3. 55 _____
4. 186 _____	5. Daniel saw 16 trees, 12 bushes, 23 flowers, and 2 lizards on his walk in the woods. How many items did Daniel see? _____	

Compound Words

Find these compound words in the puzzle.

backyard

lipstick

somebody

bookmark

mailbox

toothbrush

friendship

sailboat

f	k	m	c	g	f	z	r	s	t
d	r	a	y	k	c	a	b	o	a
m	a	i	l	b	o	x	o	m	o
t	m	l	e	c	t	t	i	e	b
n	k	z	i	n	h	d	n	b	l
i	o	t	r	b	d	s	k	o	i
s	o	u	r	x	g	s	h	d	a
g	b	u	c	i	v	s	h	y	s
h	s	r	g	c	k	s	k	i	p
h	k	c	i	t	s	p	i	l	p

 Writing Practice: Practice your letter writing skills. Write a letter to your teacher.

Rounding

Round to the nearest 10 for problems 1–4. Then solve number 5.

1. 26	2. 79	3. 452
4. 1,658	5. Ellen made an 89, 92, 97, 88, and 100 on her spelling tests. What is her average of all 5 grades?	

Adjectives

Choose the correct adjective in each sentence.

1. That is the (badest, worst) accident I've ever seen.

2. She is the (goodest, best) student in the class.

3. Marty has the (silliest, sillyest) sense of humor.

4. Who is (smartest, smarter), Joanna or Ellen?

5. Which sister is (shorter, shortest), Joy or Jill?

6. I have the (higher, highest) grades in my math class.

7. Max is (funnier, funniest) than his brother Malcolm.

8. We should be (carefuller, more careful) when playing close to the street.

 Writing Practice: Finish this story.

Joan wanted to give her mom a present, but she didn't have any money. So she decided to . . .

Rounding

For problems 1–4, round each number to the nearest ten. Then solve problem 5.

1.	2.	3.
123 = _____	565 = _____	791 = _____

4.	5. A long distance phone call costs $0.25 the first 3 minutes and $0.40 for any additional minutes. How much would it cost for a 10-minute phone call?
637 = _____	_____

Plurals

Circle the correct plural.

1. **bridge**   a. bridges   b. bridgies

2. **boss**   a. boss's   b. bosses

3. **speech**   a. speechs   b. speeches

4. **chicken**   a. chickens   b. chickenes

5. **box**   a. boxs   b. boxes

6. **kiss**   a. kiss's   b. kisses

7. **bush**   a. bushses   b. bushes

8. **tomato**   a. tomatos   b. tomatoes

 Writing Practice: An igloo is a house made of blocks of snow. Write what you would like your house to be made of and why.

Rounding

Round to the nearest 100. Then solve problem 5.

1. 864 _____	2. 729 _____	3. 671 _____
4. 5,329 _____	5. Greta is 6 years younger than her brother. Her brother is 13. How old is Greta? _____	

Contractions

Circle the correct contraction for each sentence.

1. We (won't, willn't) arrive at school late.

2. The food (wasn't, was'nt) cooked properly.

3. They (hav'nt, haven't) done their chores this week.

4. (I'ave, I've) seen a meteor fall from the sky.

5. It looks like (it's, its') going to rain.

 Writing Practice: Write about your favorite foods. What are they, and why do you like them? Then draw a picture of them.

Rounding

Round to the nearest hundred. Then solve problem 5.

1. 123 _____	2. 789 _____	3. 2,713 _____

4. 22,503 _____

5. Count the number of students in your classroom. Add 10 to the total. Then multiply by 2. Subtract the number of students in your room. What number did you end up with? _____ What would you have to do next to get the number you started with?

_____

_____

Plurals

Circle the correct plural form.

1. woman
   (womans, women, womens)

2. child
   (childs, child's, children)

3. box
   (boxes, boxs, box's)

4. deer
   (deers, deer's, deer)

5. city
   (citys, cities, cityes)

6. brush
   (brushs, brushes, brushses)

 Writing Practice: Explain in a paragraph why you would or would not like to get married someday.

Rounding

Round to the place value that is underlined. Then solve number 5.

1. 6,<u>7</u>89 _____	2. 5,3<u>2</u>9 _____	3. 9<u>8</u>2 _____
4. 2<u>3</u>,087 _____	5. Roberto lives 134 miles from the nearest mountain. Round this distance to the nearest 10 miles. _____	

Suffixes

Underline each word that contains a suffix.

comfortable	foolish	uncover
unwrap	prepaid	teacher
argument	singer	election
laziness	finalist	jumping
prearrange	careless	beautiful

Writing Practice: Write a story about the wildest dream you've ever had.

Rounding

Round to the nearest place. Then solve problem 5.

1. tens place 176 = _____	2. hundreds place 349 = _____	3. ones place $3.69 = _____
4. thousands place 8,764 = _____	5. Jeff needs 15 quarts of potting soil. He can only find 4-quart bags. How many 4-quart bags will he need? _____ How much will not be used? _____	

Predicate (Verb)

Fill in the blank with the correct tense of *run*.

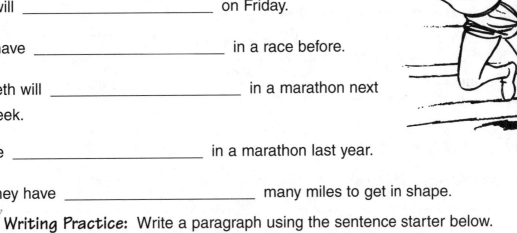

1. I _____ yesterday.

2. I will _____ on Friday.

3. I have _____ in a race before.

4. Seth will _____ in a marathon next week.

5. He _____ in a marathon last year.

6. They have _____ many miles to get in shape.

Writing Practice: Write a paragraph using the sentence starter below.

If I could plan my own day at school, I would . . .

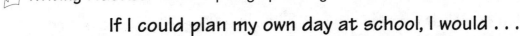

Rounding

For problems 1–4, round **428,146** to the nearest value shown. Then solve problem 5.

1. nearest hundred	2. nearest thousand	3. nearest ten
_____	_____	_____

4. nearest hundred thousand	5. The population of a southern city was 61,822. What rounded number would be used if a brochure about the city was printed?
_____	_____

Subjects

Circle the simple subject in each sentence.

1. Only Lena had her homework.

2. Ivan said, "That homework was difficult."

3. The sick children stayed home from school.

4. You play the piano well.

5. Our uncle came to visit us.

6. Can we play a game of jacks?

 Writing Practice: Describe your favorite television show.

Rounding

Solve the problems below.

1. Round 71,845 to the nearest hundred. _____	2. Round 459,056 to the nearest ten. _____	3. Round 6,752,653 to the nearest million. _____
4. Round 495, 056 to the nearest hundred thousand. _____	5. Mr. Paul bought 20 assignment books for his classroom. They cost $0.49 each. Can he pay for them with a $10 bill? How do you know? Write a number sentence to show the answer. _____	

Clauses

Underline the clause in each sentence.

1. While Toby waited for the school bus, he read a book.

2. The baby yawned when she was ready for a nap.

3. We will have P. E. outside unless it rains today.

4. Until the clock strikes noon, we will work on science.

5. He received a good grade on his test although he missed three problems.

Writing Practice: Write a paragraph about how you could be famous one day.

Rounding

Round to the nearest hundred and thousand and then solve problem 5.

1. 23,329 hundred: _____ thousand: _____	2. 3,574 hundred: _____ thousand: _____	3. 4,725,210 hundred: _____ thousand: _____
4. 165,372 hundred: _____ thousand: _____	5. Andy's family drove a total of 1,793 miles during their two-week vacation. About how many miles did they travel each day? _____	

Alphabetical Order

Write the names of these Civil Rights leaders in alphabetical order by last name.

Martin Luther King, Jr.   _____

Mary McCloud Bethune   _____

Harriet Tubman   _____

Rosa Parks   _____

A. Philip Randolph   _____

Thurgood Marshall   _____

Oliver Brown   _____

Frederick Douglass   _____

Jesse Jackson   _____

Sojourner Truth   _____

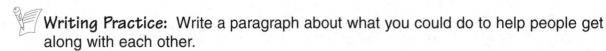

Writing Practice: Write a paragraph about what you could do to help people get along with each other.

Rounding

Round each number to the nearest thousand. Then solve problem 5.

1. 703 _____	2. 28,619 _____	3. 14,005,221 _____

4. 340,530 _____	5. Irene made a 97, 73, 82, and 91 on her tests in biology. How much higher was her best score than her lowest? _____

Sentences

Rewrite these fragments as complete sentences.

1. burning leaves

_____

2. ran to the door

_____

3. caught in the escalator

_____

4. the famous man

_____

5. a noise outside

_____

6. with his homework

 Writing Practice: April 1 is April Fool's Day. Describe a time when someone really fooled you.

Rounding

Choose the correctly rounded number. Then solve problem 5.

1.	2.	3.
2,631 to nearest 10 a. 2,630 b. 2,600	27,982,703 to nearest million a. 27,000,000 b. 28,000,000	$15.45 to nearest dollar a. $16.00 b. $15.00

4.	5.
4,103,067 to nearest thousand a. 4,100,000 b. 4,103,000	5. Andrew's mother bought groceries for a party. Estimate how much she spent if she bought the following: chips $1.69, soda $1.09, cookies $2.39, and cupcakes $3.89. _____

Author's Purpose

Using the choices from the box below, select the author's purpose.

_____ 1. The most common last name is Smith.

_____ 2. He ran the last part of his race crying with pain, yet he still finished.

_____ 3. There will be new rules for the cafeteria!

_____ 4. Buy "Super X Cereal" and start your day out right!

_____ 5. The blue whale is the largest of all whales.

_____ 6. But Wilbur said, "I don't want to die. Save me Charlotte!"

a. give information   b. persuade   c. entertain   d. arouse emotions

Writing Practice: Who do you think was the most important person in history? Why?

Rounding

Round each number and then solve problem 5.

1. Round 459,056 to the nearest hundred thousand.	2. Round 71,845 to the nearest ten thousand.	3. Round 6,572,653 to the nearest hundred.
4. Round 4,867,890 to the nearest million.	5. Pablo drove 521 miles in two days. He drove 67 more miles the first day than on the second day. How many miles did he drive on the second day?	

Fact or Opinion

Write *fact* or *opinion* beside each statement.

_____ 1. My school has 22 teachers.

_____ 2. My teacher is the best in the school.

_____ 3. There are 27 students in my class.

_____ 4. Our gym is larger than any classroom.

_____ 5. Our basketball team has the coolest uniforms.

_____ 6. The team's record is 11–3.

Writing Practice: Write a short story with the title:

A Terrific Day

Estimation

Estimate by rounding, then write your estimated sum or difference. Then solve problem 5.

1. Round to the nearest hundred. 123 + 456	2. Round to the nearest hundred. 798 − 144	3. Round to the nearest thousand. 6,198 + 2,781
4. Round to the nearest thousand. 5,110 − 1,529	5. If Caleb read 12 pages on Monday, 56 pages on Tuesday, and 9 pages on Wednesday, how many pages did he read in all? _____	

Adverbs

Fill in the blank with the correct adverb.

1. He walked _____ to the car.

2. We have to get up early _____.

3. The team _____ ran around the field.

4. My sister sings _____.

5. His friend is _____ considerate of others.

tomorrow
beautifully
slowly
quickly
very

Writing Practice: You've won a contest and you are on your way to the moon. Write a paragraph about your adventures.

Estimation

Do not work each problem. Estimate the answers. Write it in the blank. Then solve problem 5.

1. Estimate to the nearest hundred. 436 + 157 _____	2. Estimate to the nearest hundred. 713 − 324 _____	3. Estimate to the nearest ten. 29 x 65 _____
4. Estimate to the nearest ten. 24) 442 _____	5. Daphne had 75 tulip bulbs to plant. She planted 5 bulbs in a row. How many rows did she plant? _____	

Kind of Sentences

Fill in the blanks with the words: *declarative, interrogative, imperative,* or *exclamatory.*

1. Have you ever been on a farm? _____

2. You get to see all kinds of animals on a farm. _____

3. "I like pigs the best," said Leeann. _____

4. Don't step in the mud. _____

5. What a beautiful countryside! _____

6. Did you know that people work hard on a farm? _____

7. They grow many fruits and vegetables that we eat. _____

8. "I love fresh corn!" exclaimed Markel. _____

9. "Don't make a pig out of yourself," said Markel's mother. _____

10. May we come back and visit again? _____

 Writing Practice: Write a persuasive paragraph to convince your teacher that you are serious about school.

Estimation

Estimate each answer.

1. About how much more money would you need to buy a sweater that cost $29.95 if you have $15.00? _____	2. You want to buy paper and 2 pencils for $1.89 and you have $5.00. About how much would your change be? _____	3. What is the estimated total of students in your class if there are 18 girls and 13 boys? _____
4. How many movie tickets could you buy with a ten dollar bill if each ticket cost $4.00? _____	5. Sue bought 10 stamps that cost 32¢ each. Estimate how much she paid for her stamps. _____	

Punctuation

Add punctuation marks where needed in the following paragraph.

My mother took me to a picnic on Memorial Day
There were so many people there so we had to
park far away We ate the following foods hot
dogs hamburgers potato salad and baked beans
Then it started to rain so we had to go home

 Writing Practice: What do you think life would be like if people were invisible?

Estimation

For problems 1–4, choose which answer is closest to what you have estimated. Then solve problem 5.

1. How many bites does it take to eat a banana?	2. How much does your book bag weigh?	3. How many students are in your grade?
a. 10 b. 20 c. 30	a. 10 lbs. b. 20 lbs. c. 30 lbs.	a. 50 b. 100 c. 150

4. How tall is your math teacher?	5. Cleo bought lunch at the mall. She had $13.00 in her purse. If a sandwich cost $4.00, a soda cost $1.50, and a piece of cake cost $2.00, how much change will she receive?
a. 5 ft. b. 6 ft. c. 7 ft.	_____

Prepositions

Circle the prepositions in each sentence.

1. The blanket is laying over the chair.

2. The pencil is under the oak stool.

3. Please get me the cleaner above the shelf.

4. Maggie is sitting beside David.

5. Place the napkins on the table.

6. The dog went under the ball.

7. We live by the noisiest street.

8. The glass cleaner is below the laundry soap.

 Writing Practice: Sometimes pets act like members of the family. Do you have a pet like that? If you do, write about how your pet acts. If you don't have a pet, write a story about a pet.

Estimation

Estimate each answer.

1. $769 \rightarrow$ $+ 4{,}364 \rightarrow$	2. $691 \rightarrow$ $+ 189 \rightarrow$	3. $345 \rightarrow$ $+ 707 \rightarrow$
4. $6927 \rightarrow$ $+ 18{,}350 \rightarrow$	5. $25{,}467 \rightarrow$ $+ 8{,}649 \rightarrow$	

Subject

Write a subject part for each sentence.

1. _____ were going to watch television.

2. _____ was hard to do.

3. _____ had been reading their books.

4. _____ is painting a picture.

5. _____ uses a blue ink pen.

6. _____ likes to swim.

Writing Practice: Use this writing prompt to write a short paragraph:

We went to the circus to watch the lions and tigers. Suddenly, things got out of hand...

Estimation

Estimate by rounding to the nearest thousand. Then solve problem 5.

1.	2.	3.
12,378 – 9,629 est. _____	4,862 – 2,153 est. _____	34,692 – 18,023 est. _____

5.	5. In 1840, 458 patents were given to inventors, but 4 years earlier only 103 were given. How many more were given in 1840 than in 1836?
6,823 + 8,346 est. _____	_____

Clauses

Underline the dependent clause in each sentence.

1. When he was a young boy, he moved to Wyoming.

2. Until baseball season is here, Joshua plays basketball.

3. He watched quietly as the paramedic helped his brother.

4. Because their car broke down, he had to walk to school.

5. I waited for an hour before the bus came.

6. I jumped back when the door slowly opened.

 Writing Practice: Imagine that you are an astronomer and discover a new planet. Describe what the physical features of the planet are and what life on it is like.

Addition

Write corresponding numbers to the alphabet under each letter. (Example: A = 1, B = 2, C = 3, etc.) Add up the numbers in these words. Then solve problem 5.

1. paper	2. glue	3. pencil
4. notebook	5. Which word added up was the largest number?	

Following Directions

Follow the steps. Begin by putting your pencil on the center square. Circle each letter you stop at. Write it in the space provided.

1. Go 1 block West
2. Go 2 blocks North
3. Go 3 blocks East
4. Go 4 blocks South
5. Go 1 block West
6. Go 4 blocks North
7. Go 1 block West

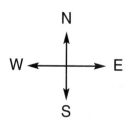

E	R	S	D	I
T	P	A	H	A
K	F	★	M	B
Q	C	G	L	D
S	K	J	N	E

What do all people need? ____ ____ ____ ____ ____ ____ ____

 Writing Practice: If you had x-ray vision, what would you use it for? Write a paragraph telling about this special gift.

Addition

Solve each problem below.

1. 69 + 96	2. 459 + 391	3. 6,765 + 4,364
4. 47,889 + 52,093	5. An ice cream store had 2 pints of ice cream for $5.00. How many pints would you get for $20.00?	

Friendly Letters

Match the part of the friendly letter with its name.

_____ 1.   Dear Julie,   a. heading

_____ 2.   the thoughts and ideas of your letter   b. greeting

_____ 3.   January 1, 2001   c. body

_____ 4.   the name of person writing the letter   d. closing

_____ 5.   Your friend,   e. signature

 Writing Practice: Write a friendly letter to a friend or a relative about something interesting happening in your life.

Addition

Add the numbers in each column. Then solve problem 5.

1.	98	2.	145	3.	2,965
	76		163		4,526
	54		237		2,632
	+ 32		+ 846		+ 5,038

4.	10,132	5. Doreen went shopping and spent all of her money. Her total purchases were $87.35. How much change did she receive? What else do you need to know about this problem?
	12,573	a. what she bought
	35,742	b. how much money she gave the cashier
	+ 54,624	c. you have all you need to know

Adverbs

Write a word before each **-ly** to make a sentence using adverbs.

1. _____ly he sang to the baby.

2. I listened _____ly to the teacher.

3. She worked _____ly on her assignment.

4. They _____ly joined in the search for the missing wallet.

5. The band played _____ly.

6. That is a _____ly nice picture you painted.

Writing Practice: When you are feeling unhappy, what do you do? Write about how you begin to feel happy again.

Addition

Solve the problems.

1. 7,283 3,854 + 9,103	**2.** 987 986 + 985	**3.** 682 607 + 643

4. 2,218 3,210 + 4,216	**5.** Kenisha bought 2 folders for 29 cents each, 2 pencils for 12 cents each, and notebook paper for 39 cents. She had $5.00. What would be her change? _____

Predicate (Verb)

Write a sentence with each verb.

1. has taken _____

2. bought_____

3. has flown_____

4. went _____

5. have seen _____

6. walked_____

7. was going _____

8. is _____

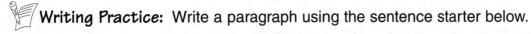 **Writing Practice:** Write a paragraph using the sentence starter below.

Playing in the snow is fun because . . .

52

Addition

Solve each problem below.

1.
 	
     723
     588
+ 396
	2.
	
	  71,259
	  55,169
	+ 543
		3.
		
		 4,635,640
		 3,550,518
		+ 1,756,170

4.
 	
  215,705
  376,156
+ 89,912
		5. Kevin and Kimberly are going to Spain to visit their aunt. They estimate their cost at $690.00 each. They've saved only half. How much have they each saved?
		
		     _____

Pronouns

Choose the correct reflective pronoun that makes each sentence complete.

____ 1. Dan taught _____ how to ride a bike.　　　a. ourselves

____ 2. We made _____ sick from eating too much candy.　　b. myself

____ 3. The students are setting high goals for _____.　　　c. yourself

____ 4. "Help _____ to a cookie after dinner," said Mom.　　d. himself

____ 5. I couldn't help _____ from falling asleep.　　　e. itself

____ 6. The tree seemed to lean _____ toward the sky.　　f. themselves

 Writing Practice: Choose an object in the room. Write five clues that would help someone discover what it is.

Addition

Find the minuend of each subtraction problem by using the numbers already given. Then solve problem 5.

1.	2.	3.
[ ] – 73,281 ——— 115,765	[ ] – 48 ——— 26,154	[ ] – 45,439 ——— 72,786

4.	5. After spending $342.80 for a television, D. J. had $186.20 left. How much did she have before she bought the television?
[ ] – 1,764 ——— 5,783	_____

Nouns

Fill in each blank with a common (C) or proper (P) noun.

1. _____ was born in the _____ of May.
        (P)   (C)

2. The _____ visited the _____ Zoo.
             (C)   (P)

3. On _____ we will take a spelling _____ .
            (P)   (C)

4. _____ sold magazines to his _____ .
        (P)   (C)

5. Our _____ is named _____ School.
          (C)   (P)

6. We drove through the _____ in the beautiful state of _____ .
                      (C)   (P)

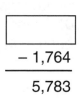 **Writing Practice:** Describe what your life would be like if you lived underwater.

Addition

Solve each problem below.

1. $\begin{array}{r} 26,407 \\ 389 \\ 1,683 \\ +\quad 42 \\ \hline \end{array}$	**2.** $\begin{array}{r} 705 \\ 3,060 \\ 129 \\ +\ 5,783 \\ \hline \end{array}$	**3.** $\begin{array}{r} 5,863 \\ 19,700 \\ 85,708 \\ +\quad 635 \\ \hline \end{array}$

4. $\begin{array}{r} 595 \\ 1,460 \\ 3,790 \\ +\ 295 \\ \hline \end{array}$	**5.** During the month of November, Shawn spent $42.00 for lunches, $14.00 for movies, and $67.23 for clothes. How much did he spend in all? _____

Figurative Language

Tell what you think each figurative statement really means.

1. He's all ears! _____

2. Get off my back! _____

3. Lend me your ear. _____

4. Give me a hand. _____

5. Who let the cat out of the bag? _____

6. I've got my eye on you. _____

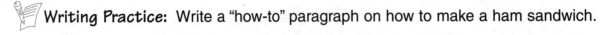 **Writing Practice:** Write a "how-to" paragraph on how to make a ham sandwich.

Addition and Average

Add the scores of each bowler. Write the bowler who had the highest total of pins. Then solve problem 5.

1. Jeb's Scores	2. Parth's Scores	3. Micah's Scores
120	132	90
114	98	144
105	111	122
Total = _____	Total = _____	Total = _____

4. Who was the winner?

_____

5. Kevin bowled 3 games in a tournament. What is the average of his score?

Game	Score
1	158
2	172
3	211

Average = _____

Capitalization

Circle the words that should be capitalized.

1. i live on bryan street.

2. i have lived there since last february.

3. we moved in our new house on a saturday.

4. we used to live near salt lake city.

5. i was born in chicago on january 10.

6. on my birthday i am going to see niagra falls.

7. my mother speaks spanish.

8. she was born in mexico.

 Writing Practice: Write a paragraph about a favorite book or story. Describe why it is your favorite.

Subtraction

Solve each problem.

1.	2.	3.
841 − 30	644 − 132	891 − 105

4.	5. Jim has to leave for school at 7:30 A.M. It is 6:45 A.M. How long does he have before he leaves for school?
85 − 18	_____

Sequencing

Put these sentences in order by looking at the time-order words.

_____ When we got there, we checked into the hotel and unpacked our bags.

_____ There we rode rides and saw Mickey Mouse.

_____ Then we went for a swim.

_____ My family and I went to Florida.

_____ Finally, we left all tired and worn out.

_____ Next, we changed clothes and left for Disney World.

 Writing Practice: Write a paragraph using the sentence starter below.

Rainy days make me feel . . .

Subtraction

Solve each problem below.

1. 82 − 36 ⎯⎯⎯	2. 503 − 88 ⎯⎯⎯	3. 2,000 − 392 ⎯⎯⎯
4. 30,415 − 4,776 ⎯⎯⎯⎯		5. A passenger car on a train can carry 67 passengers. How many passengers can a train with 12 passenger cars carry? ⎯⎯⎯⎯⎯⎯⎯

Pronouns

Rewrite the underlined words with a pronoun.

1. <u>The girl and her friend</u> played on a soccer team.   ⎯⎯⎯⎯⎯⎯⎯

2. Jonah said, "<u>Jonah</u> like to eat corn on the cob."   ⎯⎯⎯⎯⎯⎯⎯

3. <u>My mother</u> used to live in South Carolina.   ⎯⎯⎯⎯⎯⎯⎯

4. Why don't <u>the children</u> play outside?   ⎯⎯⎯⎯⎯⎯⎯

5. The rabbit ate <u>the rabbit's</u> food.   ⎯⎯⎯⎯⎯⎯⎯

6. <u>Katie and I</u> share the same birthday.   ⎯⎯⎯⎯⎯⎯⎯

7. The next day <u>Emilio and Caren</u> walked home together.   ⎯⎯⎯⎯⎯⎯⎯

8. <u>Rubert</u> found a watch in his backyard.   ⎯⎯⎯⎯⎯⎯⎯

 Writing Practice: Describe an eventful day at school and the different things that you did.

Subtraction

Solve each problem below.

1.	2.	3.
32,000 − 8,671	1,000,000 − 537,112	9,000 − 5,523

4.	5. A whale eats an average of 800 pounds of fish a day. How many would he eat in one week? One month?
7,040,200 − 64,344	week _____ month _____

Dictionary Skills

Write each vocabulary word with its definition. Use the dictionary, if needed.

1. leave ship or aircraft ___ ___ ___ ___ ___ ___ ___ ___ ___

2. unhappy ___ ___ ___ ___ ___ ___ ___ ___ ___ ___ ___

3. break up ___ ___ ___ ___ ___ ___ ___

4. offend ___ ___ ___ ___ ___ ___ ___

5. show unjust favor ___ ___ ___ ___ ___ ___ ___ ___ ___ ___ ___

6. release ___ ___ ___ ___ ___ ___ ___ ___ ___

disband	disembark	disgust
disconsolate	discharge	discriminate

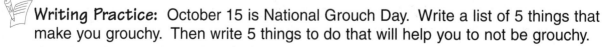

Writing Practice: October 15 is National Grouch Day. Write a list of 5 things that make you grouchy. Then write 5 things to do that will help you to not be grouchy.

Subtraction

Subtract the number at the top from each number listed below. Then solve problem 5.

1. subtract 32		2. subtract 21		3. subtract 19	
44		67		48	
58		42		39	
63		29		27	
33		90		19	

4. subtract 8

91	
87	
73	
60	

5. California has about 65 times more pets than the state of Georgia. If Georgia has 283,000 pets, how many does California have?

_____

Prefixes

Write what each word means by looking at the meanings of the following prefixes.

uni = one	*tri* = three	*inter* = between	*pre* = before
bi = two	*semi* = half	*intra* = within	*sub* = under

1. unicycle _____

2. bicentennial _____

3. triangle _____

4. semicircle _____

5. interstate _____

6. intravenous _____

7. prepay_____

8. subway _____

 Writing Practice: Write a newspaper article for your school newspaper convincing students and teachers to recycle.

Subtraction

Write the missing addend to complete each problem.

1.
 	
    20,482
+ _____
    55,169
	2.
	
	    $67.31
	+ _____
	    $108.90
		3.
		
		    73,281
		+ _____
		    89,046

4.
 	
    3,807
+ _____
    8,331
	5. Mrs. Patten ordered 73 fiction, 51 nonfiction, and 38 biographies for the library. How many books did she order?
	
	_____	

Fact or Opinion

Write **F** if the statement is a fact or **O** if the statement is an opinion.

_____ 1. Every child should have a pet dog.

_____ 2. We should all brush our teeth to keep them healthy.

_____ 3. November has 30 days.

_____ 4. Ice cream is the most popular dessert.

_____ 5. Peanut butter and jelly sandwiches are delicious.

_____ 6. School is a place where children learn.

Writing Practice: You've been given an unusual gift from your aunt. What is it? Write her a thank you note.

Subtraction

Solve each problem.

1. $2,000$ $-\,1,385$	2. $\$10.00$ $-\,\$9.43$	3. $\$56.00$ $-\,\$19.93$
4. $7,000$ $-\,4,928$	5. On July 4th the high temperature in Sacramento was 93˚. The low temperature that evening was 67˚. What was the change in temperature for that day? _____	

Adjectives

Circle the adjectives that describe a Christmas tree.

star	green
shiny	stand
present	big
beautiful	bright
ornament	round
lights	branches
sharp	under
tall	decorative

 Writing Practice: Martin Luther King, Jr. had a dream. We also have dreams or wishes. Write a paragraph with the title, "I Have a Dream."

62

Subtraction

Solve each problem.

1. $40.40 − $12.98	2. 1,620 − 1,598	3. $30.05 − $ 8.67
4. 3,000 − 1,542		5. Mrs. Morgan bought her students Christmas gifts that totaled $16.98. What is her change if she pays with $20.00? _____

Cause and Effect

Tell which part of the sentence is the cause and which is the effect. Write **C** if it is the cause; write **E** if it is the effect.

1. _____ Because of playing in the rain, I got a bad cold ____.

2. _____ To make good grades, I study hard and do my homework ____.

3. _____ We went to the zoo because our class won a contest ____.

4. _____ I went to bed early so I could get up in time for school ____.

5. _____ Since Tory and Alfonzo are good friends, they play at each other's house ____.

6. _____ I have to write Don a letter, because he moved to Illinois ____.

 Writing Practice: If you could meet any famous person, who would it be, and why? Write a paragraph explaining your answer.

Addition and Subtraction

For problems 1–4, write each problem in words and solve. Then solve problem 5.

1. 27 + 46 _____ _____ _____	**2.** 106 − 85 _____ _____ _____	**3.** 99 + 23 _____ _____ _____

4. 243 − 19 _____ _____ _____	**5.** Jason collected books. He had 13 mysteries, 5 insect books, 7 joke books, and 21 picture books. How many books did he have in all? _____

Subject

Underline the subject in each sentence.

1. The children ate pizza for lunch.

2. June and Susan traveled to Florida.

3. The boy and his dog played with the ball.

4. Good stories are found in books.

5. The little girl talked to the clown.

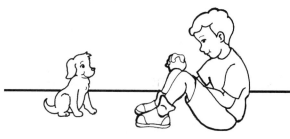

 Writing Practice: Write a paragraph about how you feel beginning this new school year. Include things you would like to do this year.

Addition and Subtraction

Solve the problems.

1. 472 + 29	2. 482 + 19	3. 921 − 19

4.

839
− 228

5. Tonya bought a cheeseburger for $1.50, French fries for $0.50, and a soda for $0.50.

How much did she pay for her meal?

_____

How much change would she get back if she paid with a $5.00 bill?

_____

Adjectives

Write an adjective in each blank.

1. A _____ girl walked down the street.

2. Mom bought us _____ pads of paper.

3. The _____ car had a flat tire.

4. The children built a _____ snowman.

5. The _____ grapes tasted sweet.

 Writing Practice: Which sport do you like to play? Write a persuasive paragraph telling why your sport is the best.

Addition and Subtraction

Solve the problems. Be careful to follow the signs.

1. $\begin{array}{r} 346 \\ + 421 \end{array}$	2. $\begin{array}{r} 259 \\ + 630 \end{array}$	3. $\begin{array}{r} 987 \\ - 183 \end{array}$
4. $\begin{array}{r} 906 \\ - 412 \end{array}$	5. One shark ate 64 fish. Another shark ate 21 fish. How many fish were eaten in all? _____	

Pronouns

Fill in the blanks with the correct pronoun. Capitalize when necessary.

it	my	our	her	we	I	they

1. _____ sister, Ana, and _____ friend went to the mall.

2. _____ shopped for two hours.

3. Ana and _____ went back the next day.

4. _____ bought _____ mother a birthday present.

5. Mom said she liked _____ very much.

Writing Practice: Finish the statement below and write a paragraph about your adventures. Then draw what you would look like.

If I were a fish . . .

Addition and Subtraction

Subtract and then check by addition. Then solve problem 5.

1. 423 − 187	**2.** 804 − 355	**3.** 1,201 − 987

4.

4,000
− 1,284

5. The sports store is having a 50% off sale. If T-shirts cost $8.00, shorts cost $5.00, and tennis shoes cost $24.00, how much will each item be at 50% off?

_____

_____

_____

Verbs

Replace each underlined verb with a more vivid verb.

1. Mom <u>made</u> a cake. _____

2. Steven <u>made</u> a race car. _____

3. I <u>went</u> to the store. _____

4. Dad <u>went</u> next door. _____

5. The girl <u>came</u> to school. _____

6. He <u>came</u> to the party. _____

 Writing Practice: Write a paragraph using the sentence starter below.

One of the best things I can do is . . .

Addition and Subtraction

Use the map provided to answer the questions.

1. What is the difference in miles between Memphis and Chattanooga and between Memphis and Nashville? _____	2. Which city is the closest from Nashville— Chattanooga or Knoxville? By how much? _____	3. What is the distance from Knoxville to Nashville to Memphis? _____

4. Would it be closer to travel to the Tri-Cities from Memphis by way of Nashville, or Chattanooga and Knoxville?

_____

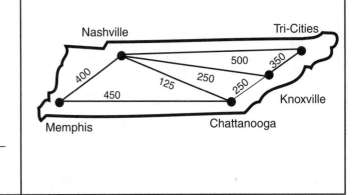

Study Skills

Determine if you would find the following information in an atlas, thesaurus, or almanac.

1. Which country is north of Spain? _____

2. What is a synonym for the word program? _____

3. Which continent is an island? _____

4. Which state has more tornadoes than any other? _____

5. Which state population is larger—Georgia or Alabama? _____

Writing Practice: What is the best thing your parents have ever done for you? Write a paragraph about it.

Multiplication

Fill in the squares by multiplying the numbers.

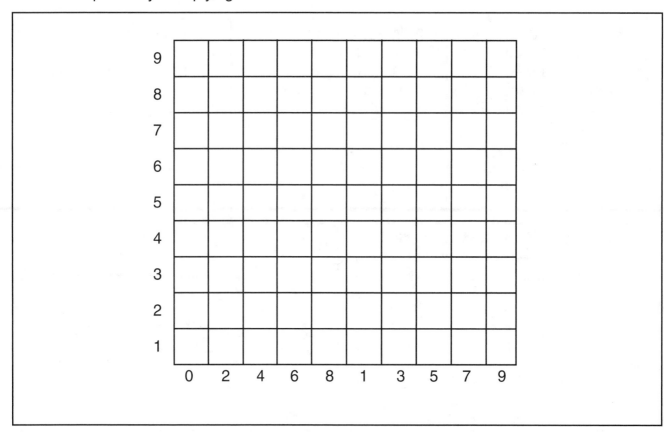

Dictionary Skills

Look at the page numbers and their guide words. Write which page you would find the entry word.

| page 23 **candle → card**   page 26 **common → conflict**   page 31 **corner → crawl** |

1. conceal _____

2. counter _____

3. captive _____

4. crane _____

5. confetti _____

6. carbon _____

7. compare _____

8. cover _____

9. count _____

10. canopy _____

Writing Practice: Write a descriptive paragraph about going on a safari in Africa.

Multiplication

Solve each problem.

1. 438 x 4	**2.** 312 x 5	**3.** 2,263 x 8
4. 3,259 x 4	**5.** The Titans scored 3 touchdowns and 1 field goal when they played the Cowboys. The Cowboys scored 2 touchdowns and 3 field goals. What was the score? (**Hint:** touchdown = 7 points [with extra point], field goal = 3 points) Titans _____ Cowboys _____ Who won? _____	

Punctuation

Underline or add quotation marks for each title.

1. Charlotte's Web (a book)

2. Beauty and the Beast (a movie)

3. Expanding the West (a chapter in a book)

4. Titanic (a ship)

5. People (a magazine)

6. How to Make a Cake (an article)

7. The Boston Globe (a newspaper)

8. West Side Story (a play)

Writing Practice: Write a paragraph describing what you think a Titan is. Then draw a picture of a Titan.

Multiplication

Solve each problem.

1. 42 x 8	2. 124 x 3	3. 235 x 4
4. 2,346 x 2	5. Kym watched television for 2 hours on Friday, 3 hours on Saturday, and on Sunday twice as much as on Friday. How many hours did she watch over the three days? _____	

Nouns

Write these nouns under the correct heading.

Spain
tears
girl
book
Houston
love
student
cat
desk
cousin
state
happiness

Person	Place	Thing	Idea

 Writing Practice: September is "All-American Breakfast Month." Write a paragraph about your favorite breakfast.

Multiplication

Solve each problem.

1. 34 x 6	2. 65 x 5	3. 123 x 4
4. 456 x 2	5. Sherry had 4 pairs of white socks, 5 pairs of black socks, and 6 pairs of brown socks. How many pairs of socks did Sherry have? _____ Since a pair is two, count each sock. How many socks is that? _____	

Spelling

Rewrite each misspelled word correctly.

1. auther _____   6. tommorrow _____

2. frite _____   7. twelth _____

3. abcense _____   8. suprise _____

4. certian _____   9. cheif _____

5. Wendesday _____   10. fourty _____

 Writing Practice: Write a paragraph about the best birthday you ever had.

72

Multiplication

Solve each problem.

1. $$\begin{array}{r} 46 \\ \times\ 8 \\ \hline \end{array}$$	2. $$\begin{array}{r} 102 \\ \times\ 8 \\ \hline \end{array}$$	3. $$\begin{array}{r} 16 \\ \times\ 32 \\ \hline \end{array}$$
4. $$\begin{array}{r} 22 \\ \times\ 24 \\ \hline \end{array}$$	5. Shelia wanted to buy stickers for her sticker book. They cost $.05 each. How many stickers can she buy with $2.15? _____	

Addressing an Envelope

Address the envelope with the following addresses:

- Return address: Write your own name and address.
- Address the letter to: Marcus Chatham, 409 McDonald Dr., St. Clair, PA 12390

 Writing Practice: Write a paragraph about things you've always wanted to do but never got to do.

Multiplication

Solve each problem.

1. 23 x 27	2. 98 x 23	3. 46 x 25
4. 43 x 18	5. Tim and Jill ordered French fries. There were 36 fries in the packet. If Tim ate 13 and Jill ate 11, how many more fries would each of them eat if they ate the same number of additional fries? _____	

Verbs

Circle each action verb below.

shirt	punches	hat	child	leaped	sing
cape	run	reads	shoes	kicks	suit
wishes	eye	dishes	washes	flew	sky

Writing Practice: Write a paragraph using the sentence starter below.

My goal for the New Year is . . .

Multiplication

Solve each problem.

1. 340 x 2	2. 176 x 4	3. 226 x 3

4.	5.
$1.92 x 5	Carlos has $10.00 to spend on a gift for his brother. He buys a football for $3.99 and also buys a helmet. If his change is $1.02, how much did the helmet cost? _____

Verb Tense

Write the correct form of the verb in each sentence. The verb follows the sentence.

1. Nathan and Natalie _____ to school together. *(walk)*

2. "Something _____ funny," I said as we got to school. *(smell)*

3. The science teacher was _____ an experiment. *(do)*

4. Our teacher _____ to get out our homework. *(say)*

5. I couldn't find my homework so I _____ in my desk. *(look)*

6. She said I could _____ it to her after math class. *(give)*

7. Renee _____ up and said, "I found it. It fell on the floor." *(stand)*

8. On the way home, a bee _____ me. *(sting)*

9. It hurt so badly that I _____, "Ouch!" *(scream)*

10. Mom put an ice pack on it, and it _____ better. *(feel)*

Writing Practice: Write a paragraph using the sentence starter below.

If I could travel anywhere in the world, it would be to . . .

Multiplication

Solve the problems.

1. 82 x 13	2. 46 x 25	3. 307 x 14
4. 224 x 63	5. Mrs. Stolz has 13 boxes of pencils. Each box has 24 pencils in it. How many pencils does she have in all? _____	

Plurals or Possessives

Choose the correct word to complete each sentence.

1. This recipe is for chocolate _____.
   a. cookie's   b. cookies'   c. cookies

2. It was _____ job to help with the dishes.
   a. Dads   b. Dad's   c. Dads'

3. James and Melissa saw the _____ kittens first.
   a. cat's   b. cats   c. cats'

4. Mr. Adams is a wonderful teacher who _____ fifth grade.
   a. teach's   b. teaches   c. teaches'

5. The _____ coats were hung in their lockers.
   a. students' b. student's   c. students

 Writing Practice: Write a story about a job you would like to do when you get older. Tell why you chose that job.

Multiplication

Solve each problem.

1. 974 x 63	**2.** 290 x 76	**3.** 794 x 13
4. 69 x 42	**5.** Jenny bought a car for $17,936.29. Miguel bought a car for $25,000.00. How much more did Miguel spend than Jenny? _____	

Adjectives

Fill in the blanks with an adjective.

1. I saw a _____ cat running down the street.

2. We like to eat _____ candy.

3. I read _____ books last month.

4. The lady has _____ children.

5. We sat on a _____ couch.

6. We ate a _____ cake for dessert.

7. Mom baked _____ cookies for my party.

8. My _____ doll was broken.

Writing Practice: Pretend you are an astronaut. Write about your adventures in space.

Multiplication

Use the information about the different symbols provided on the chart to solve each problem.

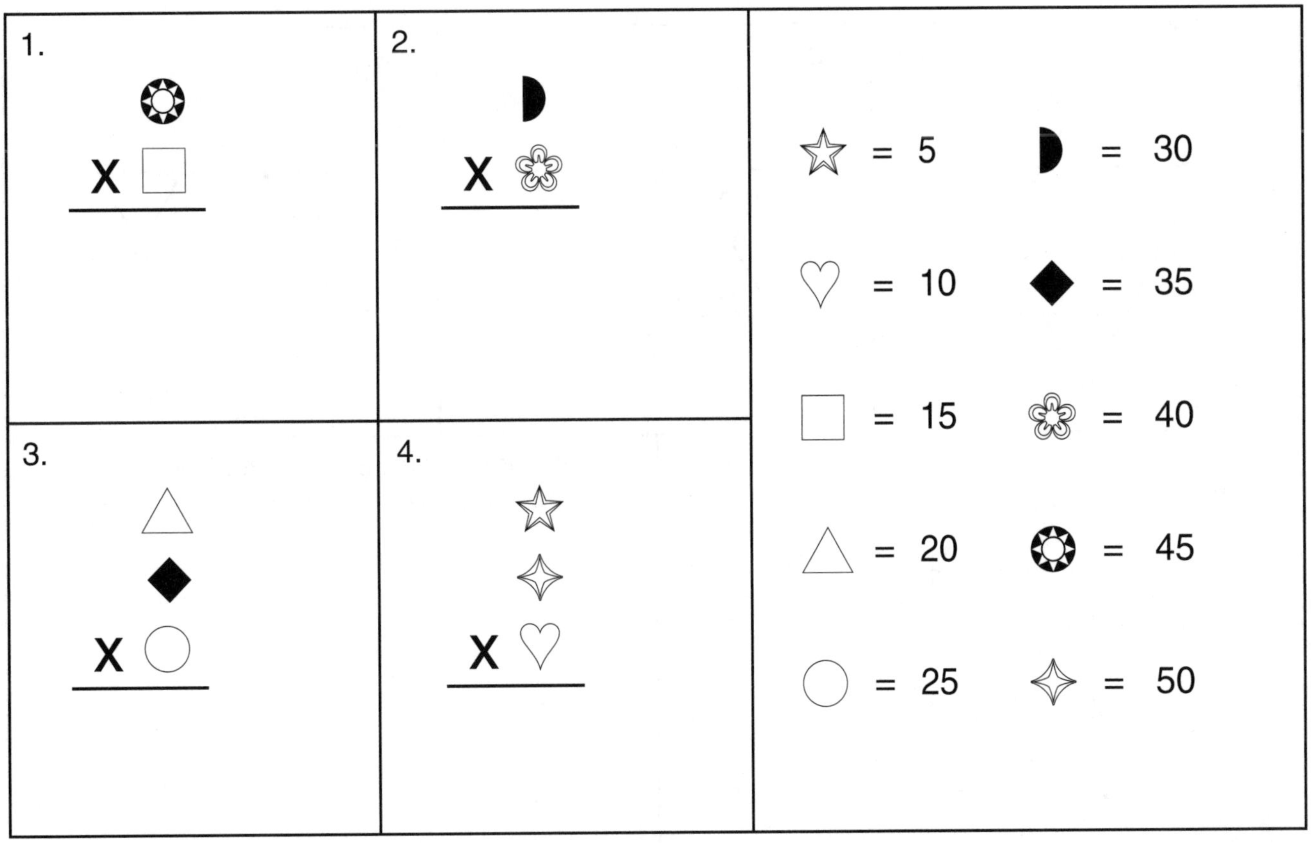

1.

✵

X □
___

2.

☽

X ❀
___

☆ = 5		☽ = 30	
♡ = 10		◆ = 35	
□ = 15		❀ = 40	
△ = 20		✵ = 45	
○ = 25		✧ = 50	

3.

△
◆

X ○
___

4.

☆
✦

X ♡
___

Adverbs

Cross out every third letter to find the names of adverbs. Write the adverb in the space provided, then write a sentence with it.

1. somftaly _____

2. menrreilay _____

3. fuyrimoukslpy _____

4. bepaudtilfusllcy _____

5. thderae _____

Writing Practice: If you combined two fruits or vegetables into a new product, how would you advertise this new product?

Multiplication

Multiply the number in the center by each point. Write the answer by the point. Then solve problem 5.

1.

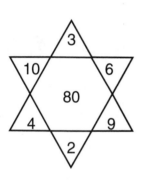

2.

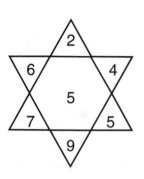

3.

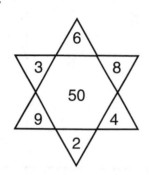

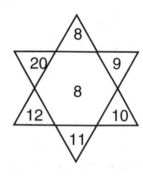

4.

5. If Cyndi was born in 1982, how old will she be in the year 2005?

_____

Subject/Verb

Add a simple subject or a simple predicate (verb) to each sentence.

1. My younger _____ was born last week.

2. Barry _____ his homework to his Algebra teacher.

3. Pedro _____ a snake in a tree in his backyard.

4. The _____ of the tree slowly fell to the ground.

5. Elizabeth _____ her hand to answer the teacher's question.

6. _____ were found at the space center.

Writing Practice: Think of your favorite music group or singer. Write a short article about him or her for the school newspaper.

Multiplication

Write the answer to each multiplication problem below.

1. 9 x 20 x 5	2. 12 x 9 x 7	3. 3 x 8 x 2 x 11
4. 8 x 15 x 3	5. 3 x 4 x 6 x 10	

Word Order

Rearrange the words in each group to make a complete sentence. Write each sentence.

1. Sweep   The   the   class   Toning   wanted   story   to   the   hear

_____

2. grades   good   get   classwork   do   have   You   to   your   to

_____

3. Marcia   best   and   friends   Barbie   in   were   grade   sixth

_____

4. anything   try   be   can   you   You   if   want   you

_____

5. Yesterday   school   to   player   CD   a   brought   Alex

_____

Writing Practice: Write about a family vacation that you are going to take or have already taken.

Multiplication

Circle each correct problem. Then solve problem 5.

1. 49 x 9 = 421	**2.** 338 x 7 = 2,366	**3.** 742 x 36 = 25,712

4. 482 x 65 = 31,330	**5.** A dog fell in a 12-foot well. Everyday, he climbed up 3 feet and slipped back 2 feet. How many days did it take him to reach the top? _____

Adjectives

Write two adjectives to describe the noun. Be sure they begin with the same letter as the noun.

1. children

   _____

   _____

2. pie

   _____

   _____

3. book

   _____

   _____

4. leaf

   _____

   _____

5. sister

   _____

   _____

6. dog

   _____

   _____

 Writing Practice: If you were a fashion designer, what kind of clothing and shoes would you design? Write a short descriptive paragraph about your fashion collection.

Multiplication

Solve each problem below.

1. 1,962 x 53 _____	**2.** 638 x 86 _____	**3.** 302 x 95 _____

4. 3,509 x 72 _____	**5.** Kari had $34.98 left of her birthday money. She saw a sweater for $15.88 and a pair of shoes for $24.69. How much more money does she need to buy both items? _____

Comprehension

Answer the questions after reading the paragraph.

The Nobel Prize is awarded annually for outstanding works in science, literature, and world peace. It was named after Alfred Nobel, a Swedish chemist. He was best known for his invention of dynamite. When he died, he left almost 10 million dollars to fund future awards. Americans like Woodrow Wilson and Martin Luther King, Jr. have won the Nobel Prize.

1. Who is the Nobel Prize named after? _____

2. What did he invent? _____

3. Name the three fields that the Nobel Prize is awarded._____

_____

4. What was the money that Nobel left used for? _____

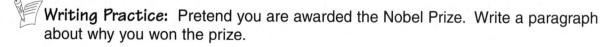 **Writing Practice:** Pretend you are awarded the Nobel Prize. Write a paragraph about why you won the prize.

82

Multiplication

Fill in the missing factors for each set of multiplication problems. Then solve problem 5.

1.	**2.**	**3.**
5 x ___ = 30 ___ x 8 = 48 7 x 9 = ___	10 x 2 = ___ 9 x ___ = 81 ___ x 5 = 15	4 x ___ = 32 ___ x 9 = 36 ___ x 5 = 25

4. 2 x ___ = 24 ___ x 3 = 45 9 x ___ = 99	**5.** Jessica saved $92 last month and $120 this month. She spent $125 on clothes. How much does she have left? _____

Word Order

Rearrange the words in each sentence to make a complete sentence.

1. speaker We a special in had library. the

   _____

2. Theodor She a read story to Geisel. our about class

   _____

3. Geisel Seuss. is Theodor known as Dr. also

   _____

4. 1904. in born was He

   _____

5. favorite he book is *and Green* My *Eggs Ham*. wrote

   _____

6. writing wonder why I he use name his when real didn't books?

   _____

 Writing Practice: You have been given the chance to create and publish your own magazine. What kind of articles and stories would it feature? What kind of magazine would it be?

Multiplication

For problems 1–4, find the GCF (greatest common factor) of the numbers listed below. Then solve problem 5.

1. 12, 15 _____	2. 6, 9 _____	3. 5, 15 _____

4. 18, 24 _____	5. During the school's reading contest, a group of four students read a total of 50 books. Carol read twice as many books as Joe. Amy read 12 books. Joe read two less books than Amy, but two more books than Ling. How many books did they each read? Carol = _____ Amy = _____ Joe = _____ Ling = _____

Verb Usage

Write *sit* or *set* in each blank.

1. We don't _____ on the table.

2. Please _____ the book on your desk.

3. Al, _____ your lunch in your locker.

4. Lou, _____ here.

5. Did he _____ on my glove?

6. Where did Mrs. Johnson _____ the box of books?

Writing Practice: Write a paragraph using the sentence starter below.

We all make mistakes, and mine was . . .

Multiplication

Solve each problem below.

1. 464 x 183	2. 814 x 572	3. 8,723 x 602
4. 3,435 x 242	5. There are five chairs in the front row. Each successive row has two more chairs. How many chairs are in the sixth row? _____	

Homographs

Write sentences showing the different meanings of each pair of words.

_____

_____

_____

_____

6. shed_____

✍ **Writing Practice:** What was the happiest moment of your life?

Multiplication

Solve each problem below.

1. 6,728 x 123	2. 59 x 38	3. 3,604 x 49

| 4.

234
x 153 | 5. The local middle school sponsored a skating party for its students in 5th and 6th grades. The cost per child was $6.00. How much did the school pay if 213 students went?

_____ |

Real/Unreal

Write **R** if real or **U** if unreal.

_____ 1. book about Harry Potter

_____ 2. Dorothy in the *Wizard of Oz*

_____ 3. Martin Luther King, Jr.

_____ 4. novel read in English class

_____ 5. Wilbur said, "Charlotte, you have to save me."

_____ 6. book about kinds of animals

Writing Practice: Use this writing prompt to write a short paragraph:

Something important I learned this year was...

Multiplication and Fractions

Use multiplication to solve the problems below.

1. $\frac{2}{3}$ x 20 =	2. 15 x $\frac{4}{5}$ =	3. 6.48 x .23 =
4. 3.729 x 45 =	5. Sean is $\frac{1}{3}$ as old as his brother. His brother is 21. How old is Sean? _____	

Direct Object

Underline the direct object in each sentence.

1. Robin hit a homerun during the ballgame.

2. He brought a friend to the game.

3. We liked the trip to the museum.

4. They played some music by Bach.

5. Pete wrote a story about caves.

6. Bats eat insects flying around at night.

Writing Practice: What type of music do you like to listen to? Why?

Multiplication and Division

Solve each problem.

1. 234 x 91	2. 6,124 x 52	3. 6)763

4. 3)12,982

5. Dad needed to buy four tires for the car. He could buy them for $28.99 each or four for $108.00. Which way would cost the least?

_____

Figurative Language

Match the statement with the correct kind of figurative language.

_____ 1. He's fast as lightning!   a. personification

_____ 2. He's a pig!   b. simile

_____ 3. The tree wanted to rest.   c. alliteration

_____ 4. The wind blew with a whoosh!   d. metaphor

_____ 5. She sings the song sweetly.   e. onomatopoeia

 Writing Practice: You've just been given a pen pal. Write a letter to your pen pal describing yourself and telling him or her about yourself.

Multiplication and Division

Solve each problem.

1.	2.	3.
22.35 x 22	1,244 x 12	2)74.50

4.	5. Donny needs 42 birthday invitations. The invitations are sold in packages of 5.
2)1,555	How many packages will Donny need to buy? _____ How do you know? _____ _____

Dictionary Skills

The pronunciation of words are given in the dictionary. Write what letter is silent in each word. You may use a dictionary, if needed. For numbers 11–15, create your own words and write the silent letter.

1. autumn _____   6. know _____   11. _____ _____

2. knots _____   7. shake _____   12. _____ _____

3. climbing _____   8. gnome _____   13. _____ _____

4. Wednesday _____   9. mechanic _____   14. _____ _____

5. thumbs _____   10. maze _____   15. _____ _____

Writing Practice: Write a story and use words that have silent letters in them. After you have finished writing, circle the silent letters.

Division

Divide and then solve problem 5.

1. 28 ÷ 7 = _____	2. 64 ÷ 8 = _____	3. 72 ÷ 9 = _____

4. 42 ÷ 6 = _____	5. Juanita wanted to divide the cookies she made between her and her 3 friends. She made 2 dozen cookies. How many cookies did each girl get? _____

Adverbs

Unscramble these adverbs.

1. stfa   _____

2. ryelal   _____

3. nyoilis _____

4. yadot   _____

5. dably   _____

6. lelw   _____

7. vyer   _____

8. lyetuiq   _____

 Writing Practice: Write a persuasive paragraph telling someone why the state you live in is the best state there is.

Division

Solve each problem.

1. $2 \overline{)14}$	2. $5 \overline{)36}$	3. $3 \overline{)36}$

4. $6 \overline{)52}$	5. Four buses were driven to school. There were 52 students on each bus. How many students were on all four buses? _____

Homographs

Write two sentences with each homograph showing different meanings. Then think of one more homograph and write two sentences with it.

1. rose   _____

_____

2. leaves   _____

_____

3. _____   _____

_____

 Writing Practice: Write a story about visiting a farm and seeing farm animals up close.

Division

Solve each problem.

1. 6)‾36	2. 9)‾810	3. 4)‾284
4. 5)‾450		5. The students in Mr. Marcos' class bought school supplies for their class. They bought 3 packs of paper at \$0.69 each, 12 pencils at \$0.09 each, and 6 bottles of glue at \$0.49 each. How much did all the supplies cost? _____

Parts of a Friendly Letter

Name the parts of a friendly letter.

Keli Smith
328 Village St.
Anytown, USA 87654

1. _____

Dear Jane,

2. _____

How are you doing? I've been thinking about you ever since you moved to Anytown. Do you like your new school? How is your new house? Have you found any new friends?

Maybe you could come visit me during the summer. Talk to your mother about it. Write me back. I miss you!

3. _____

Love,

4. _____

Keli

5. _____

✍ **Writing Practice:** Your best friend just moved away. Write a letter to him or her. Don't forget to write about what you are doing since he or she moved away.

92

Division

Circle the correct set of numbers that is divisible by the specific number given. Then solve problem 5.

1. What set of numbers is divisible by 2? a. 8, 15, 18, 23 b. 16, 24, 28, 32	2. What set of numbers is divisible by 3? a. 9, 18, 21, 39 b. 5, 15, 30, 36	3. What set of numbers is divisible by 5? a. 60, 75, 90, 100 b. 36, 40, 45, 55
4. What set of numbers is divisible by 12? a. 122, 130, 145, 152 b. 60, 84, 108, 144	5. A famous author was at the local bookstore signing copies of his book. Over 4,000 people showed up, but the author only signed 2,677 books. How many didn't get an autograph? _____	

Pronouns

Circle the word that the italicized pronoun replaces.

1. The house was dark, as though the family moved from *it*.

2. Peel the orange and separate *it* into sections.

3. Women used to stay at home and teach *their* children.

4. Mildred studied piano, and *she* became a great pianist.

5. Jasmine went home and wrote *her* friend a letter.

6. Sequoyah was a Cherokee Indian; *he* invented the Cherokee alphabet.

Writing Practice: Use this writing prompt to write a short paragraph:

One of my favorite memories when I was younger was...

Division

Solve these division problems. Then solve problem 5.

1. 6 ⟌ 39	2. 4 ⟌ 97	3. 7 ⟌ 590
4. 5 ⟌ 641	5. At the bookstore, paperback books cost $3.00 and hardback books cost $7.00. What is the total cost of 3 paperback and 4 hardback books? _____	

Syllables

Divide these words into syllables.

1. hardy _____

2. palomino _____

3. material _____

4. phonograph _____

5. appoint _____

6. chili _____

7. sideline _____

8. umbrella _____

9. computer _____

10. movie _____

 Writing Practice: If a relative gave you $500.00 to buy anything you wanted, what would or wouldn't you buy?

Division

Solve each problem below.

1. 9)327	2. 5)199	3. 18 2,965
4. 22)5,392		5. Art supplies for 5 girls cost $295.00. What is the cost for each girl? _____

Writing Practice

Write a creative limerick in the space provided below.

Writing Practice: December 15 is Bill of Rights Day. Write a list of rights you think all kids should have.

Division

Solve each problem.

1. $8\overline{)8,923}$	2. $5\overline{)45.95}$	3. $12\overline{)24,840}$
4. $11\overline{)776,655}$		5. Shawn read 78 pages in the novel *The Giver*. If there are 321 pages, how many more pages does he have to read? _____

Vocabulary

Match the word with the definition.

_____ 1. moving air   a. air

_____ 2. water falling to the earth in drops   b. wind

_____ 3. study of weather   c. rain

_____ 4. cloud close to the ground   d. sleet

_____ 5. frozen rain   e. barometer

_____ 6. sound that follows lightning   f. fog

_____ 7. instrument used to measure air pressure   g. meteorology

_____ 8. invisible mixture of gases surrounding the earth   h. thunder

 Writing Practice: Have you ever wanted to be a famous athlete? What sport would you be famous for? Write about how you would become famous.

Division

Solve the problems below.

1.	2.	3.
72)‾3,520‾	40)‾290‾	26)‾9,224‾

4.	5. If Bobby eats pizza 3 days each week at school, how many days does he eat pizza the whole school year? (36 weeks in a school year)
44)‾386‾	_____

Figurative Language

Complete each simile with a noun. You may add *a*, *an*, or *the* before each noun.

1. as soft as _____

2. as clear as _____

3. as little as _____

4. as bright as _____

5. as sweet as _____

6. as hard as _____

 Writing Practice: Would you rather be around a person who says what they think or a person who is a good listener? Write a paragraph describing why.

Division

Calculate the quotients. Then solve problem 5.

1. $60\overline{)417}$	2. $23\overline{)281}$	3. $51\overline{)673}$

4. $40\overline{)837}$	5. Andie is making a quilt that is 1.5 meters long and 1.25 meters wide. What is the area?
	_____

Forms of Literature

Match the form with its description.

_____ 1. an informational story about real things   a. legend

_____ 2. a made-up story   b. fiction

_____ 3. a story of a person's life written by someone else   c. poetry

_____ 4. a story that has come down from the past   d. biography

_____ 5. a story of a person's life written by the person   e. nonfiction

_____ 6. a composition written in verse   f. autobiography

 Writing Practice: Imagine that you are a zoologist and have recently discovered a new species of animal. Describe the physical features of this new species and how and where you discovered it.

Mixed Review

Solve each problem.

1. 2,396 + 3,784	2. 7,040 − 4,965	3. 3,681 x 63

4. 6)5,328	5. Mrs. Ling wants to buy 100 pepper plants. The plants are sold in trays of 6 plants. How many trays does she need to buy? _____

Punctuation

Choose the sentence with the correct quotation marks.

1.
   a. Emilee asked "Do you like my new outfit"?
   b. Emilee asked, "Do you like my new outfit?"
   c. Emilee asked, "do you like my new outfit?"

3.
   a. "Swimming is fun" said Kevin.
   b. "Swimming is fun," said Kevin.
   c. "Swimming is fun, said Kevin."

2.
   a. "Yes!" yelled Jodie.
   b. Yes! "yelled Jodie."
   c. "Yes! yelled Jodie."

4.
   a. Gina replied "I like to dive."
   b. "Gina replied," I like to dive.
   c. Gina replied, "I like to dive."

 Writing Practice: Write a story by finishing the statement below.

I was chosen to be a character on television. I got to play . . .

Mixed Review

Solve the problems.

1.	2.	3.
3,261 + 1,879	3,261 − 1,879	3,261 x 9

4.	5. Sammy went to the store. He bought 35 apples. They cost 9 cents each. How much did he spend?
9) 3,261	_____

Sequencing

Rewrite the following paragraph in sequence. Then circle the key words that show sequencing.

> Finally, put both slices together and enjoy! Then get out the peanut butter and jelly. Afterwards, spread jelly on the other slice of bread. Next, spread peanut butter on one slice of bread. To make a peanut butter and jelly sandwich, you first need two slices of bread.

_____

_____

_____

_____

_____

Writing Practice: Write a paragraph about "How To Make a Grilled Cheese Sandwich."

100

Mixed Review

Solve each problem.

1.	2.	3.
483 + 849	400 – 263	25 x 14

4.	5. Barbara plans to buy a tennis racket for $26.00 and shoes for $13.00.
6) 892	How much does she plan to spend? _____ If she has $50.00 to spend, will she have enough money left over to buy a can of tennis balls for $3.97? _____

Proofreading Skills

Write each sentence correctly.

1. when do mary walk her dog _____

2. she walk's scruffy at 400 pm _____

3. how much do a hamburger costs _____

4. julie bout french fries, and a soda _____

5. yesterday we had homework in spelling math and reading _____

_____

6. the first monday in september is labor day_____

_____

7. were going to my grandma house said john_____

_____

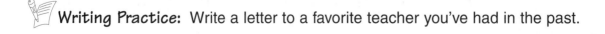 **Writing Practice:** Write a letter to a favorite teacher you've had in the past.

Mixed Review

For numbers 1–4, copy each problem vertically. Then solve the problems.

1. 47,508 + 16,893 =	2. 7,203 – 805 =	3. 842 x 7 =
4. 93 ÷ 6 =	5. Wesley needs 6 ounces of paint for each model car he makes. If he has a 30 ounce can of paint, how many cars can he paint? _____	

Predicate

Underline the predicate of each sentence.

1. Our family went on a vacation to the mountains.

2. We rented a cabin and stayed in the forest.

3. One night I heard a bear outside my window.

4. The bear was going through the garbage cans.

5. The next morning, trash was everywhere!

6. We stayed in the mountains for three more days.

7. Would you like to see a bear?

Writing Practice: Write a paragraph using the title below.

Things I've Always Wanted but Never Had

Mixed Review

Solve each problem.

1.	2.	3.
482 658 + 217	3,040 − 1,829	$87.54 x 72

4.	5. A farmer has 43 cattle. 19 are sold. He then buys 22 more. How many cattle does he have now?
6) 2,516	_____

Dictionary Skills

Which word has the same sound? Circle the answer.

1. n<u>ee</u>dle: a. let   b. ceiling   c. eight

2. l<u>ea</u>n: a. better   b. best   c. sneeze

3. cl<u>aw</u>:   a. boat   b. bought   c. clay

4. <u>Au</u>gust: a. out   b. brown   c. jaw

5. f<u>ai</u>r: a. plane   b. mare   c. clean

Circle the vowel sound that completes the word.

6. a person in a circus: cl___n
   a. ou   b. aw   c. ow

7. head of indian tribe: ch___f
   a. ie   b. ei   c. ee

8. what the pig built his house of: str___
   a. ay   b. aw   c. ew

9. a sandwich is made of: br___d
   a. ai   b. ea   c. ei

10. a trip on a ship: cr___se
   a. oo   b. ou   c. ui

 Writing Practice: Write a paragraph describing your Mondays.

Mixed Review

Solve each problem.

1. 906,370
    3,912
  +   658
	2. 1.27
	  x 29
		3. 6,175
		  – 967

4. 8)467̄	5. Bertha has 37 marbles. Her friend, Anthony has 41 marbles. They decide to put all the marbles together and then divide them up evenly. How many marbles would each person get? _____

Nouns

Circle all words in the fish that are nouns.

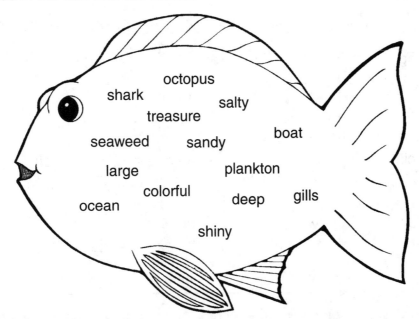

octopus
shark   salty
treasure
seaweed   sandy   boat
large   plankton
colorful   deep   gills
ocean
shiny

Writing Practice: Write a story using eight of the words above.

Mixed Review

Solve the problems.

1. 7,245 ÷ 6 =	2. 8,042 – 2,679 =	3. 1,023 x 42 =

4. 23 + 46 + 179 + 245 =	5. Johnnie wanted to watch the Olympics at 7:00 P.M. It was only 2:23 P.M. How much time did he have before the Olympics would come on television?

Prepositions

Find these prepositions in the puzzle.

after

among

beside

between

by

for

from

in

to

with

q	a	a	h	e	l	e	a	p	a	p
n	s	v	i	d	l	u	d	r	e	o
x	z	h	t	i	w	r	i	p	j	i
c	v	b	n	s	m	s	f	g	p	u
n	a	f	t	e	r	d	b	h	l	i
f	m	m	j	b	e	t	w	e	e	n
b	o	f	h	f	y	l	w	t	y	y
v	n	r	g	d	u	o	r	k	u	t
c	g	o	t	s	a	q	e	h	g	r
x	z	m	g	f	d	r	s	a	w	e

 Writing Practice: If you could be in either the summer or winter Olympics, which one would you choose? What would you do, and why?

Mixed Review

Solve each problem.

1.	2.	3.
14,132 + 2,478	$60.00 − $13.95	$87.54 x 15

4.	5. A camera store ordered 56 cameras. Each cost $68.00. What was the cost of the order?
7) 231	_____

Consonant Blends

Write which sound the *ch* makes in each word. Choose from **k**, **ch**, or **sh**.

1. church _____

2. couch _____

3. choir _____

4. chandelier _____

5. chapter _____

6. chair _____

7. echo _____

8. aches _____

9. chef _____

10. school _____

11. chauffer _____

12. each _____

 Writing Practice: What is a friend? What makes a good friend? Do you have a special friend? Write a paragraph by answering these questions.

Mixed Review

Solve each problem.

1. 468 + 129	2. 700 − 124	3. 325 x 32

4. 5⟌365	5. The library has about 140 mystery books, rounded to the nearest ten. What is the least number of mystery books in the library? _____

Capitalization

Circle all letters that should be capitalized in the following titles. Then rewrite them correctly.

1. "the big snow"

   _____

2. "clifford gets a job"

   _____

3. "all in the morning"

   _____

4. "i can read about birds"

   _____

5. "the prince and the pauper"

   _____

6. "georgie to the rescue"

   _____

7. "the story about ping"

   _____

8. "a weed is a flower"

   _____

Writing Practice: Write a paragraph using the sentence starter below.

I really get angry when . . .

Mixed Review

Solve each problem.

1.	2.	3. Which of these symbols should go in the box to get the smallest answer?
43 x 28	181 x 22	100 ☐ 20 = a. + c. x b. − d. ÷

| 4. Which one would show the largest answer?

    a. +   c. x
    b. −   d. ÷ | 5. Marilynn has 5 pencils, Alfred has 7 pencils, Jasmine has 8 pencils, and Ryan has 2 pencils.

How many pencils do they all have together? _____

How many more pencils do Marilynn and Alfred have than Jasmine and Ryan? _____ |

Subject

Find the subject in this mixed-up sentence. Circle the subject.

1. Down the street came Felipe.

2. Across the room sat Ned.

3. Under the table was her nickel.

4. Over the hill ran a deer.

5. On the floor were his shoes.

6. Into the classroom came the teacher.

7. Through the woods scampered a rabbit.

8. Around the corner came a barking dog.

 Writing Practice: You've just found an old bottle. You clean it up and . . . Poof! A genie appears. What three wishes will you make?

108

Mixed Review

Solve each problem.

1. 481 + 369 = _____	2. 4,800 − 1,469 = _____	3. 482 x 23 = _____
4. 879 ÷ 4 = _____	5. A suitcase fell off a 40-story building. Someone caught it on the 16th floor. How many stories did it fall? _____ How many stories were left before it would have hit the ground? _____	

Abbreviations

Write the abbreviations to these units of measurement.

1. ounce _____   4. yard _____   7. gallon _____

2. inch _____   5. centimeter _____   8. pint _____

3. milligram _____   6. quart _____   9. mile _____

Next, write the words for which these abbreviations stand.

10. P.M. _____   13. min. _____   16. A.D. _____

11. A.M. _____   14. hr. _____   17. c. _____

12. sec. _____   15. B.C. _____   18. ml _____

 Writing Practice: Write a poem using the title, "If."

Mixed Review

Solve each problem.

1. 426 + 879	2. 3,024 − 1,883	3. 552 x 6
4. 7)49	5. Isaiah planted 4 rows of beans. Each row had 23 bean plants. How many bean plants are there in all? _____

Dictionary Skills

Circle all words you would find on a dictionary page with these guide words.

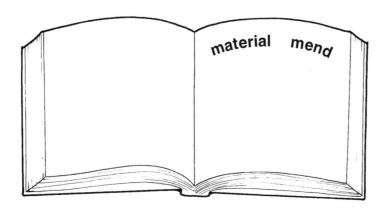

material   mend

measure	match
memory	meet
menial	medical
mean	merge
matron	master
matter	mate

 Writing Practice: Write a story about watching a scary movie on television on a stormy night.

Mixed Review

Solve the problems below.

1. $\begin{array}{r} 243 \\ + 76 \\ \hline \end{array}$	**2.** $\begin{array}{r} 500 \\ - 23 \\ \hline \end{array}$	**3.** $\begin{array}{r} 325 \\ \times\ \ 4 \\ \hline \end{array}$
4. $\begin{array}{r} 632 \\ + 378 \\ \hline \end{array}$	**5.** Mrs. Spadafino drives 20 miles to school. Mrs. Hutchison drives 13 miles, Mrs. Martin drives 8 miles, and Mrs. Olive drives 6 miles. How many total miles do they drive? _____	

Kinds of Sentences

Write the correct letter beside each sentence.

_____ 1. Pass the butter, please.   D. Declarative

_____ 2. There was a shooting star out last night.   E. Exclamatory

_____ 3. What a beautiful sunrise this morning!   I. Imperative

_____ 4. Did you see a movie on Saturday?   Q. Interrogative

 Writing Practice: Write a paragraph about your favorite place to eat. Tell why you like it and what you like to eat there.

Mixed Review

Solve each problem.

1.	2.	3.
241 362 + 103	2,000 − 1,782	4,553 x 4

4.	5. Joe and Jeff entered the 100 yard dash in the school race. Joe practiced 1 hour a day for 5 weeks, and Jeff practiced 2 hours a day for 3 weeks. Who spent more time practicing for the race?
7)498	_____

Nouns

Circle the nouns in the following paragraph.

My pet

I have a pet named Scruffy. He is a special dog called a Lab. He came to live at our house nine years ago. You should have seen him. He was a puppy and was so small. He weighed only 3 pounds. He is a good dog and never barks. He is also very cute, especially when he sleeps. My family has enjoyed having a pet like Scruffy.

 Writing Practice: Write a story about a pet you have. If you don't have a pet, write a story about a pet you would like to have.

Mixed Review

Solve each problem.

1. $\begin{array}{r} 37,777 \\ + 25,666 \\ \hline \end{array}$	**2.** $\begin{array}{r} 6,001 \\ - 2,594 \\ \hline \end{array}$	**3.** $\begin{array}{r} 67 \\ \times 49 \\ \hline \end{array}$
4. $8\overline{)96}$	**5.** Mrs. Lewis' class is going on a field trip. There are 20 students going, and 4 children can ride in each car. How many cars will be needed? _____	

Possessive Nouns

Circle the group of words with the correct possessive form.

1. A. the girls doll
   B. the girl's doll
   C. the girls's doll

2. A. Maria's desk
   B. Marias' desk
   C. Marias desk

3. A. my moms car
   B. my mom's car
   C. my moms's car

4. A. the children's pets
   B. the childrens pets
   C. the childrens' pets

 Writing Practice: Write a scary story beginning with the phrase below.

I could not believe my eyes . . .

Mixed Review

Solve each problem.

1. $\begin{array}{r} 746 \\ 832 \\ +\ 295 \\ \hline \end{array}$	2. $\begin{array}{r} 6,035 \\ -\ 2,475 \\ \hline \end{array}$	3. $\begin{array}{r} 1,271 \\ \times\ \ \ \ \ 9 \\ \hline \end{array}$
4. $4\overline{)144}$	5. Jan sold 120 boxes of Girl Scout Cookies. Sharyn sold 109 boxes, and Alex sold 283. How many boxes did they sell in all? _____ How many more boxes did Alex sell than both Jan and Sharyn together? _____	

Possessive or Contraction

Write a sentence showing the correct usage of each word.

1. its _____

2. it's _____

3. their _____

4. they're _____

5. your _____

6. you're _____

 Writing Practice: Write a paragraph using the title below.

What I Learned from a Grandparent

114

Mixed Review

Solve each problem below.

1.	2.	3.
1,382 9,217 + 463	11,846 − 7,271	3,240 x 81

4.	5. Gina had $1,000 in a savings account. In six months, she received $25 interest. How much would she have earned with $5,000 in her savings account?
17) 734	

Sentences/Conjunctions

Combine the sentences by using a conjunction *(and, but, or, nor, for, yet)*.

1. I like to watch television. I don't watch it too much.

   _____

2. I watch movies. I watch sports.

   _____

3. Don went to camp in Missouri. He really wants to go to Florida.

   _____

4. JoAnn came to help us move. We had lots of heavy boxes.

   _____

5. Bones are easily broken. They are not easily mended.

   _____

6. You can play. You can sit on the bleachers.

   _____

 Writing Practice: Have you ever had or wanted to have a slumber party? What did/would you do during the party?

Mixed Review

Solve each problem below.

1. $(35 \div 5) + 6 = $ _____	2. $(12 - 8) \times 4 = $ _____	3. $15 - (21 \div 3) = $ _____
4. $8 \times (4 \times 2) = $ _____	5. What is the perimeter of a soccer field 110 yds. by 80 yds.? What is the area? perimeter = _____ area = _____	

Conjunctions

Circle the conjunction in each sentence.

1. Jose and Maria are exchange students from Mexico.

2. They enjoy American food, but they like Mexican food the best.

3. Maria's mom used to make tortillas or tacos everyday for lunch.

4. Now she cooks hamburgers or hot dogs some days.

5. They like school but have difficulty with the English language.

6. Math and science are most interesting to them.

 Writing Practice: Use this writing prompt to write a short paragraph:

The sky was a clear blue, and the clouds above looked like...

116

Mixed Review

For problems 1–4, fill in the blanks. Then solve problem 5.

1. One-fourth of 28 is _____.	2. Three weeks and 4 days would be _____ days in all.	3. Four cartons of eggs (Each carton equals a dozen.) is _____ eggs in all.
4. There are _____ degrees in a right angle.	5. Our club collected money to buy a gift for a sick classmate. In all, we collected 82 quarters, 90 dimes, 45 nickels, and 79 pennies. How much money was collected in all? _____	

Homonyms

Write *your* or *you're* in the blanks. Capitalize when necessary.

1. _____ cake was delicious.

2. _____ my closest friend.

3. I need _____ advice.

4. What is _____ name?

5. _____ from Minnesota.

6. _____ invited to my party.

7. _____ late for school.

8. _____ cat licked my hand.

 Writing Practice: Write a persuasive paragraph telling why you agree or disagree with having no smoking in public places.

Mixed Review

For problems 1–4, fill in the blanks. Then solve problem 5.

1. The average of 6, 18, and 12 is _____.	2. In October, there are four full weeks and _____ days.	3. The time between 10:25 A.M. and 11:10 A.M. is _____ minutes.

4. One-third of the number 12 is _____.	5. In the classroom, there are 24 students. $\frac{1}{3}$ are reading, $\frac{1}{2}$ are doing math, and the rest are working on spelling. How many are working on spelling? _____

Rhyming Words

Fill in the blanks of this poem with a word that rhymes.

Groundhog Day

This furry friend might come out once a year
To keep his shadow if the day is _____.
And on this very special Groundhog Day
If his shadow is seen, winter will _____.
For six more long weeks we'll have to keep warm,
But if it's cloudy, his shadow's not there
There'll soon be warm weather and days will be _____.
So please, Mr. Sun, just this one day,
Find a big dark cloud—and stay _____!
—Unknown

 Writing Practice: Write a story about a surprising turn of events when the groundhog sees his shadow.

Mixed Review

Solve each problem.

1. (40 + 3) − (20 + 12) =	2. (60 + 8) − (34 + 8) =	3. (6 x 9) − (9 x 4) =

4. (8 x 8) − (7 x 7) =

5. 28 fifth graders were asked about their favorite ice cream. 14 said chocolate, and the others said vanilla. What percentage likes chocolate?

Prefixes

Answer each question about prefixes.

1. If **mis** means *wrong*, what does:

   a. mistreat mean?_____

   b. misread mean?_____

2. If **re** means *do again*, what does:

   a. repaint mean? _____

   b. retell mean? _____

3. If **un** means *not*, what does:

   a. untied mean? _____

   b. uncover mean?_____

 Writing Practice: Write a story with the title below.

The Case of the Missing Clock

Mathematical Terms

Circle the correct mathematical term for the underlined numbers. Then solve problem 5.

1. $10 - 8 = \underline{2}$ a. product b. sum c. difference d. quotient	2. $23 + 23 = \underline{46}$ a. product b. sum c. difference d. quotient	3. $20 \div 5 = \underline{4}$ a. product b. sum c. difference d. quotient
4. $3 \times 5 = \underline{15}$ a. product b. sum c. difference d. quotient	5. Cleveland had 104,238 in population, Columbus has 679,234 in population, and Dayton has 414,757 in population. What is the total population of all three cities? _____	

Homonyms

Eight homonyms are used incorrectly in this story. Circle each of them and write the correct word in the blanks below.

> It was a beautiful blew sky. We were playing football with hour friends. Stephan through the ball at me. It wood have dropped, but I fell forward to get it. Suddenly, I screamed! I had fallen on a be. I ran home sew hard my feat began to hurt. Later that knight, I went to bed with my leg hurting from the bee sting.

_____, _____, _____, _____,

_____, _____, _____, _____

 Writing Practice: Write a story using the sentence starter below.

We heard a "thump" outside the window . . .

Mathematical Terms

Circle the correct term to the underlined part of each number sentence. Then solve problem 5.

1. <u>81</u> divided by 9 = 9 a. subtrahend b. addends c. multiplier d. dividend	2. 6 x <u>6</u> = 36 a. subtrahend b. addends c. multiplier d. dividend	3. <u>33</u> − 11 = 22 a. subtrahend b. addends c. multiplier d. dividend
4. <u>10 + 10</u> = 20 a. subtrahend b. addends c. multiplier d. dividend	5. It takes 24 inches of string to wrap a package. How much string will be needed to wrap 25 packages? _____	

Verb Usage

Circle the correct verb in each sentence.

1. The sun has (rise, rose, risen) brightly this morning.
2. The Founder's Day program has (begin, began, begun) late.
3. The swim team has (swim, swam, swum) five laps.
4. The walnuts have (fall, fell, fallen) off the trees.
5. Watermelon was (grow, grew, grown) on my uncle's farm.
6. My mother and I will (go, went, gone) to the basketball game tonight.
7. The window pane was (break, broke, broken) by a rock.
8. The principal has (tell, told, telled) us the announcements.
9. Where was Kate (hid, hide, hidden)?
10. The *Titanic* was (sink, sank, sunk) many years ago.

 Writing Practice: Write a story using the following words: *shrub, caterpillar, leaf, change, butterfly, crawl, sleepy, home.*

Money

Count the total change. Write it on the blank provided.

1. _____	2. _____	3. _____
3 dollars 3 half dollars 3 quarters 3 dimes 3 nickels 3 pennies	2 quarters 12 dimes 5 nickels 24 pennies	12 dollars 4 quarters 2 dimes

4. _____	5. Terell saved 12 quarters, 6 dimes, 14 nickels, and 13 pennies. Shamika saved 10 quarters, 8 dimes, 12 nickels, and 20 pennies. Who saved the most money?
5 dollars 5 quarters 5 nickels 5 pennies	 _____

Dictionary Skills

Look up these words to find their origin.

1. parrot

_____

2. raccoon

_____

3. chocolate

_____

4. automobile

_____

5. piano

_____

6. chimpanzee

_____

7. pajamas

_____

8. tea

_____

9. pretzel

_____

10. cookie

_____

 Writing Practice: A *fable* is a story that teaches a lesson, and animals are usually the characters. Write your own fable about a chicken and a cow.

Money

Write what type of bills and coins equal each money value.

1. $17.53	2. $107.65	3. $75.25
_____ _____ _____	_____ _____ _____	_____ _____ _____

4. $63.71	5. Erica bought cereal for $2.39, juice for $1.59, and flour for $1.25. How much did she spend?
_____ _____ _____	_____

Prefix/Suffix

Add a *prefix* to each word and then write a sentence with each word.

1. _____clear   _____

2. _____do   _____

3. _____order   _____

4. _____trust   _____

Add a *suffix* to each word and then write a sentence with each word.

5. care_____   _____

6. kind_____   _____

7. sail_____   _____

8. help_____   _____

Writing Practice: You are sleeping soundly when the phone rings and wakes you up. Write a story about what happens.

Money

Solve each word problem using money.

1. Jerome spent between $12.00 and $13.00. Which two food items did he buy? a. steak $5.50 b. hot dog $2.75 c. shrimp $7.00 d. French fries $1.50	2. Lacey went to the bookstore for her teacher. The teacher gave her $1.00. Mrs. Woodson gave Lacey the following change: a quarter, 2 nickels, and 3 pennies. Which item did Lacey buy? a. pencil $0.25 b. notebook $0.62 c. eraser $0.10 d. ruler $0.68
3. The fourth grade hired a bus to take a trip to Mammoth Cave. It cost $15.00. Each student paid $0.50. How many students rode the bus? _____	4. The second graders collected money for charity. They collected 50 quarters, 65 dimes, 105 nickels, and 245 pennies. How much money did they collect? _____

Antonyms/Synonyms

If the words are antonyms, write **A** in the space. If the words are synonyms, write **S** in the space.

_____ 1. difficult/easy

_____ 2. brave/coward

_____ 3. empty/full

_____ 4. finish/end

_____ 5. residence/home

_____ 6. shouted/whispered

_____ 7. cent/penny

_____ 8. swift/slow

_____ 9. friend/foe

_____ 10. liberty/freedom

 Writing Practice: It rains so hard one afternoon that your bus gets stuck in the mud. Write a story about the unusual bus ride.

Money

Calculate the correct change. Then solve problem 5.

1. pizza	$1.50		2. pencil	$0.25		3. shampoo	$1.89	
soda	$0.75		paper	$1.89		conditioner	$2.09	
cookies	$0.35		notebook	$7.69		comb/brush	$1.49	
money given	**$10.00**		**money given**	**$20.00**		**money given**	**$10.02**	
change	_____		change	_____		change	_____	

4. magazine	$2.50		5. Mr. Douglas needs $500.00 for a down payment on his car. He earns $275.00 a week and has saved $426.00. How much does he still need to save?
lip gloss	$1.68		
gel pens	$4.72		
money given	**$20.00**		
change	_____		_____

Main Idea

Fill in the web with details to go along with the main idea.

winter

✍ **Writing Practice:** Now write a paragraph about winter using the details you wrote in the above web.

Addition with Money

Solve each problem.

1. $654.88 + $98.92 = _____	2. $9,832.11 + $903.45 = _____	3. $54.00 + $87.38 = _____
4. $99.99 + $11.11 = _____	5. Amanda bought 5 shirts in the mall for $9.99 each. How much did she spend in all? _____	

Parts of Speech

Match each part of speech with its definition.

_____ 1. noun   a. describe noun or pronoun

_____ 2. pronoun   b. names a person, place, thing, or idea

_____ 3. verb   c. connects words

_____ 4. adjective   d. express action or state of being

_____ 5. adverb   e. takes the place of a noun

_____ 6. preposition   f. shows emotion or surprise

_____ 7. interjection g. describes a verb

_____ 8. conjunction   h. relates a noun to another word

 Writing Practice: You're walking on the beach and you look down and see a bottle. It has a message inside. Write about what it says.

126

Addition with Money

Solve each problem.

1. $20.00 + $ 2.43	2. $6.02 + $3.45	3. $3.94 + $3.08

4. $70.00 + $29.95	5. If you bought snacks that totaled $6.89, how much change would you get if you paid with $10.00? _____

Plurals

Write the plural of the nouns below. Then write a sentence containing the plural word.

1. boy   (_____) _____

2. dish   (_____) _____

3. song   (_____) _____

4. fox   (_____) _____

5. knife (_____) _____

6. ship   (_____) _____

 Writing Practice: Write a paragraph about fun things you can do outside during the fall season. Then circle all plural words.

Addition with Money

Solve each problem.

1. $10.20 + $ 3.42	2. $8.74 + $3.65	3. $27.19 + $18.03
4. $4.03 + $1.87	5. Sue bought a sweater for $13.47. She gave the cashier $20.00. What was her change? _____	

Proofreading Skills

Write each sentence correctly.

1. i go to tom joy elementary school _____

2. the fourth grade will be a goode yer _____

3. the robin be mine favorite bird _____

4. all birds has feather said matt _____

5. jim please right there names _____

6. we red a play at schol this weak _____

7. three duck swimmed in the pond _____

8. i saw an mother duck and her babys _____

 Writing Practice: If you could change anything about your life, what would it be? Write a paragraph explaining your wishes.

Subtraction with Money

Solve each problem.

1. $0.96 – $0.34	2. $1.09 – $0.21	3. $7.42 – $6.71
4. $4.50 – $3.28	5. Sharon bought a piece of candy for 14 cents. If she gave the cashier $1.00, what five coins would she get back? Draw and label each coin.	

Story Comprehension and Following Directions

Read the story about insects. From the description, draw an insect and label each part.

Insects An insect is a six-legged invertebrate. It has 3 oval-shaped parts that connect to each other. The first part is a head. Then it has a thorax, and last it has an abdomen. Insects also have eyes and a pair of antennas.	*(drawing)*

 Writing Practice: Finish this statement with a descriptive paragraph.

This weekend I . . .

Subtraction with Money

Solve each problem.

1. $654.88 − $98.92 =	2. $9,832.11 − $903.45 =	3. $54.00 − $37.38 =

4. $99.99 − $11.11 =	5. A 12-pack of soft drinks sells for $3.99. If bought separately, the cans would cost $0.60 each. How much do you save by buying the 12-pack?

Context Clues

Circle which meaning best describes the underlined word.

1. The grackle flew through the air.
   a. shark   b. bird   c. insect

2. The scull went so fast, it almost tipped over into the water.
   a. boat   b. car   c. ski

3. Treating the animal with kindness was humane.
   a. horrible   b. not acceptable   c. merciful

4. The fallow seeds were still laying on the ground.
   a. unplanted   b. planted   c. rooted

5. If you don't brush your teeth, they may have caries.
   a. decay   b. enamel   c. caps

6. The lapidary was careful to not break the gems.
   a. someone who protects animals   b. someone who protects stones
   c. someone who protects people

Writing Practice: Can you imagine yourself as a parent? What would you do if you were a parent? How would you raise your children?

Subtraction with Money

Solve each problem below.

1. $4.60 − $1.80	**2.** $0.90 − $0.42	**3.** $542.46 − $267.95

4. $13.82 − $9.40	**5.** The distance around a field is 59.81 meters. The total length of three sides is 37.05 meters. What is the length of the other side?

Sequencing

Put the steps of this recipe in order from 1 to 8.

Ham Omelet

_____ Then chop up the ham into small pieces.

_____ Serve with orange juice and toast.

_____ Before you start, break the eggs in a bowl.

_____ Flip one side over the other side.

_____ Whip the eggs with a wire whisk.

_____ Add the chopped ham in the skillet.

_____ Turn with a spatula to lightly brown the other side.

_____ Pour the eggs in the skillet.

 Writing Practice: Write a short descriptive paragraph about the current President of the United States and what this person has accomplished.

Addition and Subtraction with Money

Solve the problems.

1. $4.87 + $1.87	2. $10.23 + $ 7.64	3. $6.20 − $1.11
4. $8.23 − $2.50	5. Mrs. Mayberry bought pencils for $3.18, and Mrs. Penn bought notebooks for $8.76. How much money did they spend in all? _____	

Sentence or Fragment

Read each group of words. Then write an **S** if it is a sentence, or write an **F** if it is a fragment.

_____ 1. Wrote my homework down.

_____ 2. She is a good friend.

_____ 3. Mrs. Green a nice teacher.

_____ 4. Sit down and do your work quietly.

_____ 5. Hey, being in the fourth grade is going to be fun!

 Writing Practice: You just earned $50.00. Write a story about how you earned the money and what you would buy with $50.00.

Addition and Subtraction with Money

Solve each problem.

1. $4.20 + $3.99	2. $28.99 + $41.35	3. $10.50 − $ 5.42

4.

$58.14
− $26.25

5. The product of two numbers is 24. The sum of the same two numbers is 11. What are the two numbers?

_____

Homonyms

Circle the correct homonym for each sentence.

1. I went to the dentist (four, for) a check-up today.

2. He said I had (four, for) cavities.

3. My mom likes to (sew, so) clothes for my doll.

4. I want to make good grades, (sew, so) I study for my tests.

5. The sky is a light-colored (blew, blue).

6. Jessie (blew, blue) his trumpet in band class.

7. The (be, bee) on the sunflower was a bright yellow and black in color.

8. Mom said we should leave it alone and let it (be, bee).

 Writing Practice: Write a story about playing outside when suddenly you see an angry bee heading towards you.

Multiplication with Money

Solve each problem.

1. 471 x 8	2. 652 x 3	3. $21.18 x 4

4. $7.98 x 5	5. Shawn had $20.00. He buys a sweater for $12.99 and socks for $2.99. What will his change be when he pays for his clothes? _____

Capitalization

Circle which group of names below are capitalized correctly.

1. Mrs. melba Moore
   mrs. melba moore
   Mrs. Melba Moore

2. Chanori and I
   chanori and I
   Chanori and i

3. Dr. D.l. moody
   Dr. D.L. Moody
   Dr. D.L. moody

4. Dequan Williams, Jr.
   dequan williams, jr.
   Dequan Williams, jr.

5. Aunt Jill
   aunt Jill
   aunt jill

6. mister Antonio Proctor
   Mister Antonio Proctor
   mister antonio proctor

 Writing Practice: Your class gets a new student. He has never worked with a computer before, so your teacher says you can show him how to use the Internet. Write a paragraph about what you would tell him about the computer.

Multiplication with Money

Solve each problem.

1. $45.21 x 21	**2.** $3.82 x 14	**3.** $5.25 x 30

4.

$92.98
x   8

5. During Columbus' last voyage, only 116 men survived. One hundred forty men began the voyage. How many did not survive?

_____

Contractions

Rewrite the underlined words with a contraction.

_____ 1. <u>There is</u> time to read before going to bed.

_____ 2. <u>That is</u> the first one I have read in a while.

_____ 3. <u>I would</u> like to read a mystery novel.

_____ 4. I <u>cannot</u> read for very long.

_____ 5. The book <u>should not</u> take but a few days to read.

_____ 6. It <u>does not</u> look too hard.

_____ 7. <u>I will</u> get a new book when I finish.

Writing Practice: Write a paragraph using the sentence starter below.

My goals for the new year are . . .

Multiplication with Money

Solve each problem.

1. $1.63 x 9	**2.** $2.41 x 8	**3.** $16.84 x 5
4. $27.15 x 4	**5.** Suo Yao bought 5 pairs of earrings for her mother. They cost $5.64 for each pair of earrings. How much did she spend? _____	

Kinds of Sentences

Read the following sentences. Write **D** if the sentence is Declarative, **I** for Imperative, **E** for Exclamatory, or **INT** for Interrogative. Then place the correct punctuation mark at the end of the sentence.

1. _____ How many pencils did Juan have ___

2. _____ Give me one of your pencils, Jamal ___

3. _____ Sheryln bought a dozen pencils at the bookstore ___

4. _____ She gave each girl in her class a pencil ___

5. _____ Mrs. Sagrages exclaimed, "What a nice gesture ___"

6. _____ Javier asked, "Why didn't the boys get a pencil ___"

 Writing Practice: Write an invitation inviting your friends to a Halloween party.

Division with Money

Solve each problem. Round to the nearest penny.

1. $2\overline{)\$11.97}$	2. $4\overline{)\$34.63}$	3. $3\overline{)\$49.06}$

4. $4\overline{)\$87.61}$	5. Sandra was given $12.00 for lunch at school for 5 days. How much can Sandra spend each day? _____

Homonyms

Write a sentence using each homonym.

1. hear _____

    here _____

2. sail _____

    sale _____

3. do _____

    dew _____

4. ate _____

    eight _____

Writing Practice: Write a paragraph using the sentence starter below.

I couldn't believe I got caught . . .

Division with Money

Solve each problem.

1. $6\overline{)\$36.60}$	2. $3\overline{)\$98.79}$	3. $8\overline{)\$73.60}$

4. $2\overline{)\$56.92}$	5. There are 365 days in a year. How many days are there in 9 years? _____ How many days are there in 15 years? _____

Spelling

Complete all words with correct spelling by adding **el** or **le** to the word.

1. wrigg_____

2. princip_____

3. app_____

4. nozz_____

5. marv_____

6. tow_____

7. purp_____

8. cab_____

9. cam_____

10. lev_____

11. ank_____

12. mot_____

13. chann_____

14. unc_____

15. trav_____

 Writing Practice: After eating in a Chinese restaurant, you get a fortune cookie. You open it, and to your surprise, the message was not what you expected. Write a story about the fortune you received in your cookie.

Multiplication and Division with Money

Solve each problem.

1. $1.29 x 3	2. $3.42 x 6	3. 6)$3.60
4. 7)$4.20	5. There were 28 people in Ruth's class. There were 12 boys. How many were girls? _____	

Subjects and Predicates

Circle the subject and underline the predicate in each sentence.

1. My friends and I went trick-or-treating.

2. I was a spooky ghost.

3. Our neighbors gave us lots of candy.

4. Jordan tripped over his costume.

5. We ran and jumped all the way down the street.

6. Halloween is a time to have fun with your friends.

 Writing Practice: Write an informative paragraph for the school newspaper about the school dance in two weeks.

Mixed Review with Money

Solve the problems below.

1. $4.82 + 6.58 ————	2. $30.40 − 18.23 ————	3. $8.74 x 21 ————
4. 6) 25.16	5. Miko and his father traveled to San Francisco on a train. The total cost was $96.00. However, Miko's ticket was $32.00 less than his dad's ticket. How much was his dad's ticket? ————————

Dictionary Skills

Circle all words you would find on a dictionary page with these guide words.

intermission   irrigate

interplay	interlock	inward
inventory	irritate	itch
intense	interval	intrude
install	interim	invest

 Writing Practice: What kind of hobbies do you have? Write a descriptive paragraph about your favorite hobby/hobbies.

Problem-Solving with Money

Look at the menu. Four families from the neighborhood ordered fast food one evening. Compute the cost of each family's meal, using the menu.

1. Family 1 ordered 2 hot dogs, 2 French fries, 1 potato salad, and 2 sodas. Total = _____	2. Family 2 ordered 1 hamburger, 3 pizzas, 1 milkshake, and 3 sodas. Total = _____	3. Family 3 ordered 2 corn dogs, 1 pizza, 2 potato chips, and 3 milkshakes. Total = _____

4. Family 4 ordered 1 of each item on the menu. Total = _____	**Fast Food Menu** hot dog $1.25 hamburger $1.50 pizza $1.50 corn dog $1.25 French fries $1.00 potato salad $0.90 potato chips $0.75 soft drink $0.50 milkshake $1.15 ice cream cone $0.80

Pronouns

Write the pronoun above the underlined word.

1. Marques ran fast. <u>Marques</u> won the race.

2. The boys like to play baseball. <u>The boys</u> play it every Saturday.

3. Mom went to the grocery store. <u>Mom</u> bought food for our lunches.

4. Barbara and I are friends. <u>Barbara and I</u> like to talk on the phone.

Circle the possessive pronoun in each sentence.

5. "That's my book," said Emily.

6. Did the baby play with her ball?

7. The blue backpack is mine.

8. The dog ate its bone.

Writing Practice: Write a paragraph using the sentence starter below.

The art of being friendly . . .

Problem-Solving with Money

Solve the problems.

1. If a wristband cost $1.39 and a headband cost $1.85, how much will it cost Jenny to buy both items at the store? _____	2. What would be Jenny's change if she paid with $5.00? _____	3. What would be her change if she paid with $10.00? _____

4. Could Jenny buy two of each item with $7.00? _____	5. There are 24 hours in one day. How many hours are in $\frac{1}{2}$ of a day? _____ In 3 days? _____

Consonant Blends

Choose the correct blend (**CH**, **SH**, **TH**) to complete each word.

1. BEA ___ ___

2. FLA ___ ___

3. ___ ___ AIN

4. REA ___ ___

5. PEA ___ ___

6. ___ ___ AIR

7. ___ ___ OVEL

8. ___ ___ ESE

9. RI ___ ___

10. ___ ___ EM

11. SQUA ___ ___

12. ___ ___ IMNEY

 Writing Practice: Do you like to take tests? Why or why not? Write about it.

Problem-Solving with Money

You've just inherited one million dollars, but there's one catch. You have to spend all of it or you lose it. Answer the questions. Choose from the items listed in the box below.

1. List the 4 items that you would buy.	2. What is the total cost of all 4 items?	3. How much money do you have left?
_____ _____ _____ _____	_____	_____

house	$250,000.00	**ten-speed bicycle**	$250.00
sports car	$25,000.00	**trip to Disney World**	$1,200.00
swimming pool	$15,000.00	**fast-food restaurant**	$56,000.00
boat	$31,000.00	**roller skating rink**	$100,000.00

Suffixes

Write what each word means by looking at the meanings of the following suffixes.

(-er) one who does something	*(-ee)* one who receives something	*(-meter)* device for measuring
(-ation) act of	*(-less)* without	*(-y)* having
(-ous) having	*(-ful)* full of	

1. teacher _____
2. thermometer _____
3. employee _____
4. transportation _____
5. careless _____
6. chilly _____
7. joyous _____
8. beautiful _____

Writing Practice: Write a paragraph using the sentence starter below.

One of the strangest sights I ever saw was . . .

Problem-Solving with Money

Look at the prices of each baseball item. Answer the questions.

glove	$29.87
bat	$17.74
cleats	$22.00
uniform	$42.28
pair of socks	$3.97
baseball	$2.69

1. Which item cost more, the glove or the bat?

_____

What is the difference?

_____

2. How much more does the uniform cost than the socks?

_____

3. Could a player get the uniform and cleats for $50.00? _____

How do you know?

_____

_____

_____

4. How much is the total if a player buys one of each item? _____

Adjectives

Adjectives tell *which one*, *what kind of*, or *how many*. Write the adjectives below under each heading.

tough one
juicy spotted
old red
cold fresh
better many
curly black
friendly few
fast first

Which One	What Kind Of	How Many

 Writing Practice: Write a descriptive paragraph about waking up one morning and finding yourself in a cartoon.

144

Problem-Solving with Money

List the fewest coins and paper money you would receive as change in the following problems and then solve problem 5.

1. If a customer spent $0.84 and paid with a dollar bill, how much change will the customer receive? _____ _____ _____	2. If a customer spent $1.73 and paid with two dollar bills, how much change will the customer receive? _____ _____ _____	3. If a customer spent $3.22 and paid with a five dollar bill, how much change will the customer receive? _____ _____ _____

4. If a customer spent $16.55 and paid with a twenty dollar bill, how much change will the customer receive?

_____

_____

_____

5. George spent 1 dollar, 2 quarters, 3 dimes, and 1 nickel on candy. His friend spent 1 dollar, 3 quarters, and 1 nickel. How much did each spend and who spent more?

George_____

George's friend _____

Who spent more? _____

Adverbs

Choose the right adverb to complete each sentence.

1. The play ended _____.   carefully

2. They acted _____ in the mall.   quickly

3. Jorge plays football very _____.   badly

4. She _____ hiked up the mountain.   suddenly

5. The sunset was _____ seen.   well

6. Mrs. Johnson walked _____ to her car.   clearly

 Writing Practice: Write a paragraph about how you feel you're doing in school this year.

Problem-Solving with Money

Use the information in the chart to answer the questions.

		Christmas Sale	

1. How much would it cost for 2 small ornaments and 1 large ornament?
 	
 _____
	2. Would it cost more for 1 regular set of lights or 2 boxes of cards?
	
	 _____
		ornaments
		     small
		     large
		 lights
		     regular
		     icicle
		 cards
		 wrapping paper
		 bows in bag
			
			 2/$3.00
			 2/$5.00
			
			 $4.89
			 $5.89
			 $2.25 box
			 $1.99/roll
			 $0.59/bag
			 2 bags/$1.00

3. Will $5.00 be enough to purchase 1 roll of wrapping paper, 3 bags of bows, and 1 small ornament? _____	4. What would the total cost be if you purchased 1 of each item? _____		

Verbs

Underline any verb and helping verb in each sentence.

1. It seemed colder yesterday.

2. We were walking down the street.

3. Bob was going to play football.

4. It began to snow heavily.

5. It was so cold, so I went inside.

6. Maybe tomorrow it will be warmer.

 Writing Practice: Write a persuasive paragraph explaining your position on students going to school for nine months versus year-round school.

Addition with Decimals

Solve each problem below.

1.	2.	3.
46.8 + 9.6	8.982 + 24.83	0.84 + 0.67

4.	5. The cost of 2 books is $10.50. One cost $2.50 more than the other. What is the cost of each book?
36.341 + 22.8	Book 1 _____ Book 2 _____

Nouns

Underline 11 common nouns in the paragraph about whales.

Whales are one of the most intelligent animals. They are mammals,

which mean they give birth to live young and use lungs to breathe.

They migrate thousands of miles each year. When there isn't much

food, they can live off their blubber.

 Writing Practice: October is National Clock Month. Write about a time you lost track of time and were late for an important event/appointment.

Addition with Decimals

Add each group of numbers with decimals. Then solve problem 5.

1. 15,873 + 5.32 = _____	2. 15.873 + 53.2 = _____	3. 1,587.3 + .532 = _____

4.

1.5873 + 532 = _____

5. There are 24 hours in one day. How many hours are there in one week?

_____

How many hours are in 12 weeks?

_____

Predicate (Verb)

Choose the correct verb for each sentence.

1. _____ the students play kickball. (Let, Leave)

2. Please don't _____ on the floor. (sit, set)

3. We _____ our bird to talk. (taught, learned)

4. Where _____ you yesterday? (was, were)

5. There _____ two bikes in the yard. (is, are)

6. Where have you _____ my picture? (took, taken)

7. We _____ our lunch in our classroom. (ate, eaten)

8. _____ I go to the mall with you? (may, can)

Writing Practice: Write a paragraph using the sentence starter below.

I have some good memories about . . .

148

Addition with Decimals

Add. Then solve problem 5.

1. 2.9461 + 56.03 = _____	2. 294.61 + 560.3 = _____	3. 2,946.1 + 5,603 = _____
4. 29.461 + 5.603 = _____	5. The Hundred Years War was fought from 1337 to 1453. How many total years did the war go on? _____	

Main Idea

Circle the topic that doesn't belong under the main idea. For problem 4, write four topics under the main idea.

1. Animals in the zoo
   a. bears
   b. dogs
   c. tigers
   d. monkeys

2. Favorite hobbies
   a. stamp collecting
   b. collecting dolls
   c. reading books
   d. doing homework

3. Why school is important
   a. learn how to clean your room
   b. learn new things
   c. learn to use the library
   d. learn to get along with others

4. You can learn a lot in social studies.
   a. _____
   b. _____
   c. _____
   d. _____

 Writing Practice: Write a story with the writing starter below.

It was a wonderful surprise . . .

Multiplication with Decimals

Solve each problem.

1. 0.06 x 0.6 = _____	**2.** 0.4 x 30.2 = _____	**3.** 5 x 0.05 = _____
4. 6.0 x 0.7 = _____	**5.** 25 students were asked how often they read a book. 10 said they read at least 5 days a week. What percentage of the students read at least 5 days a week? _____	

Analogies

Complete each analogy.

1. Wings are to butterflies, as fins are to _____.

2. Chimney is to house, as _____ is to mountain.

3. Mother is to child, as cow is to _____.

4. Pen is to chicken, as _____ is to horse.

5. 5 is to pentagon, as 8 is to _____.

6. Grapes are to jelly, as apples are to _____.

7. Antlers are to deer, as _____ are to unicorns.

8. Pencils are to writing instruments, as _____ are to tools.

 Writing Practice: Picture yourself 10 years from now. What do you think you'll be doing? Write about it.

Multiplication with Decimals

Solve each problem.

1. 9.34 x 10	2. 0.5 x 1,000	3. .98 x 100
4. 76.4 x 10	5. Nicole earned $8.50. She spent $3.75 at the store and saved $3.00 in her piggy bank. How much money does she have left to spend? _____	

Sentences

Write four sentences about any fairy tale using each kind of sentence.

1. Declarative

   _____

   _____

2. Imperative

   _____

   _____

3. Interrogative

   _____

   _____

4. Exclamatory

   _____

   _____

 Writing Practice: Write a letter to a new pen pal describing yourself.

Multiplication with Decimals

Solve each problem below.

1. 4.2 x 0.6	2. 0.73 x 4	3. 1.6 x 3.7
4. 1.06 x 5	5. What is the mode of Sarah's history grades if she had the following grades? Sarah's history grades: 77, 58, 82, 95, 65, 100, 96, 95 _____	

Punctuation

Add commas where needed.

1. My sister brother and cousin went to camp with me.

2. Jim my uncle took us last week.

3. Emily said "Let's go back next year."

4. I want this book but I will have to read it later.

5. We went to the library to the grocery store and then back home.

6. The poodle which is noted for its small size can be a great pet.

✎ **Writing Practice:** Use this writing prompt to write a short paragraph:

My favorite belonging is...

Multiplication with Decimals

Solve the problems below.

1.	2.	3.
39.37 x .21	11.89 x .33	91.44 x .16

4.	5. Kareem is two years older than his brother, Javier, but is 5 years younger than his sister, Janis. If Janis is 19, how old are Kareem and Javier?
40.47 x .25	Kareem is _____. Javier is _____.

Alphabetical Order

Write these mathematical terms in alphabetical order.

perimeter   _____

ratio   _____

multiply   _____

percent   _____

division   _____

place value   _____

decimals   _____

geometry   _____

 Writing Practice: What is your favorite food dish? Why? What is your least favorite food dish? Why?

Rounding Decimals

Round to the nearest whole number and then solve problem 5.

1. 6.29 = _____	2. 1.7 = _____	3. 0.96 = _____

4.

21.39 = _____

5. Sarah, Ricardo, and Dominique rode their bikes. Sarah rode 2.1 miles, Ricardo rode 3.7 miles, and Dominique rode 5.5 miles. About how many miles did they ride altogether? Find the answer by rounding each decimal to the nearest whole number.

_____

Context Clues

Decide on the meaning of the underlined word in the sentences below. Circle its meaning below each sentence.

1. I used my dad's <u>shears</u> to cut a rope.
   a. knife   b. scissors   c. brush
2. His statement was <u>muddled</u> and could not be understood.
   a. knowing   b. stubborn   c. confusing
3. Carlos <u>deleted</u> his letter from the computer.
   a. removed   b. added   c. changed
4. Eagles are <u>scarce</u> because there are not many around.
   a. plentiful b. common   c. uncommon
5. In the early morning, fog makes it looks <u>hazy</u>.
   a. cloudy   b. clear   c. sunny
6. The stick <u>jabbed</u> me in the side when I fell down.
   a. cut   b. poked   c. scraped

 Writing Practice: Write a short story about two friends running against each other in a race.

Rounding Decimals

Round to the nearest whole number. Then solve problem 5.

1. 4.3 = _____	2. 9.78 = _____	3. 85.03 = _____

4. 7.1 = _____	5. Merlin walked 2.3 miles, Arnold walked 7.5 miles, William walked 3.1 miles, and Franklin walked 8.7 miles. Round each to the nearest whole number. How many miles did they walk in all? _____

Verbs

Fill in the chart with the correct form of the verb.

Present	Past	Past Participle
sing		sung
	rang	rung
read	read	
think		thought
	walked	walked
take		taken
sit	sat	
blow		blown

 Writing Practice: Write a story using the sentence starter below.

In the middle of the night, I was thirsty. When I got up, I couldn't believe my eyes . . .

Mixed Review with Decimals

Solve each problem.

1. 　　97,035.6 　+ 33,461.2	2. 　　39.87 　x　 .23	3. 　　6.470 　+ 3.998

4. 　　2.34 　x　 .56	5. Janice spent $12.46 at the store on Friday and $72.90 on Saturday. How much money did Janice spend in both days? _____ How much more money did she spend on Saturday than on Friday?_____

Adjectives

Write an adjective (a descriptive word) in front of each noun.

1. _____ stone
2. _____ shoes
3. _____ movie
4. _____ baseball game
5. _____ tree

6. _____ flower
7. _____ elephant
8. _____ classroom
9. _____ pizza
10. _____ cake

 Writing Practice: You are the President of the United States for one day. Write a paragraph and tell about what you did and what decisions you made for the country.

156

Mixed Review with Decimals

Solve each problem.

1. 27.83 + 9.75	2. 96.70 − 54.82	3. 43.03 x 6
4. 8)‾20.8‾	5. Miguel and his three friends found $33.60 on the ground in his yard. If they decide to split the money between each of them, how much would each person get? _____	

Possessives

Rewrite each group of words to make them show ownership.

1. the shoes of Josh   _____

2. the desks of the students _____

3. the wings of the geese   _____

4. the toys of the baby   _____

5. the homework of Julie   _____

6. the coats of the girls   _____

7. the flowers of the florist _____

8. the leaves of the tree   _____

 Writing Practice: Write a paragraph using the sentence starter below.

If I had a million dollars, I would . . .

Mixed Review with Decimals

Solve each problem below.

1.	2.	3.
3,461.8 + 88.75	2.4 − 1.63	6.03 x 8.4

4.	5. Write any number down. Add 10. Multiply by 4. Add 200. Divide by 4. Subtract the number you write down. What answer did you get? Everyone's answer should be the same.
2.3) 31.05	_____

Context Clues

Write the meaning of each underlined word by seeing how it is used in each sentence.

1. He <u>bellowed</u> with a loud voice.

   _____

2. I was <u>flabbergasted</u> at the outcome of the game.

   _____

3. Bradley <u>grimaced</u> with pain after he broke his foot.

   _____

4. The <u>massive</u> ship held 2,500 passengers.

   _____

5. Mom was <u>bewildered</u> when her watch wouldn't work.

   _____

6. The <u>replica</u> of the original flag was almost exact.

   _____

 Writing Practice: You get home from school, and you can't find your keys. No one is home. Write about what you would do.

158

Division with Decimals

Solve each problem.

1. $6\overline{)1.38}$	2. $5\overline{)49.5}$	3. $16\overline{)1.44}$

4. $32\overline{)2.88}$	5. Rope is 30¢ a meter. What is the cost for 1.8 meters of rope? _____

Sentences

Identify each sentence with an **S** (Simple Sentence) or with a **C** (Compound Sentence).

_____ 1. My sister and her friend like to ski.

_____ 2. JoAnn is my favorite skier, but she hasn't won a medal.

_____ 3. The competition was crowded, but we found a seat near the middle.

_____ 4. Jackson and JoAnn skied in the Olympics.

_____ 5. Someday I want to ski in the Olympics and win a medal.

_____ 6. Jackson was in a race, and he won the silver medal.

Writing Practice: Imagine you were in a race and won. Write a news report about your victory.

Division with Decimals

Solve each problem below.

1. $2\overline{)3.15}$	2. $4\overline{)7.82}$	3. $9\overline{)34.56}$

4. $4\overline{)19.48}$	5. Darryl worked 23 hours last week at $6.25 an hour. How much did he earn the entire week? _____

Sequencing

Put these steps in order.

Making a Mask

_____ Next, cut out eye holes.

_____ You need colored paper, scissors, an elastic band, and glue to make a mask.

_____ Then cut the mask to be the shape you want.

_____ First, cut a piece of paper to fit your head.

_____ Finally, punch holes on both sides and secure elastic bands.

_____ Now glue any decorations you want on your mask.

Writing Practice: If you could meet any person in history, who would it be? Why?

Division with Decimals

Solve the problems below.

1. $3\overline{)5.52}$	2. $4\overline{)8.24}$	3. $5\overline{)6.35}$

4.

$6\overline{)7.68}$

5. What is the median of the scores in Mr. Field's German class if they were the following scores: 100, 65, 60, 95, 80, 85, 65, 80, 90, 95, 75?

_____

Possessives

Write **C** if a possessive is used correctly. Write **I** if it is used incorrectly.

_____ 1. a few of Anna's friends

_____ 2. the science teachers' meetings

_____ 3. the books' author

_____ 4. the childrens' rooms

_____ 5. the cat's litter box

_____ 6. a box of women's clothes

Writing Practice: Use this writing prompt to write a short paragraph:

The thing I like best about myself is...

Division with Decimals

Solve each problem below.

1. 45.6 ÷ 100 = _____	2. 0.98 ÷ 10 = _____	3. 556 ÷ 100 = _____

4. 32.92 ÷ 100 = _____	5. The original price of a CD is $13.00. If it is on sale at $1.29 off, what is the price now? _____

Punctuation and Capitalization

Choose the correctly punctuated words.

1. a. J. K. rowling
   b. J K Rowling
   c. J. K. Rowling

2. a. Dr. T C Trane
   b. Dr. T. C. Trane
   c. Dr. t c Trane

3. a. Mesa verde Park
   b. Mesa Verde Park
   c. Mesa Verde park

4. a. James Lee, Jr.
   b. James Lee, jr.
   c. James Lee jr.

5. a. Turner St
   b. turner st.
   c. Turner St.

6. a. Mrs. Bette L. Scott
   b. Mrs. Bette L Scott
   c. Mrs Bette L. Scott

 Writing Practice: Write the safety rules for leaving your classroom and the school during a fire drill or actual fire.

Decimals and Fractions

Write the following decimals as a fraction. Then solve problem 5.

1. 0.67 = _____	2. 0.9 = _____	3. 0.212 = _____
4. 0.49 = _____	5. A grasshopper can jump 3 feet high and 20 times its length. If a grasshopper is 3.5 inches long, how far can it jump? _____	

Abbreviations

Unscramble the name of the state. Then match it to its abbreviation.

Nickname	State	Abbreviations
1. Heart of Dixie	(AAAAMBL) _____	_____
2. Last Frontier	(AAAKSL) _____	_____
3. Grand Canyon State	(AANROZI) _____	_____
4. Land of Opportunity	(AAASKRNS) _____	_____
5. Gem State	(IOHAD) _____	_____
6. Land of Lincoln	(IIILSLNO) _____	_____
7. Hoosier State	(IIAANND) _____	_____
8. Hawkeye State	(IAOW) _____	_____

Abbreviations

IA

ID

IN

IL

AZ

AR

AL

AK

Writing Practice: Hawaii is the only state that is a group of islands. Write a story about being alone on an island.

Decimals and Fractions

Write each problem as a fraction. Then solve problem 5.

1. .15 = _____	2. 3.6 = _____	3. 7.52 = _____
4. 1.07 = _____	5. There were 15 yards of material bought to make curtains for the school play. The total cost was $135.00. How much did each yard of material cost? _____	

Antonyms

Write an antonym for each word.

1. above _____

2. add _____

3. easy _____

4. leave _____

5. happy _____

6. heavy _____

7. many _____

8. brave _____

9. large _____

10. up _____

11. fat _____

12. long _____

13. clean _____

14. hard _____

15. shiny _____

16. wet _____

Writing Practice: If you were a talk show host, what two guests would you invite to be on your show? What two questions would you ask them?

Decimals and Fractions

For problems 1–2, write each fraction as a decimal. For problems 3–4, write each decimal as a fraction. Then solve problem 5.

1. $\dfrac{6}{10} =$ _____	2. $\dfrac{4}{10} =$ _____	3. .7 = _____
4. .2 = _____	5. The Watsons had a pizza for supper. It was divided into 8 slices. Joey, his mom, and his dad each had $\frac{1}{4}$ of the pizza. How many slices did each person eat? _____	

Alphabetical Order

Write these words in alphabetical order.

penny   _____

person   _____

pansy   _____

particular   _____

period   _____

ponder   _____

pick   _____

 Writing Practice: You have been chosen to make a speech at school about recycling. Write what you would say in your speech. Be sure to include the reasons why we should recycle.

Ratios

Write the ratio for each problem. Then solve problem 5.

1. triangles to squares	2. nickels in a dollar to pennies in a dollar	3. seconds in an hour to minutes in an hour

4. circles to rectangles

5. Milk, butter, yogurt, cheese, and juice are on a refrigerator shelf. If milk is between the yogurt and cheese, yogurt is between the milk and butter, and cheese is directly to the left of the juice, in what order will you find them?

_____

_____

Word Usage

Write a word that fits each group.

1. horsefly, wasp, bumblebee, _____

2. wolf, coyote, fox, _____

3. boa, anaconda, rattlesnake, _____

4. ear, nose, eye, _____

5. cafeteria, library, gymnasium, _____

6. cowboy, baseball, visor, _____

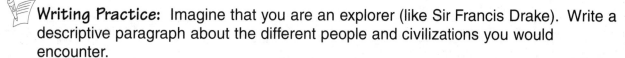 **Writing Practice:** Imagine that you are an explorer (like Sir Francis Drake). Write a descriptive paragraph about the different people and civilizations you would encounter.

Ratios

Write the ratio for each problem. Then solve problem 5.

1. shaded to nonshaded	2. X's to O's	3. numbers in a telephone number to numbers in a zip code
	OOO X X X OOO X X OO X X OO X	
_____	_____	_____

4. girls to boys in your class	5. The neighborhood grocery store donated 110 cartons of eggs to the school's annual egg hunt. If there are 12 eggs in a carton, how many total eggs are there?
_____	_____

Prefix/Suffix

Underline the base word in each word.

1. unwelcomed

2. unlovely

3. misquoted

4. misunderstood

5. renewed

6. disliked

7. misinterpreted

8. nonmetallic

 Writing Practice: What are good leadership traits?

Fractions

Write the fraction for the shaded part.

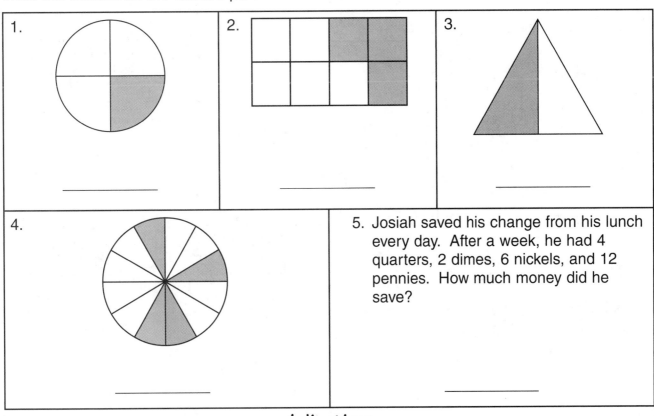

1.

_____

2.

_____

3.

_____

4.

_____

5. Josiah saved his change from his lunch every day. After a week, he had 4 quarters, 2 dimes, 6 nickels, and 12 pennies. How much money did he save?

_____

Adjectives

Unscramble each word to find an adjective. Then take the letters that are circled and fill them in order inside the boxes to find the message.

lamsl

eicn

shtor

clcethooa

erlya

ghhi

lysil

nnyuf

gunoy

renge

Message

Writing Practice: Write a paragraph describing what you would like to be when you become an adult.

Fractions

Write the mixed number represented by each picture and then solve problem 5.

1.
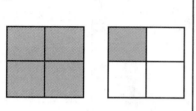
_____

2.

_____

3.
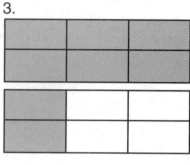
_____

4.

_____

5. The Titans' mascot weighs 186 pounds with his suit on. The suit weighs 1/6 of the total pounds. How much does the suit weigh? How much does the mascot weigh?

suit weight _____

mascot weight _____

Compound Words

Use the following words to make compound words.

life	apple	to	same
light	saver	search	board
self	morrow	your	light
side	self	pine	house

_____   _____

_____   _____

_____   _____

Writing Practice: Use this writing prompt to write a short story:

I went camping with my family. Everything was going fine until we heard a loud growl...

Fractions

Write the correct fraction expressed by the shaded part. Then solve problem 5.

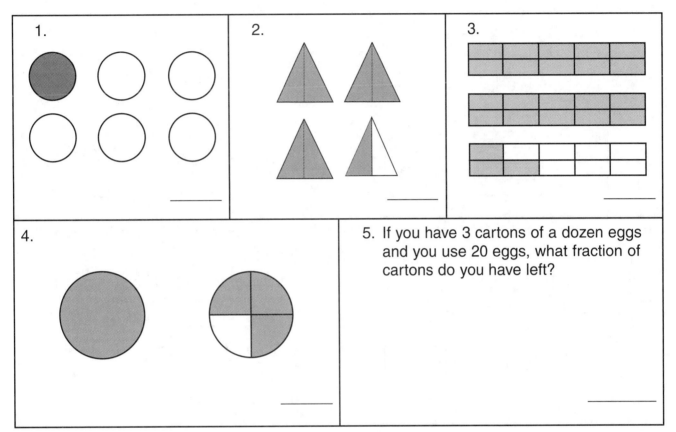

5. If you have 3 cartons of a dozen eggs and you use 20 eggs, what fraction of cartons do you have left?

Word Usage

Each word begins with the prefix *re*. Try to figure out the root word for each problem.

1. r e _____ _____ _____ _____ *(take from somewhere)*

2. r e _____ _____ _____ _____ _____ _____ *(to make as if new)*

3. r e _____ _____ _____ _____ *(to fix)*

4. r e _____ _____ _____ _____ _____ *(to have high regard for)*

5. r e _____ _____ _____ *(give answer)*

6. r e _____ _____ _____ _____ *(keeping; hold back)*

> **Riddle:** What does one do at night when he or she goes to bed?
>
> r e _____ _____ _____ _____ _____

 Writing Practice: If you had a million toothpicks, what would you build?

Fractions

Write <, >, or = between each fraction and then solve problem 5.

1.

$\frac{2}{4}$  $\frac{4}{8}$

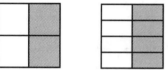

2.

$\frac{5}{8}$ $\frac{3}{8}$

3.

$\frac{4}{8}$ 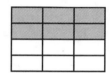 $\frac{6}{12}$

4.

$\frac{2}{10}$  $\frac{5}{20}$

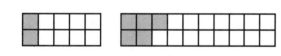

5. Aimee and her three friends ordered a pizza.

If they cut the pizza into 10 slices, how many pieces will each person get?

_____

Will there be any left over?

_____

If so, how many? _____

Homographs

Write two sentences with each word showing two different meanings.

1. star _____

_____

2. light _____

_____

3. letter _____

_____

4. stamp _____

_____

✎ **Writing Practice:** Write a paragraph explaining why schools have rules.

Equivalent Fractions

Fill in the missing number and then solve problem 5.

1. $$\frac{3}{12} = \frac{}{4}$$	2. $$\frac{2}{3} = \frac{}{9}$$	3. $$\frac{1}{2} = \frac{}{16}$$

4. $$\frac{4}{16} = \frac{}{4}$$	5. Justin's word in a word game made 12 points, but then it was doubled. Quentin's word made 20 points, but then it was tripled. What is Justin's and Quentin's score now? Justin's score = _____ Quentin's score = _____

Common/Proper Nouns

Fill in the blanks with nouns.

Common	Proper
city	_____
_____	Tennessee
river	_____
_____	Jupiter
boy	_____
_____	Dr. Simpson

 Writing Practice: Write a short story about living in the Mohave Desert. Circle each common noun and underline each proper noun.

Equivalent Fractions

For problems 1–4, write <, >, or = in each blank. Then solve problem 5.

1.

$\frac{1}{2}$ ◯ $\frac{3}{4}$

2.

$\frac{2}{3}$ ◯ $\frac{4}{6}$

3.

$\frac{1}{4}$ ◯ $\frac{1}{3}$

4.

$\frac{2}{3}$ ◯ $\frac{4}{5}$

5. How much did a team pay for jerseys if each jersey cost $9.00 and the team bought 3 dozen?

_____

Adjectives

Write the article *a* or *an* before each noun.

1. _____ house

2. _____ hour

3. _____ orange

4. _____ aunt

5. _____ job

6. _____ eye

7. _____ gorilla

8. _____ arm

9. _____ man

10. _____ old man

11. _____ elephant

12. _____ candy

13. _____ apple

14. _____ table

15. _____ chair

 Writing Practice: Write a story using the title below.

My Saddest Day

Equivalent Fractions

Fill in the blanks with the missing number. Then solve problem 5.

1.

$$\frac{1}{4} = \frac{}{16}$$

2.

$$\frac{3}{5} = \frac{}{20}$$

3.

$$\frac{5}{4} = \frac{}{16}$$

4.

$$\frac{2}{3} = \frac{}{12}$$

5. Brittani had 13 goldfish. Her mother bought her 6 more. The next day she found 2 dead. Then a week later one fish had 12 babies. How many goldfish does she now have?

_____

Prefixes

Circle each word with a prefix.

happiness	unclear	redone
jumping	helpless	preseason
careful	mender	disadvantage
misinterpret	capable	mistake

 Writing Practice: Write a paragraph using the sentence starter below.

When I get home from school, I . . .

Equivalent Fractions

Circle the correct answer for each unknown. Then solve problem 5.

1.	2.	3.
$\dfrac{4}{5} = \dfrac{?}{10}$	$\dfrac{?}{8} = \dfrac{28}{32}$	$\dfrac{2}{3} = \dfrac{14}{?}$
5 6 7 8	5 6 7 8	20 21 22 23

4.

$$\frac{11}{?} = \frac{22}{40}$$

20   21   22   23

5. Mr. Roberts bought T-shirts for his classroom of 27 students. If the total amount was $357.75, how much did each shirt cost?

_____

Spelling

Circle the correctly spelled form of each word.

1. greedly   greedily   greedlly

2. chillily   chillie   chilly

3. batty   battey   battie

4. riding   ridding   rideing

5. fortunatly   fortunately   fortunatelly

6. hideing   hidding   hiding

 Writing Practice: Write a descriptive paragraph about your neighborhood and community.

Equivalent Fractions

Cross out the fraction that is NOT equivalent to the first fraction. Then solve problem 5.

1. $\frac{4}{5}$	2. $\frac{5}{6}$	3. $\frac{2}{3}$
$\frac{16}{20}$ $\frac{20}{25}$ $\frac{18}{30}$ $\frac{12}{15}$	$\frac{10}{12}$ $\frac{20}{24}$ $\frac{30}{36}$ $\frac{15}{16}$	$\frac{4}{6}$ $\frac{10}{15}$ $\frac{16}{24}$ $\frac{8}{18}$

4. $\frac{3}{4}$

$\frac{9}{12}$ $\frac{18}{24}$ $\frac{12}{20}$ $\frac{24}{32}$

5. After 3 minutes into a basketball game, the score was 12 to 8. If this pattern continues, what would the score be after 12 minutes?

_____

Dictionary Skills

Look at the pronunciation of each pair of words. Circle the correct pronunciation that matches the definition.

1. con´ test   con test´   *competition or fight*

2. pro´ duce   pro duce´   *bring into existence*

3. re bel´   reb´ el   *person who rebels*

4. graj´ u āt   graj´ u it   *person who finishes school*

5. prez´ ent   pri zent´   *gift*

6. ob´ jekt   ob jekt´   *protest*

Writing Practice: If you were to create a charity to help others, how would it benefit your community and what would its purpose be?

Equivalent Fractions

Circle the correct answer that is equivalent to the given fraction. Then, solve problem 5.

1. $\frac{4}{5}$	2. $\frac{3}{7}$	3. $\frac{2}{3}$
$\frac{10}{18}$ $\frac{8}{10}$ $\frac{12}{22}$	$\frac{15}{35}$ $\frac{5}{14}$ $\frac{6}{12}$	$\frac{10}{16}$ $\frac{12}{20}$ $\frac{8}{12}$

4. $\frac{3}{4}$ $\frac{25}{30}$ $\frac{21}{28}$ $\frac{15}{18}$	5. Sharon wanted to buy a dress for her school dance. She had only $30.15, but the dress cost $59.87. How much more money does she need? _____

Verbs

Write sentences using these vivid verbs.

1. sobbed: _____

2. mumbled: _____

3. moaned: _____

4. protested: _____

5. gasped: _____

6. insisted: _____

 Writing Practice: Use this writing prompt to write a short paragraph:

I began my time travels by . . .

Comparing Fraction

For problems 1 and 2, arrange fractions from least to greatest. For problems 3 and 4, arrange fractions from greatest to least. Then solve problem 5.

1. $\dfrac{1}{5}$ $\dfrac{1}{2}$ $\dfrac{1}{3}$ $\dfrac{1}{6}$ _____	2. $\dfrac{2}{3}$ $\dfrac{1}{4}$ $\dfrac{3}{4}$ $\dfrac{1}{3}$ _____	3. $\dfrac{3}{9}$ $\dfrac{5}{35}$ $\dfrac{4}{16}$ $\dfrac{6}{30}$ _____

4. $\dfrac{3}{5}$ $\dfrac{1}{2}$ $\dfrac{2}{6}$ $\dfrac{1}{5}$ _____	5. If Bob has 4⅔ boxes of party favors left over from a party and gives Cindy ½ of them, how much do each get? _____

Adverbs

Circle the underlined word which is an adverb.

1. Buddy <u>said</u> that <u>math</u> <u>class</u> would start <u>soon</u>.

2. The <u>pizza</u> <u>was</u> delivered <u>promptly</u> at <u>our</u> house.

3. <u>Our</u> <u>team</u> played <u>well</u> <u>at</u> the tournament.

4. The turtle <u>walked</u> <u>slowly</u> <u>across</u> the <u>street</u>.

5. The <u>child</u> <u>ran</u> <u>away</u> <u>from</u> his mother.

6. He <u>searched</u> <u>longer</u> <u>than</u> <u>his</u> friends.

 Writing Practice: Why is it important to eat balanced, nutritional meals during the day?

178

Simplifying Fractions

For problems 1–4, Simply the fractions to lowest terms. Then solve problem 5.

| 1. $\frac{4}{6}$ = _____ | 2. $\frac{9}{18}$ = _____ | 3. $\frac{3}{15}$ = _____ |

| 4. $\frac{6}{8}$ = _____ | 5. The average speed limit on most highways is 65 miles per hour. If a car went exactly 65 mph, how far would it go in 5 hours? _____ |

Story Comprehension

Read the story and answer the following questions.

The Kiwi

The kiwi is the national emblem of Australia. The kiwi is a bird, like the eagle of the U. S., yet the kiwi cannot fly. Years ago, the kiwi was hunted for its valuable feathers, just as the American eagle was. The kiwi is a nocturnal animal, which means it comes out at night and sleeps during the day. It is considered the strangest bird of all birds.

1. What makes the kiwi a different kind of bird? _____

2. How is the kiwi like the eagle? _____

3. What is a nocturnal animal?_____

4. Why do you think the kiwi is a strange bird? _____

 Writing Practice: The turkey was almost named our national bird. Do you think the eagle was a better choice? Why or why not?

Simplifying Fractions

Simplify all fractions to their lowest terms. Then solve problem 5.

1. $\dfrac{10}{12}=$	2. $\dfrac{7}{42}=$	3. $\dfrac{9}{15}=$
4. $\dfrac{14}{20}=$	5. A can of vegetable soup contains 13 ounces. How many ounces are there in 57 cans? _____	

Spelling

Circle the word with the correct spelling.

1. receive   recieve   5. baloon   balloon

2. pade   paid   6. vacuum   vaccuum

3. rember   remember   7. ancient   anceint

4. efficient   eficcient   8. myriad   miriad

 Writing Practice: What is your favorite school subject? Why?

180

Mixed Fractions

Change each numeral to a mixed number or an improper fraction. Reduce to lowest terms. Then solve problem 5.

1. $8\frac{2}{3} = $ _____	2. $3\frac{8}{7} = $ _____	3. $15\frac{7}{10} = $ _____

4. $7\frac{4}{8} = $ _____	5. This past year the library bought 1,675 new books at the average cost of $9.00 per book. What was the total cost of books? _____

Dictionary Skills

Answer these questions about the dictionary entries.

cus´-tard	*n.* sweet milk and egg mixture; like pudding	
cus´-to-dy	*n.* 1. guardianship; care	2. legal restraint
cut´	*v.* 1. divide with sharp tool	2. wounding remark
cute´	*adj.* 1. attractive	2. clever

1. How many syllables does custody have? _____

2. What part of speech is cute? _____

3. Which syllable is accented in custard? _____

4. Which definition of cut means "her words cut me like a knife"? _____

 Writing Practice: Use this writing prompt to write a short paragraph:

The best gift I ever received was...

Improper Fractions

Change to mixed numerals. Then solve problem 5.

1. $\dfrac{17}{4}$ = _____	2. $\dfrac{23}{5}$ = _____	3. $\dfrac{47}{7}$ = _____
4. $\dfrac{99}{10}$ = _____	5. Tom played football for his school team. He made three touchdowns. His friend made two touchdowns. How many points did they score in the game? (**Hint:** touchdown = 6 points) _____	

Sentence/Fragment

Add the correct end mark to each complete sentence. Write a **F** if the sentence is incomplete.

1. Go fishing with Dad _____

2. The girls watching a scary movie _____

3. Hamilton read six books this month _____

4. He can teach his parrot to talk _____

5. A man in the boat _____

6. A million stars in the sky _____

7. We went to English class. We worked on our language sentences _____

8. Our teacher gave us treats for Valentine's Day _____

 Writing Practice: Write your own fairy tale about a frog and a princess.

Adding Fractions

Add these fractions with like denominators. Then solve problem 5.

1. $\frac{7}{8} + \frac{1}{8} =$ _____	2. $6\frac{1}{2} + 5 =$ _____	3. $3\frac{2}{7} + 1\frac{3}{7} =$ _____
4. $12\frac{7}{18} + 11\frac{2}{18} =$ _____	5. Mrs. McWilliams made treat bags for her class. She has 18 students and 86 treats. How many treats will go in each bag, if they all have equal amounts? _____	

Syllables

Circle the word that is correctly divided into syllables.

1.
 a. col-lect
 b. co-mmand
 c. conn-ect

2.
 a. ag-ain
 b. dis-tance
 c. exem-pt

3.
 a. harv-est
 b. gut-ter
 c. i-sland

4.
 a. mi-stake
 b. nec-klace
 c. op-tion

5.
 a. vap-or
 b. hot-el
 c. bi-son

6.
 a. pap-er
 b. sil-ver
 c. flo-wer

Writing Practice: If you were shipwrecked on an island, what five things would you want? Be sure to tell why you chose those things.

Adding Fractions

Add these fractions. Reduce to lowest terms. Then solve problem 5.

1. $\frac{2}{3} + \frac{4}{9} =$	2. $7\frac{7}{12} + 2\frac{4}{24} =$	3. $\frac{6}{10} + \frac{6}{12} =$

4. $12\frac{6}{7} + 4\frac{11}{21} =$

5. If it's March 1 and Felicia's birthday is 6 months and 8 days away, when is her birthday?

_____

Sentences

Write **S** for sentence, **F** for fragment, or **R** for run-on.

_____ 1. Jane reads a book I read it, too.

_____ 2. Her sister sings songs and dances.

_____ 3. Sitting quietly while she watches television.

_____ 4. Many sisters in the house.

_____ 5. Jane had a pet it was a cat.

_____ 6. Her cat was a yellow striped tabby.

 Writing Practice: Write what qualities you think would make a good teacher and a good student.

Adding Fractions

For problems 1–4, add the mixed numbers. Then solve problem 5.

1. $8\frac{2}{7} + 4\frac{3}{7} =$ _____	2. $5\frac{2}{5} + 6\frac{1}{5} =$ _____	3. $9\frac{3}{8} + 1\frac{4}{8} =$ _____

4. $6\frac{2}{9} + 6\frac{5}{9} =$ _____	5. Jimmy lives $\frac{1}{3}$ of a mile away from the baseball field. If he walks there in the morning, back home for lunch, back to the field, and then back home for dinner, how far has he walked? _____

Analogies

Complete each analogy.

1. dog is to puppy as cow is to _____

2. ship is to sail as car is to _____

3. book is to read as music is to_____

4. on is to off as here is to _____

5. come is to came as some is to_____

6. pencil is to paper as paintbrush is to _____

7. tan is to brown as pink is to _____

8. milk is to cup as coffee is to _____

 Writing Practice: Create a newspaper article with the heading below.

Extra! Extra! Read All About It!

Subtracting Fractions

Subtract these fractions with like denominators. Then solve problem 5.

1. $\dfrac{7}{8} - \dfrac{2}{8} =$ _____	2. $\dfrac{12}{15} - \dfrac{3}{15} =$ _____	3. $8\dfrac{3}{4} - \dfrac{1}{4} =$ _____
4. $5\dfrac{9}{12} - 4\dfrac{1}{12} =$ _____	5. Javier wants to buy CDs with his birthday money. He received $30.00 from his grandma. If each CD cost $14.97, how many CD's can he buy? _____	

Analogies

Complete each analogy.

1. Orange is to fruit as almond is to _____.

2. Foot is to shoe as _____ is to glove.

3. Remote is to _____ as joystick is to video game.

4. Snow is to shovel as _____ is to back-hoe.

5. _____ is to hot as black is to white.

6. Stripes are to tigers as spots are to _____.

 Writing Practice: Write a paragraph using the title below.

Things I Remember Most About Kindergarten

Subtracting Fractions

For problems 1–4, subtract the mixed numbers. Then solve problem 5.

1. $12\frac{8}{9} - 7\frac{7}{9} =$ _____	2. $15\frac{5}{8} - 9\frac{2}{8} =$ _____	3. $22\frac{2}{3} - 11\frac{1}{3} =$ _____

4. $16\frac{4}{5} - 8\frac{2}{5} =$ _____

5. The perimeter of an octagon is 40 feet. All the sides have equal length. How long are they?

_____

Capitalization

Write a sentence that corresponds with each capitalization rule. Be sure to use correct capital letters.

1. Begin every sentence with a capital letter.

   _____

2. Proper nouns begin with capital letters (city, state, street, river, etc.).

   _____

3. The pronoun I is always capitalized.

   _____

4. Titles are capitalized when they are used before names.

   _____

5. Capitalize the first and last word and all other important words in the titles of books.

   _____

6. All holidays, days of the week, and months of the year begin with a capital letter.

   _____

Writing Practice: On a separate piece of paper, finish the story below.

Yesterday, I was walking down the street and a stranger stopped me. I was frightened, but he only wanted help.

Adding and Subtracting Fractions

Solve each problem.

1. $\dfrac{3}{8} + \dfrac{2}{8} + \dfrac{1}{8} =$ _____	2. $\dfrac{11}{12} - \dfrac{9}{12} =$ _____	3. $\dfrac{20}{25} - \dfrac{4}{5} =$ _____

4.

$$12\,\frac{2}{9} + 7\,\frac{4}{18} = \underline{\hspace{2cm}}$$

5. Amy walked $\dfrac{2}{10}$ of a mile to the park. Johnson walked $\dfrac{7}{10}$ of a mile to the park.

How many total miles did they walk?

_____

Who walked the farthest?

_____

Vocabulary

Write a word from the word bank.

Word Bank

breezy	blossom	shamrock	air
spring	kite	pot-of-gold	lamb

1. a flower

_____

2. windy

_____

3. a clover

_____

4. at the end of a rainbow

_____

5. season after winter

_____

6. farm animal

_____

7. atmosphere

_____

8. child's toy

_____

 Writing Practice: Write a descriptive paragraph about spending the day at the beach.

Adding and Subtracting Fractions

Solve each problem. Reduce to lowest terms.

1. $2\frac{2}{9} + 4\frac{7}{9} = $ _____	2. $12\frac{4}{16} - 8\frac{3}{16} = $ _____	3. $32\frac{4}{7} + 4\frac{5}{7} = $ _____

4. $8\frac{8}{9} - 5\frac{6}{9} = $ _____

5. Kim Ling had 41 marbles. Her friend had 28. Kim gave her friend some of her marbles. Now Kim has 29.

How many did Kim give her friend?

_____

How many does her friend have now?

_____

Alphabetical Order

Write the following groups of words in alphabetical order.

1. ensign _____
   engine _____
   envelope _____
   enamel _____
   enormous _____
   enchant _____
   enjoy _____

2. grass _____
   grammar _____
   grassy _____
   gray _____
   grab _____
   gravel _____
   grade _____

 Writing Practice: What fun thing (or things) did you do this past weekend? Write about your adventures.

Adding and Subtracting Fractions

Add or subtract each pair of fractions and then simplify. Then solve problem 5.

1. $\dfrac{5}{12} + \dfrac{6}{12} =$	2. $\dfrac{15}{16} + \dfrac{8}{16} =$	3. $16\dfrac{7}{8} + 5\dfrac{1}{8} =$

4. $9\dfrac{13}{15} - 3\dfrac{7}{15} =$	5. In a fraction, the denominator is 6 more than the numerator. If you add the numerator and the denominator together, you get 28. What is the fraction? _____

Verbs

Write whether the verb is linking or action.

1. Carrie feels sick.   _____

   Carrie feels the dog's fur.   _____

2. The baby's diaper smells bad.   _____

   The baby smells the baby powder.   _____

3. My sister turned ten today.   _____

   My sister turned her ankle playing basketball.   _____

4. Pizza tastes delicious.   _____

   Caroline tastes pizza.   _____

 Writing Practice: Write a story using this title:

Hurray! The circus is coming to town!

Adding and Subtracting Fractions

Add or subtract and reduce to the lowest term. Then solve problem 5.

1. $\dfrac{3}{4}$ $+\ 6\dfrac{3}{8}$ ____	2. 22 $-\ 7\dfrac{4}{10}$ ____	3. $11\dfrac{1}{2}$ $+\ \dfrac{9}{12}$ ____

4. 28 $-\ 3\dfrac{3}{5}$ ____	5. Jessie Blanks set a record in the long jump of 7 ft. The old record was only $6\dfrac{3}{4}$ ft. By how much did he break the record? _____

Suffixes

Rewrite the italicized words with a suffix and a base word.

1. An act of *quality of being kind* will never be forgotten.   _____

2. The policeman was *without fear* in his daily duties.   _____

3. She was *full of care* not to spill her milk.   _____

4. The *one who skis* flew down the slope.   _____

5. Her new outfit was *able to be in comfort.*   _____

6. The students were *having worth* of a special treat.   _____

 Writing Practice: Design a futuristic car. Describe how it looks and what makes it run.

Multiplying Fractions

For problems 1–4, fill in the blanks. Then solve problem 5.

1. $\frac{1}{8} \times \frac{16}{7} =$ _____	2. $\frac{1}{3} \times \frac{24}{5} =$ _____	3. $\frac{3}{4} \times \frac{2}{8} =$ _____

4.

$\frac{1}{7} \times \frac{21}{4} =$ _____

5. It is 398 miles to Aunt Edna's house. The train goes 80 miles per hour. About how many hours will it take to get to her house?

_____

Sequencing

Read the story. Number the sentences so that they are in correct order.

The Camping Trip

Dad told Ben that their scout camping trip would be on Friday. He told him to pack his bags. Ben thought about what he should pack. Then he packed his clothes, his camping gear, his scout manual, his football, and his sleeping bag. After he finished packing, he told his dad he was ready to go! Finally, on Friday, they left for the scout camping trip.

____ Ben and his dad went camping.

____ Dad told Ben about the camping trip.

____ Dad told Ben to pack.

____ Ben packed his clothes.

____ Ben decided what to pack.

 Writing Practice: You are going to make a time capsule about yourself. What would you put in your time capsule, and why?

Multiplying Fractions

Multiply fractions. Reduce to lowest terms. Then solve problem 5.

1. $\dfrac{7}{8} \times \dfrac{2}{7} =$	2. $\dfrac{2}{5} \times \dfrac{3}{10} =$	3. $\dfrac{9}{14} \times \dfrac{7}{9} =$

4. $\dfrac{16}{24} \times \dfrac{6}{8} =$	5. If Bob ate 2/6 of the cake and John ate 1/3 of the cake, who ate more? _____

Analogies

Complete each analogy.

1. read is to library as worship is to _____

2. laugh is to cry as lively is to _____

3. students are to school as patients are to _____

4. antonym is to synonym as big is to _____

5. pickle is to jar as egg is to _____

6. fake is to real as hot is to _____

 Writing Practice: Use this writing prompt to write a short paragraph:

The best day at school was...

Dividing Fractions

Divide the fractions and reduce to lowest terms. Then solve problem 5.

1.

$$\frac{3}{5} \div \frac{8}{9} =$$

2.

$$\frac{2}{7} \div \frac{4}{5} =$$

3.

$$\frac{7}{8} \div \frac{2}{7} =$$

4.

$$\frac{12}{14} \div \frac{3}{4} =$$

5. Basset School needs two 48-seat buses to take the football team to the playoffs. They will have only 6 vacant seats. How many people will be riding the bus?

_____

Alphabetical Order

Write each group of words in alphabetical order.

1. prohibit, probate, proud, proclaim

_____

2. further, fuel, fuzz, furlough

_____

3. commune, communicate, commotion, community

_____

4. span, spatter, space, spacious

_____

5. receipt, realize, react, reason

_____

6. overlay, overlook, overhaul, overseas

_____

 Writing Practice: When does a rainbow appear? Why does it appear?

Dividing Fractions

Solve each problem below.

1. $\dfrac{2}{3} \div \dfrac{12}{18} =$	2. $\dfrac{4}{5} \div \dfrac{6}{8} =$	3. $\dfrac{7}{12} \div \dfrac{3}{4} =$

4. $\dfrac{2}{5} \div \dfrac{9}{12} =$

5. The temperature in Minnesota was -5° F. If it dropped 4°, what would be the new temperature?

_____

Main Idea

Write a category for each group of words.

1. tree
   children
   grass
   mold
   category _____

2. rose
   carnation
   marigold
   daffodil
   category _____

3. peanuts
   potatoes
   treasure
   fossil
   category _____

4. hairbrush
   comb
   headband
   barrette
   category _____

 Writing Practice: Why is it important to protect endangered animals and rain forests?

Mixed Fractions

Write +, −, ÷, or x in each box to make each equation correct. Then solve problem 5.

1. $\dfrac{2}{3} \boxed{} \dfrac{2}{3} = \dfrac{4}{9}$	**2.** $\dfrac{2}{7} \boxed{} \dfrac{8}{14} = \dfrac{6}{7}$	**3.** $1\dfrac{4}{5} \boxed{} \dfrac{3}{4} = 1\dfrac{1}{20}$
4. $\dfrac{3}{4} \boxed{} \dfrac{7}{9} = \dfrac{7}{12}$	**5.** A 35 mm camera costs \$72.00, but it's on sale for 20% off. How much does it cost now? _____	

Antonyms

Circle the antonym for the first word in each row.

1. abolish   destroy   restore

2. begin   start   terminate

3. correct   false   accurate

4. dingy   dull   bright

5. expect   surprise   anticipate

6. famous   celebrated   unknown

 Writing Practice: Write about similarities and differences between doctors and lawyers.

Percents and Fractions

For problems 1–4, write the fraction as a percentage. Then solve problem 5.

1. $\frac{1}{2} = $ _____ %	2. $\frac{1}{4} = $ _____ %	3. $\frac{1}{5} = $ _____ %

4.

$\frac{1}{10} = $ _____ %

5. In a football game, a touchdown plus the extra point gets 7 points and a field goal gets 3 points. If one team's score is 15 points, how many touchdowns and field goals have they scored?

_____

Synonyms

Write a synonym for each underlined word.

1. You are <u>correct</u>.   _____

2. It <u>arrived</u> yesterday.   _____

3. Mom sang her baby a <u>lullaby</u>.   _____

4. Ghosts don't <u>scare</u> me.   _____

5. The students were <u>quiet</u>.   _____

6. What was the <u>name</u> of the song?   _____

7. The <u>shears</u> were sharp.   _____

8. I sat on the <u>sofa</u>.   _____

 Writing Practice: Write a paragraph using the sentence starter below.

The last thing I want to do this year is . . .

Percents and Fractions

For problems 1–4, write each percent as a fraction. Make sure to reduce each answer. Then solve problem 5.

1. 17% = _____	2. 35% = _____	3. 75% = _____

4. 20% = _____	5. The perimeter of a triangle is 58 meters. One side is 18 meters long, and another side is 25 meters long. How long is the third side? _____

Possessives

Write the correct possessive in the blank.

1. The cat has a toy mouse. Evan played with the _____ toy mouse.

2. My sisters have dolls. My _____ dolls are fun to play with.

3. Sue Ellen is on the basketball team. We saw _____ team play yesterday.

4. Her uncle has a bicycle shop. Her _____ bicycle shop is on Third Street.

5. The pencils belong to the students. The _____ pencils were on their desks.

6. The birds sing merrily. The _____ song is sweet to hear.

Writing Practice: Write a paragraph using the sentence starter below.

"Well, it's about time you came . . ."

Percents

Write each number as a percent. Then solve problem 5.

1. 6 out of 100 _____	2. $\frac{43}{100}$ _____	3. 58 to 100 _____
4. $\frac{79}{100}$ _____		5. Tami had $1.00. She spent 42¢. What percent of a dollar does she have left? _____

Analogies

Complete each analogy.

1. animal is to herd as person is to _____

2. drought is to dry as rain is to _____

3. end is to begin as finish is to _____

4. clean is to neat as _____ is to grimy

5. adult is to thirty as _____ is to ten

6. small is to enormous as _____ is to difficult

 Writing Practice: Write the steps involved in baking a cake or cupcakes.

Percents

Solve each problem below.

1. 20% of 40 _____	**2.** 25% of 100 _____	**3.** 50% of 30 _____

4. $33\frac{1}{3}$ % of 99 _____	**5.** If your eyes blink about 20 times per minute, how many times will you blink in an hour? _____

Cause/Effect

Underline the word that signals a cause or effect relationship.

1. The teacher gave a retest because so many students were absent.

2. Since we had a mild winter, we will have a hot summer.

3. I didn't feel safe when the news said a tornado was coming.

4. If you work hard, you should do well on the test.

5. As the day went on, the rain turned to snow.

6. The bicycle wouldn't go since the tires were flat.

 Writing Practice: How do you feel when you accomplish a goal that you worked hard to achieve? Give a recent example of a goal that you have set and met.

Percents

Calculate the percent. Then solve problem 5.

1. 8% of 20 _____	2. 6% of 16 _____	3. 100% of 239 _____
4. 12% of 65 _____	5. Mrs. Coleman begins her first class at 8:45 A.M. If her next class starts 52 minutes later, what time does it start? _____	

Dictionary Skills

Read the entry and definitions. Identify the best meaning for each underlined word.

> **hold**   *v.* 1. have in the hand.   2. keep from moving or changing.   3. embrace.
> 4. contain.   5. remain firm or fixed.   6. cargo space (also, holding or held).

_____ a. We had to <u>hold</u> our luggage for 1 hour.

_____ b. It couldn't be put in the <u>holding</u> area.

_____ c. We <u>held</u> our niece before boarding the plane.

_____ d. Our eyes <u>held</u> each other anxiously.

_____ e. Finally, we <u>held</u> our breath as the plane took off.

_____ f. Our carry-on bag <u>held</u> pictures of our visit.

Writing Practice: If you could create a new language and alphabet, what would it be like? How would it be useful for people?

Fractions/Decimals/Percents

For problems 1–4, fill in the blanks on the chart. Then solve problem 5.

1.
Fraction = $\frac{33}{100}$

Decimal = _____

Percent = 33%

2.
Fraction = _____

Decimal = .54

Percent = 54%

3.
Fraction = $\frac{77}{100}$

Decimal = .77

Percent = _____

4.
Fraction = $\frac{12}{100}$

Decimal = _____

Percent = 12%

5. A television Joe wanted cost $185.00. He noticed the store put it on sale at 25% off. How much would the television cost after the discount?

_____

Compound Sentences

Add a connecting word and finish each sentence to make a compound sentence.

1. My best friend is nice, _____

_____.

2. Our cat likes to lay on the couch, _____

_____.

3. My math teacher is strict, _____

_____.

4. Mac sings in the shower, _____

_____.

5. Harry wants to go bowling, _____

_____.

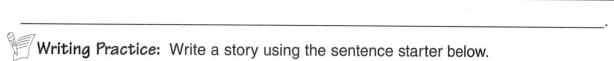 **Writing Practice:** Write a story using the sentence starter below.

I went ice skating on the pond, when suddenly I heard a cracking sound . . .

202

Time

Write how many hours are between the times given. Then solve problem 5.

1. 2:00 P.M. and 10:00 P.M.	2. 6:00 A.M. and 1:00 P.M.	3. 1:18 A.M. and 10:18 P.M.
		_____
_____	_____	

4. 12:00 P.M. and 12:00 A.M.	5. Mehul called his friend Jim at 2:23 P.M. to come over and work on their school project. If they met at 6:30 P.M., how long would it be before they began working?
_____	_____

Prefixes

Match the correct **en** prefix word with its definition.

_____ 1. get pleasure from	a. enslave
_____ 2. commit	b. engage
_____ 3. wrap	c. entrap
_____ 4. put name on a list	d. enjoy
_____ 5. make a slave of	e. enfold
_____ 6. on the way	f. enliven
_____ 7. make lively	g. enroll
_____ 8. catch	h. enroute

Writing Practice: Write a paragraph using the sentence starter below.

Everyone in the room started to laugh when . . .

Time

Read the times and write A.M. or P.M.

1. 6:30 (sunrise) _____	2. 3:00 (day) _____	3. 8:30 (bedtime) _____
4. 1:00 (night) _____		5. It is 8:00 A.M. If 12 hours go by, is it 8:00 A.M. or P.M.? _____

Dictionary Skills

Read each definition for *back*. Decide which definition best fits each sentence. Write the letter of the correct definition in each blank.

a. part of a person opposite the face	c. related to the past
b. uppermost part of an animal	d. at the rear
	e. spine

_____ 1. Tyra hurt her back playing volleyball.

_____ 2. Jerrod was told to go to the back of the line.

_____ 3. Michael likes to pet his dog on his back.

_____ 4. Shannon turned around and went back to school.

_____ 5. I combed the back of my hair.

Writing Practice: What part of the school day do you like the best? Write a paragraph telling about your favorite part of school.

204

Time

Write how many minutes are between the given times. Then solve problem 5.

1. 6:00 A.M. and 6:25 A.M. _____	2. 4:25 P.M. and 5:10 P.M. _____	3. 2:30 A.M. and 2:56 A.M. _____
4. 11:55 P.M. and 12:05 A.M. _____	5. Jan gets up at 7:20 A.M. She goes to school at 8:05 A.M. How much time does she have to get ready? _____ Her class comes back from lunch at 12:00. Is this A.M. or P.M.? _____	

Abbreviations

Choose the correct abbreviation of each state.

MA	ME	MN	MS	WA	WV
MD	MI	MO	MT	WI	WY

Maine _____   Maryland _____   Massachusetts _____

Michigan _____   Minnesota _____   Mississippi _____

Missouri _____   Montana _____   Washington _____

West Virginia _____ Wisconsin _____   Wyoming _____

 Writing Practice: If you could plan the ideal trip across the United States, where would you go and why?

Time

If 60 seconds (sec) equals 1 minute (min) and if 60 minutes (min) equals 1 hour (hr), calculate the times in the problems below and then solve problem 5.

1.	2.	3.
93 sec = _____ min _____ sec	76 min = _____ min _____ sec	12 hrs = _____ min

4.	5. Michelle walks 45 minutes everyday. How many total hours and minutes does she walk in one week?
41 min = _____ sec	_____ hrs _____ min

Proofreading

Copy each sentence correctly.

1. didn't they put on a play in november

_____

2. there class saw two playes this year

_____

3. have you ever ben to cape canaveral

_____

4. next yeare bobs aunt will work for the post office

_____

5. the olympics is fun too watch

_____

6. I like the knew sport called snowboarding

_____

 Writing Practice: Describe a sporting event you would like to compete in during an upcoming Olympics. What kind of training would be involved? What kind of time and dedication would you have to give towards your training?

Time

Calculate how much time has passed in each problem. Then solve problem 5.

1. 8:10 A.M. to 3:40 P.M. _____	2. 12:46 P.M. to 9:06 P.M. _____	3. 5:28 A.M. to 12:00 P.M. _____
4. 10:37 P.M. to 9:00 A.M. _____	5. It's 38° at 7:00 A.M. By 3:00 P.M. it is 52°. How much did the temperature rise? _____	

Possessives

Fill in the chart with the correct possessive nouns.

Noun	Singular Possessive	Plural Possessive
class		
town		
child		
beach		
whale		

 Writing Practice: Write a letter to your local newspaper expressing your concerns and views about an issue (examples: pollution, driving safety, pet adoption, etc.) that you feel needs some attention.

Time

Solve the problems below.

1. $2\frac{1}{2}$ hours after 6 A.M. _____	2. 3 hours 45 minutes before 7 P.M. _____	3. 420 seconds = _____ minutes
4. 35 days = _____ weeks	5. Find the batting average of Ty Cobb. He hit 4,191 times out of 11,429 times at bat. _____	

Synonyms/Antonyms

Determine whether each pair of words is a synonym (**S**) or an antonym (**A**).

_____ 1. grief – mourning

_____ 2. flood – drought

_____ 3. establish – settle

_____ 4. oval – oblong

_____ 5. wander – halt

_____ 6. ugly – hideous

_____ 7. special – extraordinary

_____ 8. thick – sparse

 Writing Practice: If you could design your own school, describe how it would be different from or similar to the one you currently attend.

208

Reading a Graph

Use the pictograph to answer the questions.

1. Which student was tardy the most? _____	2. Which student was tardy 3 days? _____	3. How many times was Joe tardy? _____

4. If each ✻ meant 2 days of being tardy, how many days would Beth have been tardy?

_____

Students With Tardies

Sue	✻ ✻ ✻
Tamika	✻
Joe	✻ ✻
Jamal	✻ ✻ ✻ ✻ ✻
Beth	✻ ✻

✻ = 1 tardy

Subject and Predicate

Read each sentence. Decide how the underlined words are used.

_____ 1. The <u>football team</u> played a game yesterday.

_____ 2. The rabbits <u>hopped and jumped</u> in the grass.

_____ 3. Sunshine <u>is</u> very warm on your face.

_____ 4. <u>Donna and Jane</u> are best friends.

A. Simple Subject

B. Simple Predicate

C. Compound Subject

D. Compound Predicate

 Writing Practice: August is National Invention Month. Describe something you would like to invent and then draw a picture of it.

Reading a Graph

Use the bar graph to answer the questions.

1. How many horses are on the farm? _____	2. Are there more pigs or goats? _____
3. On the farm there are 20 of what animal? _____	4. What is the total number of pigs and horses? _____

Animals on the Farm

(bar graph: horses = 80, goats = 50, pigs = 66, chickens = 20; y-axis 0 to 90)

Possessive Nouns

Add an **'s** or **'** to each word to show ownership.

1. The child _____ toy was put on the shelf.

2. Please turn your papers in the teacher _____ box.

3. Bobby found his friends _____ baseball cards outside.

4. Mrs. Saxton _____ students went on a field trip.

5. The dog _____ bone was buried under the tree.

 Writing Practice: Write a paragraph describing a time you went to a fair. Include your favorite ride and all the things you saw.

Reading a Graph

Study the graph and answer the questions.

1. How many chocolate ice cream cones were sold?	2. Which flavor of ice cream sold the most?	3. How many more strawberry cones were sold than vanilla cones?
_____	_____	_____

4. How many ice cream cones were sold in all? _____	**Ice Cream Cones Sold on Sunday** Chocolate Vanilla Strawberry Sherbet = 10 cones

Punctuation

Add a colon (:) or a semicolon (;) to each sentence.

1. Shari felt funny ___ her stomach hurt.

2. She had just been to the fair ___ it was fun.

3. She rode many rides ___ the ferris wheel, the swings, and the bumper cars.

4. Shari had eaten before the rides ___ it was a mistake.

5. Shari ate these foods ___ popcorn, a hot dog, two sodas, and cotton candy.

6. She knew her mom would come home at 5___00.

Writing Practice: Write about what you like and dislike about where you live.

Reading a Graph

Use the bar graph to answer each question.

1. Which city is the largest in population? _____	2. Which city has less than 100,000 in population? _____	3. Where does Nashville rank (first, second, third, fourth, fifth)? _____
4. Which two cities have almost the same amount in population? _____ _____	**5 Largest Cities in Tennessee** 700 600 500 400 300 200 100 0 Memphis Nashville Knoxville Chattanooga Clarksville *population in thousands	

Direct Objects

Complete each sentence with a direct object.

1. Jamal closed the _____.

2. We ate our _____.

3. He caught the _____.

4. Mr. Blair wrote a _____.

5. Someone took my _____.

6. I like to ride my _____.

7. She read a _____.

8. I like to play _____.

Writing Practice: Write a paragraph using the sentence starter.

I remember when . . .

212

Reading a Graph

Answer the questions about the graph below.

1. How many fish did Robert catch?	2. How many fish were caught altogether?	3. Who caught the same number of fish?

4. How many more fish did Jalisa catch than Ashley?

Name	Number of Fish
Robert	🐟 🐟 🐟
Ashley	🐟
J. J.	🐟 🐟
Jalisa	🐟 🐟 🐟 🐟 🐟
Dixie	🐟 🐟

🐟 = 3 fish

Proofreading

Rewrite the sentences correctly.

1. scotts father said the month of march is finalle here

_____

2. the white house is in washington dc

_____

3. Janessa alway smiles and she seem happy

_____

4. will she helps uus chek our homework?

_____

5. my Friend is leaveing next weak

_____

6. his mother weights for him and he wants to sea her

_____

Writing Practice: Write a paragraph about why you think we need our circulatory system.

Reading a Graph

Answer the questions about the graph.

1. On which days were 3 students absent?

   _____

   _____

2. Which day had the most students absent?

   _____

3. Were more students absent on Wednesday or Thursday?

   _____

4. How many more students were absent on Tuesday than Wednesday?

   _____

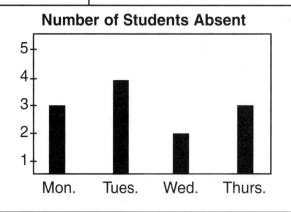

Number of Students Absent

Direct Object

Circle the direct object in each sentence.

1. Sancho threw the football to Jim.

2. Mom ate popcorn after supper.

3. Harriet Tubman led slaves to freedom.

4. The children smelled the bright flowers.

5. Ed played the trumpet in band class.

 Writing Practice: Write a story using the sentence starter below.

I was in a haunted house . . .

214

Reading a Graph

Use the graph to answer the following questions.

1. How old is Marques?	2. Who is oldest?	3. How much older is Greg than Marques?
_____	_____	_____

4. What is the difference in the ages of Greg and Maria?	
	Ages of Siblings 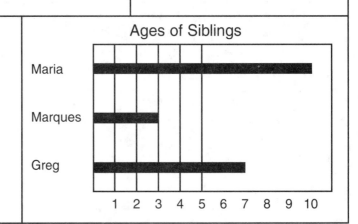
_____	

Possessive Nouns

Write the possessive form of each singular noun. Then write a sentence with each one.

	Possessive	**Sentence**
1. boy	_____	_____
2. Susan	_____	_____
3. dog	_____	_____
4. sky	_____	_____
5. teacher	_____	_____
6. mom	_____	_____

Writing Practice: Write a descriptive paragraph about the month of September. Include things you like or dislike.

Reading a Graph

Answer the questions about the circle graph.

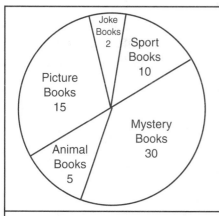

Joke Books 2
Sport Books 10
Picture Books 15
Mystery Books 30
Animal Books 5

1. How many students checked out books altogether?

_____

2. Which type of book is checked out twice as much as picture books?

_____

3. How many more students checked out mystery books than animal books?

_____

4. What is the least popular book?

_____

Which type of book is checked out the most?

_____

Fact or Opinion

Write **F** if the statement is fact and **O** if the statement is opinion.

_____ 1. Rabbits are furry animals.

_____ 2. Spiders are ugly.

_____ 3. Basketball is easier to play than baseball.

_____ 4. My dad is 6' 3" tall.

_____ 5. Squash tastes terrible!

_____ 6. Lansing is the capital of Michigan.

_____ 7. Fish breathe through gills.

_____ 8. You shouldn't watch too much television.

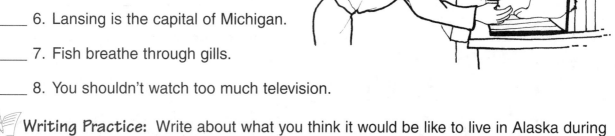

Writing Practice: Write about what you think it would be like to live in Alaska during the season when it's dark 24 hours a day.

216

Reading a Graph

Answer each question about the graph.

1. Which activity is enjoyed the most? _____	2. How many more people go on vacation than go to camp? _____	3. Which activities have the same number of people? _____ _____
4. Which activity is enjoyed the least? _____	**Things to Do During Summer** 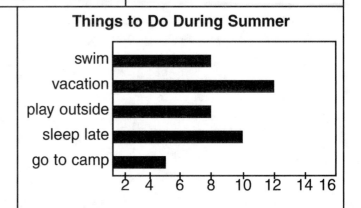	

Kinds of Sentences

Label each sentence with the correct letter.

_____ 1. Are you going today?

_____ 2. You are going today.

_____ 3. Where are you going today?

_____ 4. Please go today.

_____ 5. We're going today!

_____ 6. We're going today?

_____ 7. We're going today.

_____ 8. You need to go right now!

a. declarative
b. interrogative
c. imperative
d. exclamatory

 Writing Practice: What do you think your pencil would say if it could talk? Write a story about what your pencil would say.

Reading a Graph

Using the graph provided, answer the questions below.

1. How many people visited the Fitness Club in March?	2. How much did the visits to the gym decrease from March to April?	3. During what month did the number of visits increase to over 250?
_____	_____	_____

4. Do people visit more in the winter or fall of the year? _____	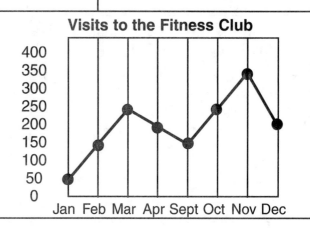 **Visits to the Fitness Club**

Abbreviations

Write the abbreviation above each underlined word.

1. Doctor John Miller is my mother's doctor.

2. On Monday, January 29, I visited Mister Serra's house.

3. She lives on 44 Jacob Street in Boston, Massachusetts.

4. We will meet for lunch at 12:00 post meridian on Tuesday.

5. The T. F. Hall Company is located on Rosswell Boulevard.

6. The Department of Agriculture had their meeting last November.

 Writing Practice: If you could be president of the United States, what kind of changes would you make to better the country?

Reading a Graph

Answer the questions using the provided pictograph.

1. How many students ate pizza?	2. How many students ate corn dogs?	3. How many students ate fries?
_____	_____	_____

4. How many more students ate pizza than salad?	**Student's Lunch on Friday** 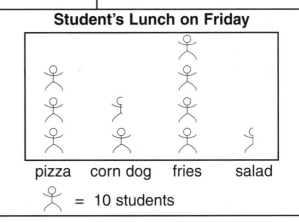
_____	

Cause/Effect

Underline the effect in each sentence.

1. I go to bed when I am tired.

2. The hunter stopped and shot the bear.

3. Because he wanted to sing, Hans joined the choir.

4. I got soaked walking home in the thunderstorm.

5. When Andrew organized his folder, he found his assignment.

6. The swimming pool was crowded after we arrived.

 Writing Practice: Write a personal narrative about going on a picnic. Underline any cause/effect statements.

Reading a Graph

Use the information provided in the bar graph to answer the questions below.

1. How many students liked chocolate the best? _____	2. How many students liked strawberry the best? _____	**Favorite Ice Cream**
3. Which was the most popular flavor of ice cream? _____	4. Which was the least popular flavor of ice cream? _____	12 10 8 6 4 2 0 chocolate strawberry vanilla Neapolitan

Sentences

Rewrite each pair of sentences to form a compound sentence.

1. The python and the jaguar are both wild animals. They live in the rainforest.

   _____

   _____

2. The canopy is a layer of the rainforest. It is below the emergent layer.

   _____

   _____

3. Mice are members of the rodent family. Most people don't like them.

   _____

   _____

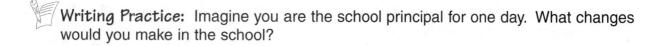

Writing Practice: Imagine you are the school principal for one day. What changes would you make in the school?

Reading a Table

Use the table to answer the questions.

1. How many more pencils does Charles have than Kim?	2. Who has more pencils, Rachel or Kim?	3. How many pencils does Taryn need in order to have the same amount as Phillippe?

4. How many pencils are there in all?

Student	Amount of Pencils
Kim	3
Charles	12
Rachel	7
Taryn	1
Phillippe	5

Punctuation

Add quotation marks where they belong.

1. We sang The Star Spangled Banner at the baseball game.

2. My mom read the poem The Raven to me.

3. Our family saw The Pearls of Parlay, a short story, at the theater.

4. The band aboard the ship played Nearer My God to Thee.

5. The newspaper printed an article entitled 2000: The Millennium.

 Writing Practice: Peace, Friendship, and Good Will Week is in October. Write a paragraph about what you think will make all of these things happen in your classroom. Then underline which ones you will work on.

Reading a Chart

Look at the chart. Answer the questions using the information from the chart.

1. Who is older, Jesse Jackson or Muhammad Ali?	2. How many years younger is Ali than Rosa Parks?	3. How many years older is Rosa Parks than Bill Cosby?
_____	_____	_____

4. Jesse Owens was famous for running in track and field events. He was born in 1913 and died in 1980. How old was he when he died?	**Black American**	**Born**
	Bill Cosby	1937
	Rosa Parks	1913
	Shirley Chisholm	1924
	Jesse Jackson	1941
_____	Muhammad Ali	1942

Cause/Effect

Underline the cause in each sentence.

1. When Sally listens in class, she makes better grades.

2. We'll go outside for P.E. because the weather is nice.

3. If Betsy cleans her room, she'll be able to go to the mall.

4. April talked on the phone and ordered a pizza.

5. Jeff tried out for the lead in *Romeo and Juliet* and was chosen to play the part of Romeo.

6. We went to the ballgame, when my uncle came for a visit.

 Writing Practice: Margaret Thatcher once said, "Being powerful is like being a lady. If you have to tell people you are, you aren't." What do you think she meant by that? Do you agree with her?

222

Reading a Chart

Answer the questions about these mountain ranges.

Mountains in Feet		1. Which mountain has the highest peak?	2. How much higher is Aconcagua than Mount McKinley?
Mont Blanc	15,771		
Mount Kilimanjaro	19,340		
Mount McKinley	20,320		
Aconcagua	22,834	_____	_____
Mount Everest	29,028		

3. Which mountain has the lowest peak?	4. In the list above, what is the difference between the highest and lowest peaks?
_____	_____

Handwriting

Write the names of the 13 original colonies in your best handwriting.

New Hampshire_____   North Carolina _____

Delaware _____   Connecticut _____

Massachusetts _____   South Carolina _____

Maryland _____   Pennsylvania _____

New York _____   Georgia _____

Virginia _____   New Jersey _____

Rhode Island _____

Writing Practice: There is a poem called "The Purple Cow." Write a poem with another colored animal.

Reading a Chart

Using the information in the chart, answer the following questions below.

1. How many more dogs were owned in 2000 than 1990?	2. What was the total number of cats and dogs owned in 2000?	3. Which pet had the smallest increase?
_____	_____	_____

4. How many pets were owned in 1990? In 2000?

1990: _____

2000: _____

Pet Population

Pet	1990	2000
Cat	540	718
Dog	622	962
Bird	83	110
Fish	51	79

Sentences

Rewrite each sentence to make more sense.

1. Under the table were her shoes.

   _____

2. For the party I had to pick her up.

   _____

3. Across the room sat Miss Michaels.

   _____

4. Near the couch was the baby's toy.

   _____

5. For quietly just a moment she sat.

   _____

6. Faster and faster came the runners.

   _____

 Writing Practice: Write a paragraph about a pet you have or a pet you've always wanted.

Reading a Chart

Use the information provided in the chart to answer the questions below.

1. How many more electoral votes do Florida and North Carolina have than Georgia and Tennessee? _____	2. Which 2 states' total electoral votes are equal to Florida? _____	3. What is the total number of electoral votes in all 8 states? _____

4. Find the average of the total electoral votes. _____	**Electoral Votes**	
	Alabama 9	Mississippi 7
	Florida 25	North Carolina 14
	Georgia 13	South Carolina 8
	Louisiana 9	Tennessee 11

Context Clues

Look at how the underlined Australian word is used. Write what you think the word means.

1. My mom will <u>flog</u> our dog's puppies when they get older. _____

2. The <u>jackaroo</u> worked on a ranch in Texas. _____

3. Our <u>chalkie</u> gave us <u>yakka</u> to do in class. _____

4. The <u>bloke</u> and <u>sheila</u> jogged around the block. _____

5. He bought new <u>clobbers</u> at the department store. _____

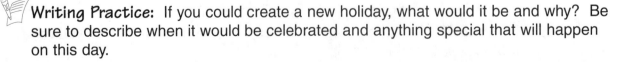 **Writing Practice:** If you could create a new holiday, what would it be and why? Be sure to describe when it would be celebrated and anything special that will happen on this day.

Reading a Chart

Use the information in the chart to answer the questions below about the different mountain ranges.

		Mountain	Elevation
1. Which mountain is the tallest? _____	2. Which mountain is only 20 ft. taller than Clingman's Dome? _____	Mt. Rainier	14,410 ft.
		Clingman's Dome	6,642 ft.
		Mt. Hood	6,225 ft.
3. Which mountain is the shortest? _____	4. Which mountain is 300 ft. shorter than Mt. Rainier? _____	Mt. Mitchell	6,662 ft.
		Mt. Lassen	10,446 ft.
		Pike's Peak	14,110 ft.

Alphabetical Order

Write the names of these patriots in alphabetical order.

Thomas Paine _____

Paul Revere _____

Deborah Sampson _____

Nathan Hale _____

Patrick Henry _____

Mary Ludwig Hays _____

Crispus Attucks _____

John Paul Jones _____

Samuel Adams _____

Baron Friedrich von Steuben _____

 Writing Practice: National Grandparent's Day is in September. Write a descriptive paragraph about your grandparents.

Reading a Chart

Use the sales tax chart to determine the amount of tax on each amount below. Write the tax below the amount. Then add for the total.

		Tax Chart	
1. $14.09 tax: _____ total: _____	**2.** $11.33 tax: _____ total: _____	**Amount**	**Tax**
		$9.00–9.49	56¢
		$9.50–9.99	57¢
		$10.00–10.49	58¢
		$10.50–10.99	59¢
		$11.00–11.49	60¢
		$11.50–11.99	61¢
3. $9.72 tax: _____ total: _____	**4.** $12.18 tax: _____ total: _____	$12.00–12.49	62¢
		$12.50–12.99	63¢
		$13.00–13.49	64¢
		$13.50–13.99	65¢
		$14.00–14.49	66¢
		$14.50–14.99	67¢
		$15.00–15.49	68¢
		$15.50–15.99	69¢

Compound Words

Underline the open compound words in each sentence.

1. He ate lunch on a picnic table in the park.

2. Mom opened up a savings account for my sister and me.

3. My friend, Antonio, became the president of the sixth grade.

4. I was the flower girl in my aunt's wedding.

5. Our Girl Scout troop had fun swimming at our neighbor's swimming pool.

6. We learned about the largest mountain range in Alaska.

 Writing Practice: Write a story using the following compound words: fire engine, vice president, parking lot, and open house.

Reading a Chart

Use the information in the chart to answer the questions below.

1. You have $50.00 to spend. Which two items would you buy if your change was $10.00?	2. You have $50.00 to spend. Which two items would you buy if your change was $3.00?	**Item**	**Price**
		shirt	$15.00
		shoes	$36.00
		blouse	$17.00
		necklace	$9.00
3. You have $50.00 to spend. Which two items would you buy if your change was $11.00?	4. You have $50.00 to spend. Which two items would you buy if your change was $21.00?	jeans	$25.00
		watch	$20.00
		skirt	$30.00
		socks	$3.00

Figurative Language

Rewrite each sentence using literal language.

1. I'm dead!

_____

2. It's raining cats and dogs.

_____

3. We're like two ships that pass in the night.

_____

4. She cried a bucket of tears.

_____

5. He's blind as a bat.

_____

6. Stanley has a chip on his shoulder.

_____

 Writing Practice: The 19th Amendment to the Constitution of the United States gave women the right to vote. If you could add an amendment for children, what would it be and why?

Coordinates

Write the coordinate pair for each point on the grid.

1. What is the ordered pair for *A*?	2. What is the ordered pair for *B*?	3. What is the ordered pair for *C*?
_____	_____	_____

4. What is the ordered pair for *D*?

_____

Noun/Verb

Write **N** if the word is a noun. Write **V** if the word is a verb.

_____	1.	sing	_____ 9.	traveller
_____	2.	song	_____ 10.	travel
_____	3.	greeting	_____ 11.	erase
_____	4.	greet	_____ 12.	eraser
_____	5.	collect	_____ 13.	measurement
_____	6.	collection	_____ 14.	measure
_____	7.	freeze	_____ 15.	see
_____	8.	freezer	_____ 16.	sea

Writing Practice: Predict the first day you think it will snow. Now write a paragraph to persuade me that you can have fun in the snow.

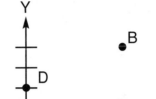

Coordinates

Write the ordered pairs of each point on the grid.

1. A = (,)	2. B = (,)	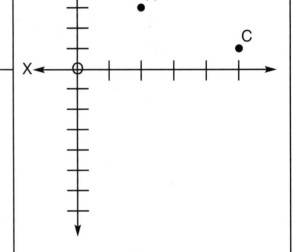
3. C = (,)	4. D = (,)	

Prepositions

Circle all prepositions in the sentences below.

1. Carol visited her sister near Chicago.

2. In the early 1900s, the telephone was invented.

3. Immigrants came to America to seek a better life.

4. The squirrel crawled through the hollow tree and onto the branch.

5. He went without playing baseball for two weeks.

6. The student sat between her friend and the principal during the program.

 Writing Practice: You only have one television at home and you and your siblings all want to watch something different. What do you do?

230

Coordinates

Use the graph and write the matching point to each set of coordinates for each problem.

1. (2, -3) _____	2. (-1, -2) _____
3. (1, 3) _____	4. (-2, 2) _____

Nouns

Write a noun for each letter in "nouns." Then write a sentence with each word.

1. N: _____

2. O: _____

3. U: _____

4. N: _____

5. S: _____

Writing Practice: Write a review of a restaurant that you have recently been to. Be sure to describe what sort of food is served there and where it is located.

Word Problems

Write a number sentence for each word problem. Then solve.

1. The judges ordered 28 ribbons and 32 trophies for the contest. How many prizes were ordered? _____	2. A circus has 7 clowns, 3 monkeys, and 6 tigers. How many are in the circus in all? _____	3. Joy baked 12 cookies. She gave 7 cookies to a friend. How many cookies are left for her? _____
4. Todd has 8 stamps. On Friday his brother bought 15. How many more stamps does Todd's brother have? _____	5. Kenya had 3 basketballs, 2 footballs, 1 soccer ball, and 5 baseballs. How many balls did he have in all? _____	

Common and Proper Nouns

Write **C** for *common* and **P** for *proper* nouns.

_____ 1. house

_____ 2. White House

_____ 3. Jill

_____ 4. sister

_____ 5. state

_____ 6. Missouri

_____ 7. toy store

_____ 8. store

_____ 9. deer

_____ 10. Deerfield St.

 Writing Practice: Write a paragraph explaining what it means when someone says "beauty is only skin deep." Then tell about someone you think is beautiful inside.

Word Problems

Write a number sentence for each word problem and solve.

1. Clarence had 139 baseball cards. He gave 23 to Allen. How many cards does he have left? _____	2. At the dollar store, I spent $6.48. I gave the cashier a 10 dollar bill. How much money should I get back? _____	3. I bought a pencil for $0.25, an eraser for $0.05, and a pack of paper for $0.75. How much did I spend in all? _____
4. Josiah had a pack of notebook paper with 150 sheets. He gave four friends 6 pieces of paper each. How many sheets does he have left? _____	5. Ramon wants to take his 375 gumballs and put them in machines. Each machine can only hold 10 gumballs. What is the greatest number of gumball machines Ramon needs? _____	

Figurative Language

Finish each hyperbole.

1. It rained so hard _____

2. It was so hot _____

3. My cat is so lazy _____

4. It was so foggy _____

5. My little sister is so annoying _____

6. The room was so crowded _____

Writing Practice: Write a paragraph using the sentence starter below.

If there's one thing I really dislike, it's . . .

Logic

Read each statement and write the results.

1. Brenda, Mona, and Dennis lined up from shortest to tallest for a picture. Dennis stood between Brenda and Mona. Mona was the shortest. Who was the tallest?

   _____

2. John is eight. His sister is 12. Thomas is five years younger than John's sister. Write their names from youngest to oldest.

   _____

   _____

3. Juan is half the age of Joe. Joe is 14 years old. Tina was born five years before Juan. Tim is three times the age of Tina. List the oldest to the youngest person.

   _____

   _____

4. Stephen, Allison, Susan, and Mark sit in the same row at school. Mark sits in front of Susan. Allison sits between a girl and a boy. Stephen doesn't sit by a boy. Write, in order, where each student sits in the row, front to back.

   _____

   _____

5. There are three frogs. The spotted frog jumped 8 feet. The tree frog jumped 6 feet. The toad jumped twice as far as the tree frog. List the frogs according to their positions from shortest to farthest distance.

   _____

   _____

Friendly Letter and Proofreading

Make corrections on the letter below and then rewrite it on a separate sheet of paper.

> 192 fielder ave
> ft. worth texas 97246
>
> february 18 1999
>
> dear charles
>
>   hey! how are you i am fine. i looking forward to seeing you on friday. have a safe trip. When you get here we will talk about what we want to do see you then.
>
>   your Friend
>   michael

 Writing Practice: If you could spend the day with one of your friends, who would it be? Tell what you would do when you spend the day together.

Logic

Read each statement and write the results.

1. Jerry is taller than Jamal. Shemeka is taller than Jerry. And Ollie is shorter than Jamal. Write in order the tallest to the shortest student. _____ _____	2. Ben sits by Joan. Kim sits by a girl, and Theron sits beside Kim. Write the order in which students are sitting next to each other. _____ _____	3. Eric runs the race faster than Loren. Bob wins the race. Mara finishes in front of Eric. Write in order first through fourth place. _____ _____
4. Emily jumped higher than Sharon. Karen jumped higher than Emily. Sara did not jump as high as Sharon. Write in order the highest to lowest jumper. _____ _____	5. Leo ate less pizza than Julio. Tyrone ate less pizza than Leo. James ate the most pizza. Write in order who ate the most pizza to who ate the least. _____ _____	

Alphabetical Order

Write the names of these presidents in alphabetical order.

George Washington _____

Abraham Lincoln _____

John Adams _____

William Harrison _____

Dwight Eisenhower _____

Ronald Reagan _____

Jimmy Carter _____

Gerald Ford _____

Richard Nixon _____

Bill Clinton _____

 Writing Practice: If you could visit any continent, which one would it be, and why? Write a paragraph about your adventures.

Magic Squares

All rows, both horizontal and vertical, when added up will equal the stated sum. Fill in the missing numbers in the puzzle. Then solve number 5.

1.

8		
		3
0	9	

sum = 16

2.

5		
	3	9
		5

sum = 18

3.

3		
	1	
1		6

sum = 11

4.

	6	7
10		
		8

sum = 19

5. James spent $104.90 on a coat. Tabitha spent $56.73 on a coat. How much more money did James spend than Tabitha?

_____

Spelling

There is a misspelled word in each sentence. Circle the misspelled word and write the correct spelling in the blank beside the sentence.

1. Have you studied for the test? _____

2. It was cloudyr yesterday than today. _____

3. Are you worryed about the exam? _____

4. Johnny caried the trash to the dumpster. _____

5. Do you have any hobies? _____

6. Nashville and Knoxville are large cityes. _____

7. Martha is the prettest girl I know. _____

8. I copyed my homework down today. _____

 Writing Practice: Write a newspaper article about your favorite team in baseball, basketball, or football.

Magic Squares

All rows, both horizontal and vertical, when added up will equal the sum. Fill in the missing numbers in the squares.

1.

5		
		2
1	8	

sum = 12

2.

8	2	
		9
6		

sum = 15

3.

		6
	4	
9		2

sum = 14

4.

		3
	8	
2		7

sum = 13

5. Janet and David picked 12 berries one day, 34 the next day, and 27 the following day. How many did they pick in all?

_____

Plurals

Write the plural forms of each word under the correct title.

tray   berry

cowboy   fly

penny   journey

city   key

fry   buy

way   cry

turkey   lady

y + s	y to i and add es

 Writing Practice: Write a story about your pet being able to talk, so you become famous. What do you do? Tell about your adventures.

Mean

For problems 1–4, find the averages of these test scores. Then solve problem 5.

1. Billy: 85, 88, 95 _____	2. Jorge: 99, 100, 81 _____	3. Joanne: 89, 89, 93 _____
4. Jaquarius: 90, 80, 88 _____	5. Simon and his friend Wayne set up a lemonade stand. A cup of lemonade cost $0.25 each. They made $5.00. How many cups of lemonade did they sell? _____	

Compound Words

Make a compound word by adding a beginning or an ending to the words below.

1. _____ground

2. grand_____

3. book_____

4. _____plane

5. him_____

6. _____age

7. every_____

8. with_____

9. sun_____

10. _____ball

11. _____man

12. home_____

 Writing Practice: Imagine waking up and finding out you're 10 feet tall. Write a story about your adventures.

238

Median

Find the median for each set of numbers and then solve problem 5.

1. 17, 24, 34, 28, 16	2. 215, 219, 225, 200, 231	3. 48, 68, 51, 65, 55
_____	_____	_____

4. $3.63, $4.74, $3.59, $4.62, $3.48	5. Mrs. Forrest gave a questionnaire to her math class of 12 boys and 13 girls. 7 boys and 7 girls returned their questionnaires. How many will she still need to get back from the boys? from the girls?
_____	boys _____ girls _____

Proofreading

Rewrite each sentence correctly.

1. the temperature in the woods were below freezing and i got two cold

_____

_____

2. the story about dr. terry were interesting

_____

3. last tuesday i go to see the movie the patriot

_____

4. canada be on the border of the united states

_____

5. do you like to ate shrimp

_____

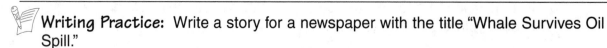 **Writing Practice:** Write a story for a newspaper with the title "Whale Survives Oil Spill."

Mode

Find the mode for each set of numbers. Then solve problem 5.

1. $20, $12, $16, $12, $30 _____	2. 46, 39, 28, 27, 39 _____	3. 100, 200, 100, 600, 300 _____
4. 75, 85, 95, 65, 75 _____	5. The 5th and 6th graders sold 98 candy bars. 12 more were sold by the 6th grade than 5th grade. How many did each grade sell? 5th grade _____ 6th grade _____	

Adverbs

Underline each adverb. Then circle where, when, or how to indicate what each adverb describes.

1. Stand there beside the tree.   where   when   how

2. Swiftly he ran toward the fence.   where   when   how

3. A man waited eagerly for his letter.   where   when   how

4. "It should arrive soon," said Mary.   where   when   how

5. The pitcher threw the ball down.   where   when   how

6. The umpire suddenly shouted for him to stop.   where   when   how

 Writing Practice: What is your favorite commercial on television? Why?

Mean, Median, Mode

The students in Mr. Dahl's math class received their tests grades back. (See below for test grades.) Find the *total*, the *mean*, the *median*, and the *mode* scores.

1. Total of All Scores = _____	2. Mean = _____	3. Median = _____

4. Mode = _____	**Test Scores**			
	Tom	97	Shelly	66
	Maria	98	Howard	88
	Juan	86	Lana	86
	Adam	86	Eugene	93
	Connie	95	Suzanne	89
	Dorothy	100		

Dictionary Skills

Circle the word that would come between each set of guide words.

1. **perennial**   **persevere**
   a. period
   b. perspire
   c. percent

2. **cope**   **correspond**
   a. costume
   b. coordinate
   c. corps

3. **gnome**   **govern**
   a. gray
   b. gossip
   c. gnaw

4. **motorcycle**   **mule**
   a. mouth
   b. motor
   c. mull

5. **stroke**   **stuff**
   a. stretch
   b. student
   c. stump

6. **black**   **blanket**
   a. blackbird
   b. blaze
   c. blast

 Writing Practice: Write a story using the sentence starter below.

I was playing outside when suddenly a UFO hovered over me. I looked and . . .

Mean, Median, Mode

Use the information provided on the list to answer the following questions.

1. What is the mean?	2. What is the median?	Jeff received these amounts of money for his birthday.
_____	_____	grandparents $40

parents $30

aunt $15 |
| 3. What is the mode? | 4. What is the total he received? | 3 brothers $10 each

sister $15

best friend $20

neighbor $5 |
| _____ | _____ | |

Nouns

Write "noun" if the word names a person, place, thing, or idea. Write "verb" if it describes action, existence, or occurrence. (*Hint:* There are some words that are not nouns or verbs)

1. Rachel _____
2. discover _____
3. socks _____
4. cheered _____
5. yellow _____
6. talked _____
7. peace _____
8. up _____
9. gratitude _____
10. her _____

 Writing Practice: Write a paragraph using at least five of the nouns listed above. Then circle any other nouns in your paragraph.

— • — • — • — • — • — • — • — • — • — • — • — • — • —

Mean, Median, Mode

If Tamara's math test scores are 96, 92, 83, 71, 83, and 91, calculate the answer for each problem. Then solve problem 5.

1. mean	2. median	3. mode
_____	_____	_____

4. range	5. Mr. Garcia bought a new car. His payments for 48 months are $185.00 per month. What is the price of the car?
_____	_____

Pronouns

Circle the underlined pronoun in each sentence.

1. The <u>coach</u> <u>was</u> <u>talking</u> to <u>him</u>.

2. He said <u>for</u> the <u>team</u> to put on <u>their</u> uniforms.

3. <u>They</u> would <u>be</u> practicing <u>after</u> school <u>tomorrow</u>.

4. <u>We</u> <u>had</u> an assembly in <u>school</u> <u>today</u>.

5. <u>It</u> was <u>about</u> <u>Black</u> History <u>month</u>.

6. My friend <u>said</u>, "<u>I</u> have <u>seen</u> the program <u>before</u>."

Writing Practice: Can you cook? Do you like to cook? Write about something you can cook or something you'd like to learn to cook.

Measurement

Circle the larger unit. Then solve problem number 5.

1. 4 in. or 4 ft.	2. 74 yd. or 74 mi.	3. 1 yd. or 1 in.
4. 60 ft. or 60 in.	5. Students at Gladeville Middle School collected 23 lbs. of aluminum cans, 18 lbs. of plastic bottles, and 78 lbs. of newspapers for the annual recycling drive. How many pounds of recycling material did they collect in all? _____	

Syllables

How many syllables does each word have? Write each word under the correct heading.

library
table
magazine
paper
globe
reference
shelf
computer
book

One	Two	Three

 Writing Practice: Write a paragraph using the sentence starter below.

I walked into a jungle and saw . . .

Measurement

Write the correct measurement (in., ft., yd., or mi.). Then solve number 5.

1. the depth of a swimming pool _____	2. the distance to Mars _____	3. the width of your hand _____
4. the material in a dress _____	5. D'Andre worked on his homework after school. He started at 4:15 P.M. and finished right before supper at 6:00 P.M. How long did he work on his homework? _____	

Compound Sentences

Combine the two simple sentences with a comma and a connecting word to make a compound sentence.

1. Joellyn woke up late. She was late to school.

   _____

2. She told her teacher she was late. She had overslept.

   _____

3. Mrs. Sagraves was teaching math. She was giving directions.

   _____

4. Her teacher said to sit down quickly. She had to take off her coat.

   _____

   _____

5. She sat down. She worked very hard.

   _____

Writing Practice: Write a paragraph about a time you were late to school.

Measurement

Circle the more reasonable temperature. Then solve problem 5.

1. football weather	2. hot cocoa	3. a store during the summer
20° F 50° F	32° F 82° F	50° F 70° F

4. soup	5. The temperature was 29° C. It rose 15°. What is the temperature now?
52° F 72° F	_____

Contractions

Choose the correct word in the parentheses.

1. We (doesn't, don't) like to eat spinach.

2. I (doesn't, don't) want to wash the dishes.

3. They (wasn't, weren't) going to the mall today.

4. She (wasn't, weren't) honest with Bill.

5. We (aren't, isn't) supposed to talk during class.

6. He (aren't, isn't) sure what to do in math.

Writing Practice: Write a paragraph about living on a space station.

Measurement

Write which metric measure you would use to measure the following: **cm** (centimeter), **m** (meter), or **km** (kilometer). Then solve problem 5.

1. the length of your pencil	2. the length of the hallway at school	3. your height
_____	_____	_____

4. the distance from your house to school	5. You sold Teri a pencil for $0.35. She gave you a dollar.
	How much change does she get back? _____
	She receives four coins back. What type of coins does she get back?
_____	_____
	_____

Nouns or Verbs

Some words can be a noun or a verb, depending on the way it is used. Read the sentences below and write whether the underlined word is a *noun* or a *verb*.

1. The <u>wind</u> blew so hard, my bicycle fell over. _____

2. The string on my yo-yo got stuck, and I had to <u>wind</u> it up again. _____

3. Kindergarten students should <u>rest</u> after lunch. _____

4. The <u>rest</u> of the animals in the zoo went to sleep. _____

5. Go down the street and <u>turn</u> left onto Front Street. _____

6. Terry said, "It's my <u>turn</u>!" _____

7. Dad's <u>suit</u> was dark gray. _____

8. He said the student's homework would <u>suit</u> him. _____

9. The <u>cut</u> on his finger was bleeding. _____

10. Mrs. Roberts said not to <u>cut</u> the picture out. _____

Writing Practice: What is your favorite fairy tale? Write your own version of it.

Measurement

Fill in the blanks for problems 1–4. Then solve problem 5.

1. 1 quart is _____ pints.	2. There are _____ ounces in a pound.	3. 4 quarts make _____ gallon.

4. $\frac{1}{2}$ of a gallon is _____ quarts.	5. Stanley's father bought a car that weighed $\frac{1}{4}$ of a ton. How much did it weigh in pounds? _____

Syllables

Circle the words that have a long vowel sound in the first syllable.

table	baby	bridle
money	apple	lucky
lady	nature	pizza
window	hero	pilot
robin	fatal	nickel
flower	drama	music

Writing Practice: Some people like to be by themselves. Others don't like to be alone. Write a paragraph explaining which one you prefer.

Measurement

Solve each problem.

1. About how long is a crayon? 3 in. or 3 ft.	2. About how much does a large bucket hold? 5 pt. or 5 gal.	3. Which is used to measure milk in a glass? cup or pint
4. About how long is a straw? 5 cm or 5.2 km		5. What was the total distance of a race if it had 4 laps, each 1,125 meters long? _____

Nouns, Verbs, and Adjectives

Write words that begin with the letter at the top of each chart.

	m
noun	
verb	
adjective	

	a
noun	
verb	
adjective	

	l
noun	
verb	
adjective	

	s
noun	
verb	
adjective	

	r
noun	
verb	
adjective	

	w
noun	
verb	
adjective	

Writing Practice: If you could give your teacher a suggestion, what would it be?

Measurement

Circle which method of measurement would be more appropriate. Then solve problem 5.

1. width of your math book ruler or yardstick	2. length of your classroom ruler or yardstick	3. height of your teacher ruler or yardstick
4. length of your arm ruler or yardstick	5. Sammy gave Antonio six apples, Samantha three apples, and Kershawn five apples. If he started with 35 apples, how many does he have left? _____	

Spelling

Unscramble these words having to do with Christmas.

1. aittesnoip _____
2. bbrion _____
3. cdar _____
4. kingcots _____
5. glena _____

6. shlgei _____
7. lloyh _____
8. rewaht _____
9. lorac _____
10. repnest _____

 Writing Practice: Write a Christmas story using six of the words above.

250

Measurement

For problems 1–4, fill in the blanks. Then solve problem 5.

1. $\frac{2}{3}$ yd. = _____ feet	2. $\frac{3}{4}$ hr. = _____ minutes	3. $\frac{1}{2}$ doz. = _____ eggs

4.

$\frac{1}{4}$ ft. = _____ inches

5. A jar of candy has 592 pieces in it. Each bag of candy used to fill up the jar contained 30 pieces.

How many bags were needed to fill the jar?

_____

How many extra pieces of candy were left over?

_____

Handwriting

Write this poem in your best handwriting.

Bugs

I like bugs.
Black bugs, green bugs,
Bad bugs, mean bugs,
Any kind of bug.
A bug in a rug, a bug in the grass,
A bug on the sidewalk, a bug in a glass,
I like bugs.
Big bugs, fat bugs,
Shiny bugs, round bugs,
Lady bugs, buggy bugs,
I like bugs.

—Unknown

(title)

Writing Practice: Write your own poem about an animal or insect that you like.

Measurement

For problems 1–4, write the correct answers. Then solve problem 5.

1. At 100° C, do you take a bath or boil eggs? _____	2. At 0° C, do you freeze ice cream or cook hotdogs? _____	3. At 35° C, do you wear a bathing suit or wear a jacket? _____
4. At 40° C, are you at the North Pole or the Sahara Desert? _____	5. If John was cold, and he looked at the thermometer and it said 32°, would it be Celsius or Fahrenheit? _____	

Adverb/Verb

Underline the verb and circle each adverb.

1. The football player fell down.

2. The old dog just lies there.

3. The fire trucks drove nearby.

4. The pool table sits downstairs in the den.

5. The young baby crawled over to me.

6. The big dogs barked loudly.

7. The jet plane landed today.

8. My good friend arrives tomorrow.

 Writing Practice: Write a story using the sentence starter below.

In the year 2020 . . .

252

Measurement

Calculate the correct equivalent measurement for each problem and then solve problem 5.

1. $\frac{1}{2}$ gal. = _____ qt.	2. 2 pt. = _____ qt.	3. $\frac{1}{2}$ c. = _____ fl. oz.

4. $\frac{1}{2}$ qt. = _____ pt.	5. Monkeys in a zoo eat 796 bananas and 283 cans of peanuts per day. How much do they eat in 1 week? bananas _____ cans of peanuts _____

Prefix

Replace the italicized words with a prefix and a base word.

1. The girl *wrote again* her science report.   _____

2. She *read incorrectly* the instructions on the list.   _____

3. Mom likes to drink a big glass of *not fat* milk.   _____

4. Dad *planned ahead* our trip to the Grand Canyon.   _____

5. The baseball game was *scheduled again*.   _____

6. I had some *opposite of comfort* after my leg broke.   _____

 Writing Practice: Write about the best dream that you've ever had or can remember.

Measurement

Write the unit (in., ft., yd., mi.) you would use to measure the items listed below. Then solve problem 5.

1. height of a light pole _____	2. length of a school bus _____	3. distance between east and west coast _____

4. length of your arm _____	5. Toni owed her sister 75¢. She paid her with a combination of 5 coins. What coins did she give to her sister? _____

Synonyms

Circle the best synonym for each boldfaced word.

1. **drill**   train   useful   lifted

2. **drab**   stylish   dreary   oppressed

3. **duty**   requirement   doubtful   created

4. **doodle**   unsteady   enhance   scribble

5. **desert**   gained   cake   abandon

6. **dainty**   courteous   delicate   helpful

Writing Practice: Write a story using this title:

The Strangest Place I've Ever Been

254

Measurement

Write the correct measurements. Then solve problem 5.

1. ___ ounces in a pound	2. ___ fluid ounces in a cup	3. ___ quarts in a gallon

4. ___ cups in a pint	5. If you add Yolanda and Wanda's ages, you get a total of 21 years. If you multiply their ages, you get 110. What age is each girl? (Yolanda is older than Wanda.) Yolanda: _____ Wanda: _____

Punctuation

Write a sentence that is an example of each punctuation rule.

1. Place quotation marks before and after a person's spoken words.

   _____

2. Underline the title of a book or newspaper.

   _____

3. Place an exclamation mark at the end of an exclamatory sentence.

   _____

4. Place a comma between the city and state.

   _____

5. Place a colon between the hour and minute in time.

   _____

6. Place a period after the abbreviated title in a person's name.

   _____

 Writing Practice: You wake up one morning and find that your skin has turned purple. Write a story about it.

Measurement

Solve each problem by using the conversion chart provided.

1. 35 cm = _____ mm	**2.** 652 m = _____ cm	**3.** 15 g = _____ mg

4. 32,000 mg = _____ g	**conversion chart** 1 cm = 10 mm 1 m = 100 cm 1 g = 1,000 mg

Dictionary Skills

Match the correct definition of the word *course* as used in the sentences below.

_____ 1. Dessert is the best *course*.　　　　a. direction

_____ 2. I took a *course* in Spanish.　　　　b. lessons or classes

_____ 3. The ship sailed on course to Fiji.　　c. part of a meal

Match the correct definition of the word *low* as used in the sentences below.

_____ 4. Speak in a *low* voice in the hall.　　a. nearly used up

_____ 5. The price of the wallet was *low*.　　b. soft

_____ 6. The battery was *low* on my CD player.　　c. less than usual

 Writing Practice: Use this writing prompt to write a short paragraph:

I feel good about myself when ...

256

Measurement

Find the volume of each object. (Remember, V = l x w x h.) Then solve problem 5.

1.

book

l = 10 in.

w = 2 in.

h = 6 in.

V = _____

2.

juice box

l = 6 in.

w = 1 in.

h = 4 in.

V = _____

3.

wallet

l = 5 in.

w = 2 in.

h = 5 in.

V = _____

4.

desk

l = 20 in.

w = 10 in.

h = 25 in.

V = _____

5. Annie traveled 722 miles in 2 days. If she traveled the same distance both days, how many miles did she travel each day?

_____

Antonyms

Write an antonym for each word.

1. miniature _____

2. powerless _____

3. never _____

4. least _____

5. depart _____

6. race _____

7. different _____

8. ignore _____

Writing Practice: Use this writing prompt to write a short paragraph:

The wind sounded eerie late in the night when...

Measurement

Match the unit of measure with its equivalent. Circle the answers then solve problem 5.

1. deci	2. deka	3. kilo
a. 100	a. 100	a. 100
b. 0.1	b. 0.1	b. 0.1
c. 1,000	c. 1,000	c. 1,000
d. 10	d. 10	d. 10

4. hecto	5. Ten campers signed up for 1 week of camp. The total amount paid was $2,025.00. How much did each camper have to pay?
a. 100　　c. 1,000 b. 0.1　　d. 10	_____

Word Usage

Use the code to find out famous authors.

code	z	y	x	w	v	u	t	s	r	q	p	o	n
letter	a	b	c	d	e	f	g	h	i	j	k	l	m
code	m	l	k	j	i	h	g	f	e	d	c	b	a
letter	n	o	p	q	r	s	t	u	v	w	x	y	z

1. plmrthyfit _____   4. ildormt _____

2. xovzib _____   5. nvbvih _____

3. wzso _____   6. hgrmv _____

Writing Practice: Write a fan letter to your favorite author.

258

Measurement

Solve each equation and give each answer in centimeters. Then solve problem 5.

1. 2 m + 32 cm = _____	2. 30 cm + 80 mm = _____	3. 24 mm + 3.6 cm = _____

4. 5 m + 16 cm = _____	5. How many squares are in this figure? 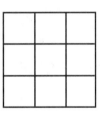 _____

Nouns/Word Usage

Fill in the blanks with a word to make each sentence complete.

1. Clark wrote his _____ and told about his trip to _____.

2. Mary Sue and _____ went to visit _____ in _____.

3. John, my _____, asked if he could give me a _____.

4. In _____, there is a special holiday called _____.

5. My sister lives on _____, right next door to _____.

6. My _____ gave me homework in _____.

Writing Practice: What is the best way to travel—by bus, car, train, plane, etc.? Why?

Measurement

Select the best unit (mm, cm, m) for measuring each object. Then solve problem 5.

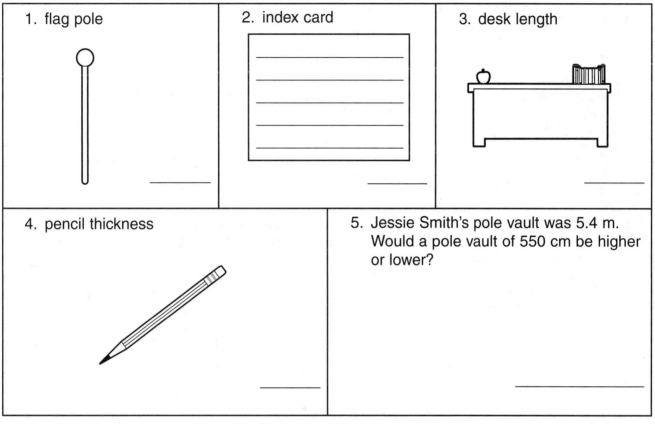

1. flag pole

2. index card

3. desk length

4. pencil thickness

5. Jessie Smith's pole vault was 5.4 m. Would a pole vault of 550 cm be higher or lower?

Writing Practice

Write the following rules in your best handwriting.

Tips for Being a Good Listener

1. Pay close attention to the speaker.

_____

2. Look at the speaker except when taking notes.

_____

3. Respond to the speaker with appropriate facial expressions.

_____

4. Compliment the speaker after the presentation.

_____

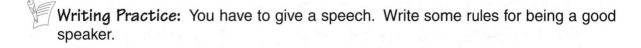 **Writing Practice:** You have to give a speech. Write some rules for being a good speaker.

Measurement

Circle the reasonable measurement for each of the listed items. Then solve problem 5.

1. width of a bulletin board a. kilometer b. meter c. millimeter d. centimeter	2. trip from Cleveland to Columbus a. kilometer b. meter c. millimeter d. centimeter	3. length of your finger a. kilometer b. meter c. millimeter d. centimeter

4. width of your desk a. kilometer b. meter c. millimeter d. centimeter	5. Camille has a portfolio of her drawings. It has 32 pages and each page has four drawings. How many drawings are in her portfolio? _____

Analogies

Write the word to complete each analogy.

1. pen : draw as boat : _____   hot

2. give : take as cold :_____   remote

3. rain : umbrella as leaves : _____   tools

4. computer : keys as television: _____   neigh

5. book : pages as tool box : _____   sailing

6. kitten : meow as horse : _____   rake

Writing Practice: Use this writing prompt to write a short paragraph:

My friend called me on the phone to tell me that...

Exponents

Solve the problems below.

1. $16^2 =$ _____	2. $7^4 =$ _____	3. $22^3 =$ _____

4. $9^4 =$ _____

5. The theater has 155 rows of seats with 35 seats in each row. How many seats are in the theater?

_____

Prefixes

Match each numerical prefix to its meaning.

_____ 1. bi		a. one	
_____ 2. uni		b. two	
_____ 3. omni		c. half or partly	
_____ 4. deca		d. three	
_____ 5. semi		e. all	
_____ 6. tri		f. ten	

 Writing Practice: What would you do if you could be a teacher for a day?

Exponents

For problems 1 and 2, rewrite each problem in exponent form. For problems 3 and 4, rewrite each problem in factored form.

1. $3 \times 3 \times 3 \times 3 \times 3 =$ _____	2. 16 cubed = _____	3. $5^4 =$ _____

4. $24^2 =$ _____	5. Meg ran 3 ½ miles on Tuesday and 4 ⅔ miles on Thursday. How many miles did she run in all? _____

Writing Practice

Write a tongue twister poem.

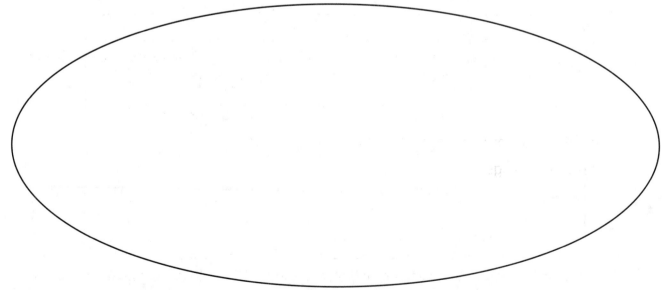

Writing Practice: Write a name poem using a classmate's first name.

Variables

Solve for *x*.

1. *x* = 17 + 5 *x* = _____	2. *x* = 21 − 3 *x* = _____	3. 6 multiplied by *x* = 54 *x* = _____
4. *x* divided by 8 = 8 *x* = _____	5. A life jacket is needed for each tourist on 8 tour boats. How many life jackets are needed if each tour boat holds 185 passengers? _____	

Main Idea

Read each group of words. Write the main idea on the blank.

1. banana, papaya, orange, grapefruit, grape

   _____

2. singing carols, shopping, wrapping gifts, decorating a tree, snow

   _____

3. goal, net, referee, kicking, black and white ball

   _____

4. guide words, definitions, pronunciation, parts of speech, spelling

   _____

Now write a list of 5 words or phrases that go with each category.

5. Thanksgiving things

   _____

6. things at a circus

   _____

 Writing Practice: Look at one of the lists above. Write a story, beginning with the main idea, and then finish the story by writing sentences with the list of words or phrases. Remember, stories have a beginning, a middle, and an end.

Variables

Find the value of *x*. Then solve problem 5.

1. $23 + x = 31$ $x = $ _____	2. $17 - x = 12$ $x = $ _____	3. $x = 3 \times 4$ $x = $ _____
4. $x = 43 \div 3$ $x = $ _____	5. LaToya went to bed at 9:36 P.M. She woke up 23 minutes later to get a drink of water. What time did she wake up? _____	

Spelling

Begin with the word, look at the clues, and change one letter each time to make a new word.

1. whole

   _ _ _ _ _ _ : mammal

   _ _ _ _ _ _ : rock

   _ _ _ _ _ _ : measures weight

   _ _ _ _ _ _ : frighten

2. plane

   _ _ _ _ _ _ : grows in the ground

   _ _ _ _ _ _ : diagonal

   _ _ _ _ _ _ : informal speech

   _ _ _ _ _ _ : bandage for arm

3. grab

   _ _ _ _ : dreary

   _ _ _ _ : heavy freight wagon

   _ _ _ _ : talk to God

   _ _ _ _ : hunted for food

 Writing Practice: Write a paragraph to complete this idea.

If I were three inches tall, I would . . .

Variables

Fill in the blanks. Then solve problem 5.

1. If 6 + a = 10,
   then a = _____
	2. If 20 − b = 15,
	   then b = _____
		3. If 4 x c = 40,
		   then c = _____

4. If 50 ÷ d = 25, then d = _____

5. Your neighbor Mr. Jones is paying you to walk his dog Tubbs. If he gives you $0.50 a day, how many days will it take to earn $10.00?

_____

Verbs

Complete each sentence by adding appropriate verbs.

1. The rabbits _____ and _____ in the forest.

2. The squirrels _____ and _____ up the tree.

3. The snake _____ and _____ along the ground.

4. The lions _____ and _____ in their cages.

5. The baby birds _____ and _____ in their nests.

 Writing Practice: Do you have a favorite poster on the wall in your room at home? Do you collect things? Write a descriptive paragraph describing your room.

266

Variables

For problems 1–4, fill in the blanks. Then solve problem 5.

1. If $10 + e = 32$,
   then $e =$ _____
	2. If $21 - f = 10$,
	   then $f =$ _____
		3. If $6 \times g = 48$,
		   then $g =$ _____

4. If $99 \div h = 11$, then
   $h =$ _____
	5. The perimeter of a square is 20 inches. How long is each side?
	
	   _____	

Commas

Write a sentence that corresponds with each comma rule. Be sure to use the comma correctly.

1. Use a comma to separate items in a list.

   _____

2. Use a comma to set off direct quotes.

   _____

3. Use a comma to separate the names of cities and states.

   _____

4. Use a comma to set off a direct address.

   _____

5. Use a comma and a connecting word to connect two clauses.

   _____

 Writing Practice: There are over 250,000 kinds of flowers. Flowers are given to people sometimes to help them feel better. Write a story about either getting flowers or giving flowers and how it made you feel.

Variables

For problems 1–4, find the variable. Then solve problem 5.

1. $56 + 6 = x + 13$ $x = \underline{\hspace{1.5cm}}$	**2.** $25 + 7 = 20 + y$ $y = \underline{\hspace{1.5cm}}$	**3.** $66 - 6 = 72 - x$ $x = \underline{\hspace{1.5cm}}$
4. $87 - 8 = y - 9$ $y = \underline{\hspace{1.5cm}}$	**5.** Samuel paid for a new jacket. The jacket cost $24.98. His change was $15.02. How much money did he give the clerk? $\underline{\hspace{4cm}}$	

Synonyms

Write a synonym for each word.

1. scarce $\underline{\hspace{3cm}}$

2. alarm $\underline{\hspace{3cm}}$

3. joyful $\underline{\hspace{3cm}}$

4. startle $\underline{\hspace{3cm}}$

5. identical $\underline{\hspace{3cm}}$

6. jersey $\underline{\hspace{3cm}}$

7. mammoth $\underline{\hspace{3cm}}$

8. valuable $\underline{\hspace{3cm}}$

 Writing Practice: Write a story using the sentence starter.

I was home by myself when I heard a noise in the attic . . .

Variables

Find the value of each expression. Then solve problem 5.

1. $x - 12 = 88$ $x = $ _____	2. $7 \times z = 49$ $z = $ _____	3. $144 \div y = 12$ $y = $ _____
4. $n + 120 = 241$ $n = $ _____	5. On the way to Mrs. Ward's classroom, the new student will pass five rooms. Mrs. Proctor's room is next to Mrs. Baker's room. Mrs. Morgan's room is between Mrs. Proctor's and Mrs. Prince's room. Mrs. Prince's room is not next to Mrs. Ward's room. Which classroom is beside Mrs. Ward's room? _____	

Nouns

Write the following nouns under the correct heading. Use capitalization where needed.

- playground
- book
- elm street
- athlete
- detroit
- caddie woodlawn
- aunt
- england

Common Nouns	Proper Nouns

 Writing Practice: Write a short story about your class at school. Underline each common noun and circle each proper noun.

Variables

Solve each problem below.

1. If $a = 3$ and $b = \dfrac{1}{2}$, then $3a + b = $? _____	2. If $a = 2.3$ and $b = 4$, then $2a + 2b = $? _____	3. $x - 1\dfrac{1}{2} = 6$ $x = $? _____
4. $6m = 24$ $m = $ _____	5. Leo and Larry work at 2 different theaters. Leo's theater employs 12 people, and Larry's theater employs 2/3 as many as Leo's. How many people does Larry's theater employ? _____	

Subjects

Write simple or compound once you identify the type of subject used in each sentence.

_____ 1. Pauline went to the mall and bought a sweater.

_____ 2. Sandy and Jason found a stray dog.

_____ 3. They nursed the dog back to health.

_____ 4. Mom and Dad played Scrabble® with us.

_____ 5. The children ran and played on the playground.

_____ 6. We all like to eat pizza.

 Writing Practice: Describe a fun day at the beach.

Variables

Solve each problem below.

1. $y + 19 = 42$ $y =$ _____	**2.** $26 - b = 14$ $b =$ _____	**3.** $23 + x = 50$ $x =$ _____

4. $\dfrac{24}{n} = 6$ $n =$ _____	**5.** The decorating committee bought crepe paper for the school party. If the total cost was $15.87, how many rolls did they buy at 69¢ each? _____

Spelling

Choose the correctly spelled word.

1. laid   layed   layied

2. hankerchief   handkerchief   handerchief

3. forty   fourty   fourtty

4. daugter   dauther   daughter

5. farer   farther   farthor

6. running   runing   runnying

 Writing Practice: Use this writing prompt to write a short paragraph:

Things I like in a friend...

Variables

Solve for *x*. Then, solve problem 5.

1. $52 + 6 = x + 12$ $x =$ _____	2. $18 + 7 = 22 + x$ $x =$ _____	3. $61 - 6 = 73 - x$ $x =$ _____
4. $82 - 8 = x - 12$ $x =$ _____	5. Marty paid for a new jacket. The jacket cost $21.99. His change was $18.01. How much money did he give the clerk? _____

Synonyms

Write a synonym for each word.

1. chimpanzee _____

2. mountain _____

3. beautiful _____

4. surprise _____

5. small _____

6. soft _____

7. trash _____

8. exhausted _____

9. boat _____

10. miniature _____

 Writing Practice: Use this writing prompt to write a short paragraph:

I was home one night when I heard a noise on the front porch.

Variables

Solve for n. Then solve problem 5.

1. $48 - 12 = 6 \times n$	2. $26 \times 3 = 122 - n$	3. $23 + 15 = 40 - n$
		_____

4. $72 \div 9 = 100 - n$	5. Frances Drake explored California in 1579 and 28 years later, Jamestown was settled by Captain John Smith. What year was that?
_____	_____

Synonyms

Complete the Venn diagram by writing the words (listed below) in each catergory.

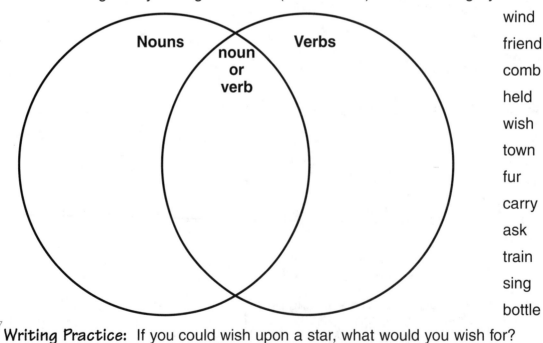

Nouns

noun or verb

Verbs

wind

friend

comb

held

wish

town

fur

carry

ask

train

sing

bottle

Writing Practice: If you could wish upon a star, what would you wish for?

Geometry

Write *point*, *ray*, *line segment*, or *line* in the correct box. Then solve problem 5.

1. •———• _____	2. • _____	3. ←———→ _____

4. •———→ _____	5. Derek saw 32 birds. Natasha saw 18 birds. How many more birds did Derek see than Natasha? _____

Homonyms

Fill in the blanks with the correct *to*, *too*, or *two*.

1. Sally has _____ dolls.

2. Hailey has the same amount of dolls, _____.

3. They like _____ play with their dolls.

4. "Let's go _____ the store and buy _____ more," said Sally.

5. "That's _____ bad," said Hailey's mother, "because we have _____ eat dinner."

Writing Practice: Write a speech to convince your classmates that you would make a good class president.

Geometry

Fill in the blanks with the correct answer.

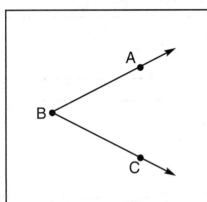

1. In angle ABC, the vertex is _____.

2. In angle ABC, one side of the angle is

_____.

3. Angle ABC is an _____ angle.

4. Angle ABC is made up of two

_____.

Handwriting

Write the following quote from William Durant, the founder of General Motors, in your best handwriting.

> "Forget mistakes. Forget failures. Forget everything except what you're going to do today. Today is your lucky day."

_____

_____

_____

_____

_____

Writing Practice: Write a paragraph explaining what the quote you just wrote means to you.

Geometry

Name the lines. Write *parallel*, *intersecting*, or *perpendicular*. Then solve problem 5.

<table>
<tr><td>

1.

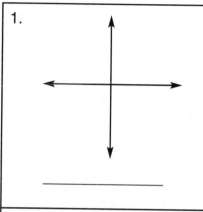

_____
</td><td>

2.

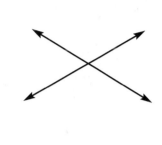

_____
</td><td>

3.

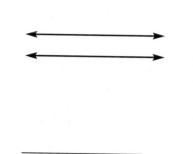

_____
</td></tr>
<tr><td colspan="2">

4.

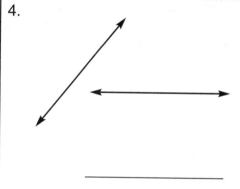

_____
</td><td>

5. At the store, you spent $4.32. You give the cashier $10.02. How much money should you get back?

_____
</td></tr>
</table>

Pronouns

Write **I** or **me** in each blank.

1. _____ danced at the party.

2. She gave her CD to _____.

3. My sister and _____ are going shopping.

4. My cousin is going with Michiko and _____.

5. They gave _____ an award for attendance.

6. Sukey and _____ won a talent contest.

 Writing Practice: Write a paragraph about winning a contest.

Geometry

Write what type of angle—*right, acute,* or *obtuse*—is being used. Then solve problem 5.

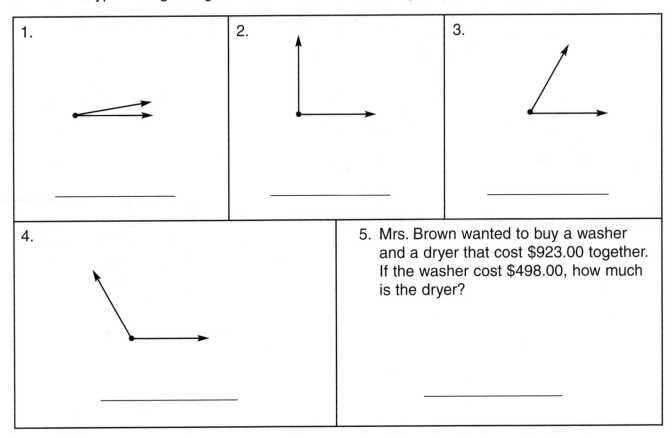

1. _____	2. _____	3. _____

4. _____

5. Mrs. Brown wanted to buy a washer and a dryer that cost $923.00 together. If the washer cost $498.00, how much is the dryer?

_____

Adjectives

Write the correct adjective in each blank. Choose between *this, that, these,* and *those.*

1. We like _____ new clothes best.

2. Do you have any of _____ blue gel pens?

3. Surely _____ kind of safety program is best.

4. _____ math problem is very hard.

5. I wore _____ old shoes to school.

6. We saw _____ movies last summer.

7. _____ kind of book interests me.

8. Al likes _____ cars.

 Writing Practice: National Book Week is in November. Tell about a book you have read recently. What did you like about it? What did you dislike about it? Then illustrate a scene in the book.

Geometry

Identify each type of triangle (right, scalene, equilateral, obtuse). Then solve problem 5.

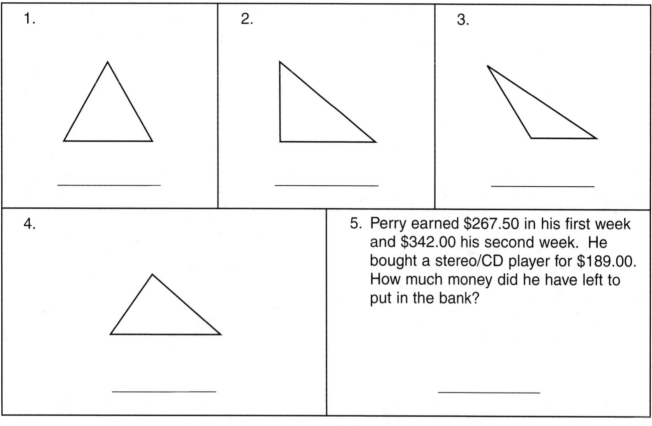

1.

_____

2.

_____

3.

_____

4.

_____

5. Perry earned $267.50 in his first week and $342.00 his second week. He bought a stereo/CD player for $189.00. How much money did he have left to put in the bank?

_____

Compare/Contrast

Decide if the sentence is comparing or contrasting. Write compare or contrast by each sentence.

_____ 1. Texas and Oklahoma are states in the Southwest U. S.

_____ 2. Like South Carolina, Virginia is also located on the east coast.

_____ 3. Michigan has cold winters, but Florida has mild winters.

_____ 4. Unlike Hawaii, Tennessee is surrounded by land on every side.

_____ 5. All the states in the U. S. have a governor who helps lead the affairs of the state.

_____ 6. Instead of bordering Mexico, Montana borders Canada.

Writing Practice: Write a paragraph about holidays using comparing and contrasting sentences.

278

Geometry

Fill in the missing answer and draw a picture of the shape. Then solve problem 5.

1. A pentagon has _____ sides.	2. A hexagon has _____ sides.	3. An octagon has _____ sides.

4. Kelly, DeWayne, Jerika, and Edgar went to a masquerade party. They were dressed as a lion, tiger, bear, and cougar, but not in that order. Jerika was not the cougar, and Edgar's costume did not have a long tail. Kelly was either the tiger or the bear. What were each person's costume?

Kelly = _____

DeWayne = _____

Jerika = _____

Edgar = _____

Consonant Blends

Add two different blends *(scr, spl, shr, spr, str, thr)* to each word ending to make two new words.

1. _____eam   _____eam
2. _____ing   _____ing
3. _____ash   _____ash
4. _____ill   _____ill
5. _____ead   _____ead
6. _____ap   _____ap
7. _____ee   _____ee
8. _____ew   _____ew

 Writing Practice: There are only a few types of animals that live in the Arctic. Write about how you would like or dislike living in the Arctic.

Geometry

Determine whether the figure is plane or solid and then solve problem 5.

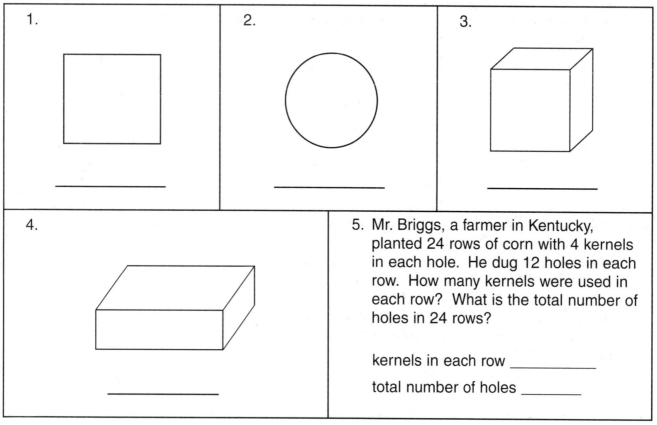

1.

_____

2.

_____

3.

_____

4.

_____

5. Mr. Briggs, a farmer in Kentucky, planted 24 rows of corn with 4 kernels in each hole. He dug 12 holes in each row. How many kernels were used in each row? What is the total number of holes in 24 rows?

kernels in each row _____

total number of holes _____

Pronouns/Possessives

Use *its* or *it's* correctly in the following sentences.

1. My father says _____ too early to go to school.

2. The prairie dog makes _____ home in a burrow.

3. _____ not going to matter if it rains today.

4. The tractor did _____ work on the farm.

5. _____ almost ten o'clock.

6. If _____ raining, be sure to take your umbrella.

7. He got off his bicycle to check _____ tires.

8. The fish swam in _____ aquarium.

Writing Practice: Many children have best friends. Write a paragraph describing your best friend. What makes this person your best friend? If you don't have a best friend, write about one of your good friends.

Geometry

Label each figure with its geometric name—rectangular prism, pyramid, sphere, cone, or cylinder.

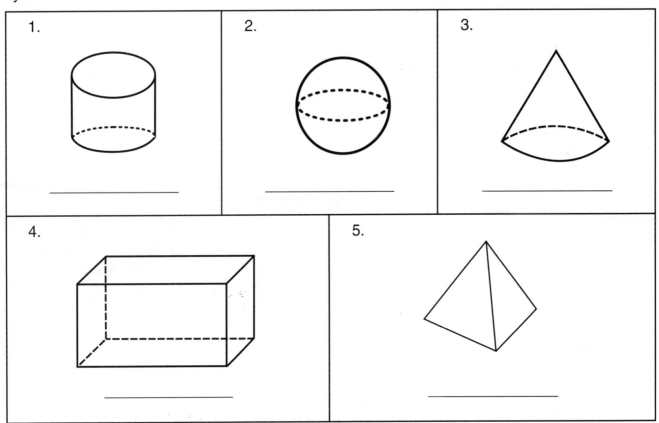

1. _____

2. _____

3. _____

4. _____

5. _____

Punctuation

Correct each sentence by underlining or adding quotation marks around each title.

1. The Firebird is a story in our reading book.

2. I like the poem The Road Not Taken by Robert Frost.

3. Did Amanda read the book Holes by Louis Sachar?

4. Frances Scott Key wrote The Star Spangled Banner.

5. The news reporter wrote an article called Education News in the daily paper The Globe.

6. Sports Illustrated has many articles about famous football players.

Writing Practice: If you were asked to design a new amusement park, what kind of rides and attractions would you put in it?

Geometry

Determine if the pair of figures is congruent or similar and then solve problem 5.

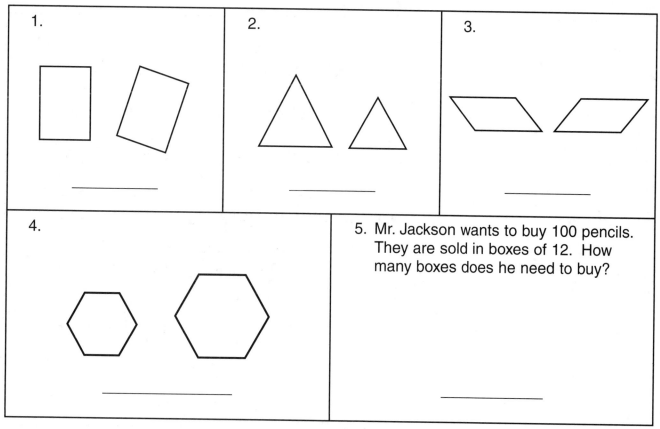

1.

2.

3.

_____

_____

_____

4.

_____

5. Mr. Jackson wants to buy 100 pencils. They are sold in boxes of 12. How many boxes does he need to buy?

_____

Homonyms

Circle the correct homonym to complete each sentence.

buy   by   1. Mom drove _____ Janet house.

break   brake   2. How did you _____ your pencil?

piece   peace   3. Countries need to have _____ with each other.

There   Their   4. _____ suitcase was packed for their vacation.

To   Too   5. _____ many people live in the city.

flee   flea   6. He swatted at the _____ on his arm.

Writing Practice: If you were in charge of the school cafeteria, what kinds of changes would you make?

Geometry

Circle each pair of congruent figures. Then solve problem 5.

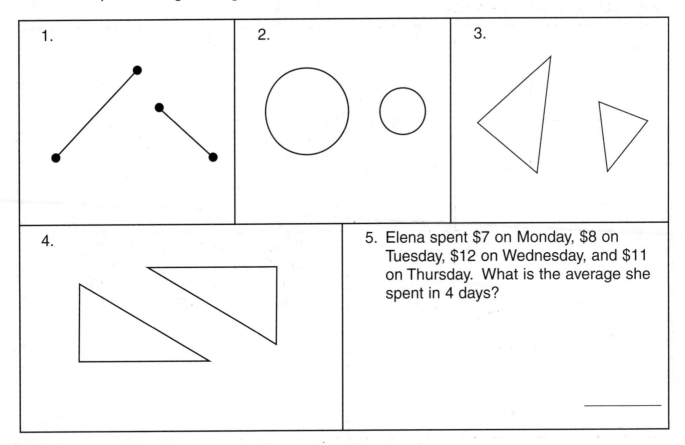

1.

2.

3.

4.

5. Elena spent $7 on Monday, $8 on Tuesday, $12 on Wednesday, and $11 on Thursday. What is the average she spent in 4 days?

_____

Verbs

Write the correct form of each verb in the sentences below.

Drink

1. Everyone _____ their milk.

2. Ellen _____ hers too fast.

3. I like to _____ mine slowly.

Take

4. Someone has _____ my book.

5. Our class _____ a trip to the museum.

6. Will you _____ me again next Tuesday?

 Writing Practice: Write a new commercial ad for your favorite product.

Geometry

Determine if each figure has a line of symmetry. Write symmetrical or not symmetrical for each problem. Then solve problem 5.

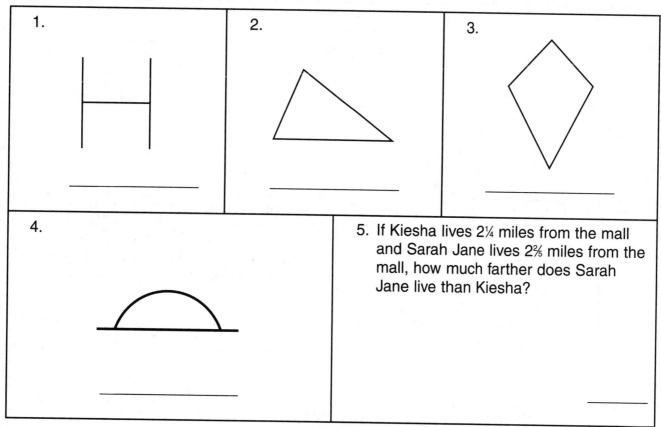

1.

2.

3.

4.

5. If Kiesha lives 2¼ miles from the mall and Sarah Jane lives 2⅗ miles from the mall, how much farther does Sarah Jane live than Kiesha?

Plurals

Circle the correctly spelled plural form of each word.

1. toy   toyies   toyes   toys

2. boss   boss's   bosses   boss

3. deer   deers   deer   deeres

4. fox   foxes   foxs   foxen

5. knife   knives   knifes   knife's

6. lunch   lunchs   lunch's   lunches

 Writing Practice: What do you do when it rains and you can't go outside?

Geometry

Write **S** if the figure is symmetrical or **N** if it is not symmetrical. Then solve problem 5.

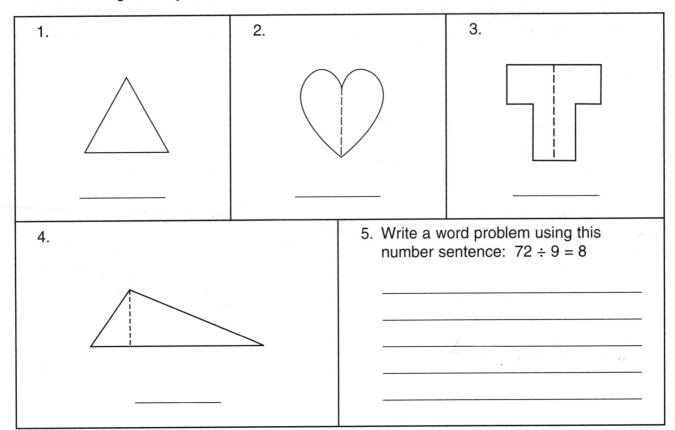

1.

_____

2.

_____

3.

_____

4.

_____

5. Write a word problem using this number sentence: $72 \div 9 = 8$

_____
_____
_____
_____
_____

Abbreviation

Write the abbreviation for each state.

1. Idaho   _____

2. Montana   _____

3. California   _____

4. Arizona   _____

5. Utah   _____

6. Washington   _____

7. Wyoming   _____

8. New Mexico   _____

 Writing Practice: Write a travel brochure about your home state and the sites and attractions it offers visitors/tourists.

Geometry

Match the correct term for each pair of shapes.

1.

2.

3.

_____

_____

_____

4.

a. similar

b. congruent

c. similar and congruent

d. neither similar nor congruent

_____

Punctuation

Add the correct punctuation for each sentence.

1. That movie was interesting ___

2. Who are the main characters ___

3. The movie last week was great ___

4. I like movies about real people ___

5. Did you see _Titanic_ ___

6. It was so sad at times ___

 Writing Practice: Write a review about a movie, TV program, or book that you recently read or saw.

Geometry

Use the diagram to solve the problems.

1. △ ABC is congruent

   to △ _____.

2. $\overline{ED}$ is equal

   to _____.

3. ∠BEC is equal

   to ∠ _____.

4.

   $\overline{AB}$ is parallel to _____.

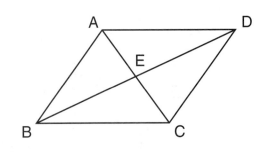

Adjectives

Fill in the acrostic with adjectives describing parents.

P _____

A _____

R _____

E _____

N _____

T _____

S _____

 Writing Practice: Write a story using this title:

The Birthday I'll Never Forget

Geometry

Match each name with the correct symbol.

1. line AB	2. ray AB	3. line segment AB

4. vertex AB	
	a. $\overrightarrow{AB}$ c. $\overline{AB}$
	b. $\overleftrightarrow{AB}$ d. AB

Homonyms

Circle the correct homonym in each sentence.

1. Charlton was the first actor to come (forth, fourth) on stage.

2. "The weather (vain, vane) looks like a rooster," said Meryl.

3. Sarah is (dying, dyeing) her dress green.

4. Margaret had a (miner, minor) part in the school play.

5. The (principal, principle) of the school made the morning announcements.

6. We (new, knew) right away that we didn't belong in the meeting.

Writing Practice: Write a persuasive paragraph to convince someone to recycle.

288

Geometry

Estimate the degrees of each angle and then solve problem 5.

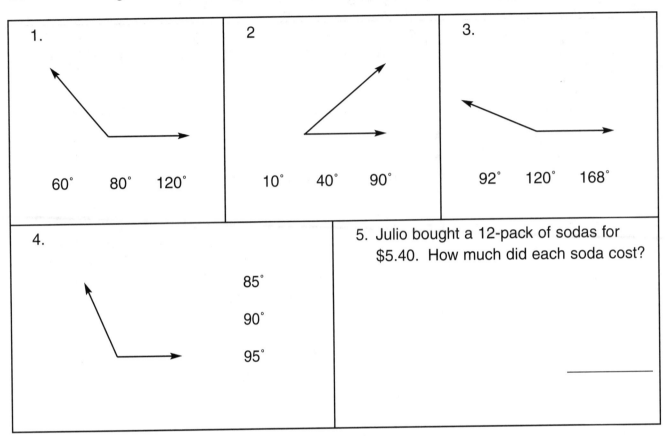

1.

60°   80°   120°

2

10°   40°   90°

3.

92°   120°   168°

4.

85°

90°

95°

5. Julio bought a 12-pack of sodas for $5.40. How much did each soda cost?

_____

Punctuation

Circle the colon (:) or semicolon (;) to make each sentence complete.

1. Ryan decided to stay after school (:   ;) I decided to go home.

2. I like to eat the following foods (:   ;) pancakes, bacon, and eggs.

3. At 6 (:   ;) 00 P.M. we eat dinner.

4. She won the race (:   ;) her teammate came in second.

5. Mr. Diaz asked the students to do three things (:   ;) listen, work quietly, and respect others.

6. It wasn't long till school would begin (:   ;) I was almost late.

 Writing Practice: National Children's Book Week is in November. Write a paragraph describing your favorite book.

Geometry

Circle the correct measurement for each angle. Then solve problem 5.

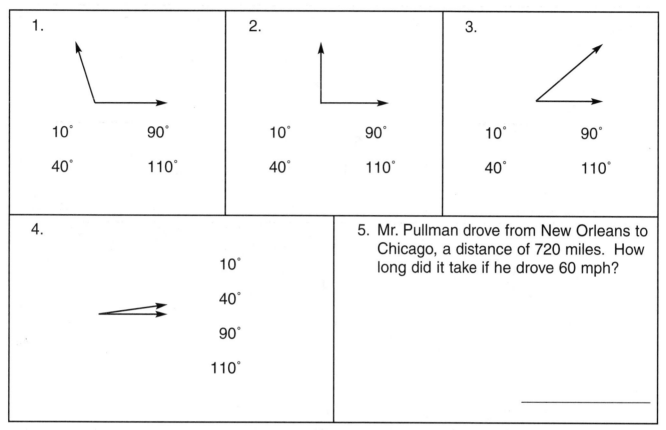

1.

10°   90°

40°   110°

2.

10°   90°

40°   110°

3.

10°   90°

40°   110°

4.

10°

40°

90°

110°

5. Mr. Pullman drove from New Orleans to Chicago, a distance of 720 miles. How long did it take if he drove 60 mph?

_____

Adjectives

Write the correct form of each adjective in the sentences below.

Good

1. The last quarter was the _____ of all.

2. She was a _____ student than her sister.

3. Alex is a very _____ reader.

Bad

4. I did _____ on this test than the one last week.

5. Benjamin felt _____ when he broke the window.

6. It was the _____ day in my life!

 Writing Practice: If you could visit any place in the world, where would it be and why?

Geometry

Find the measurement of the unknown angle. Then solve problem 5.

1.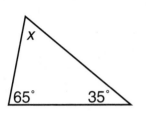

   $x =$ _____

2.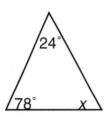

   $x =$ _____

3.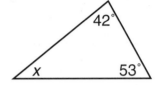

   $x =$ _____

4.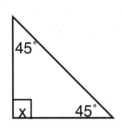

   $x =$ _____

5. Each table in the lunchroom can hold four people. How many tables are needed for 125 students?

   _____

Context Clues

Write the words that complete the paragraph.

Word Bank		
psychological	committed	mentor
psychiatrist	psychiatry	commencement

Dr. Lee, a young _____, works at a mental health clinic. She has learned much

from her _____, Dr. Harvey. They have practiced _____ together

since their _____ from Baylor University. They help people with _____

problems. They are _____ to helping others.

Writing Practice: Imagine that you are a marine biologist. Write a descriptive paragraph about the different things you would see during your sea expeditions.

Geometry

Find the perimeter. Then solve problem number 5.

1.

6 ft.

2 ft.

P = _____

2.

4 ft.

P = _____

3.

12 in.

P = _____

4.

8 cm

12 cm

P = _____

5. Barney went on vacation with his family. They traveled 125 miles the first day, and 201 miles the second day. By the end of the third day, they had traveled a total of 500 miles. How many miles did they travel the third day?

_____

Subject and Predicate

Circle the subject and underline the predicate in each sentence.

1. Mr. Jones gave us a Christmas present.

2. We opened it up on Christmas morning.

3. My brother received a toy truck.

4. My present was a board game.

5. Christmas makes me feel good inside.

Writing Practice: Write a paragraph using the sentence starter below.

I'm going to have fun this holiday season because . . .

Geometry and Measurement

Find the perimeter. Then, solve problem 5.

1. P = _____	2. P = _____	3. P = _____
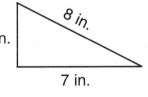 3 in. 8 in. 7 in.	7 in.	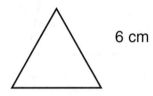 6 cm

4. P = _____	5. At basketball games, there are 20 rows of seats with 24 seats in each row. How many people can be seated at games?
4 ft. 10 ft.	_____

Syllables

Divide these words into syllables.

1. entire	5. magazine	9. because
_____	_____	_____
2. commercial	6. goblet	10. tomorrow
_____	_____	_____
3. appoint	7. wriggle	11. attention
_____	_____	_____
4. favorite	8. together	12. laughter
_____	_____	_____

 Writing Practice: Write a paragraph to complete this idea.

I wish it would snow because . . .

Geometry

Find the perimeter.

1. 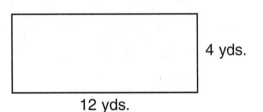 2 in. 4 in. P = _____	2. 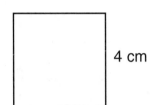 4 cm P = _____	3. 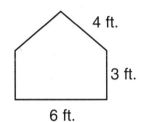 4 ft. 3 ft. 6 ft. P = _____

4.

4 yds.

12 yds.

P = _____

5. If Jo weighs 50 pounds and Jill weighs 42 pounds, how much more does Jo weigh than Jill? _____

How much do they both weigh in all?

_____

Proofreading

Rewrite this paragraph correctly.

> Wellcome to the villege of harbor Town, Each cotage, shop and warehouse looks just like it did in the 1800s? Take a carriage ride alonge the eeege of the Harbor. youll love this special plase

_____

_____

_____

_____

_____

 Writing Practice: What is the most important thing you've ever learned? Write a paragraph and share it with a friend.

Geometry

Find the area of each right triangle. (Remember, A = 1/2 bh.) Then solve problem 5.

1.

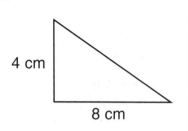

4 cm

8 cm

A = _____

2.

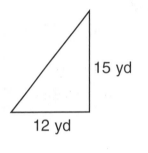

15 yd

12 yd

A = _____

3.

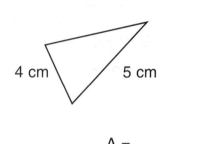

4 cm   5 cm

A = _____

4.

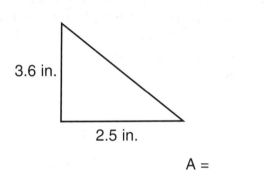

3.6 in.

2.5 in.

A = _____

5. On Saturday, Brad got up at 9:00 A. M. If he spent 3½ hours doing yard work, ¾ hours eating lunch, and 2¼ hours playing baseball, what time is it?

_____

Possessives

Underline the possessive noun in each sentence.

1. She is coming over for Jenna's party.

2. The Egyptians' pyramids are so enormous.

3. Those five girls' dolls are made of china.

4. The bird's nest is on the top branch of the tree.

5. The students' desks were rearranged differently today.

6. The teacher's desk was all the way in the back.

 Writing Practice: What board game do you like to play? Write a paragraph about playing the game.

Geometry

Find the area of each figure. (Remember, A = l x w.) Then solve problem 5.

1.	2.	3.
l = 12 cm w = 32 cm A = _____	l = 18 in w = 16.5 in A = _____	l = 4 ft. w = 4 ft. A = _____

4.	5. Marcos bought a pair of jeans at the department store for $19.99. He has to pay a 6% sales tax. What is the tax? What is his total cost?
l = 25 in. w = 5 in. A = _____	tax: _____ total: _____

Dictionary Skills

Match the correct definition of the word *mine* that goes with each sentence.

_____ 1. My friend's father mined coal in Kentucky.

_____ 2. During World War II, there were many minefields in Europe.

_____ 3. The pen he has is really mine.

_____ 4. Would you like to work in a diamond mine?

_____ 5. The coal miner has a dangerous job.

a. *pron.* my own

b. *n.* excavation for coal and mineral

c. *n.* buried or floating bomb

d. *v.* dig for a coal or mineral

e. *v.* one who works in a mine

 Writing Practice: Become a detective and write a mystery.

Geometry

Find the area. Then solve problem 5.

1.

1 m

6 m

A = _____

2.

10 in.

12 in.

A = _____

3.

8 cm

A = _____

4.

8 ft.

2 ft.

A = _____

5. Joan has 120 baseball cards. She sold 87 and then bought 23 more. How many cards does she have now?

_____

Compound Words

Match the compound words in the boxes.

your	lash	rain	paper
honey	mark	play	shell
eye	melon	birth	noon
door	moon	after	fish
water	self	cat	ground
book	light	news	day
candle	knob	sea	bow

 Writing Practice: Write five predictions about your future.

Geometry

Find the circumference of each figure. (Remember C = dπ or 2rπ. Use 3.14 for π.) Then solve for problem 5.

1. 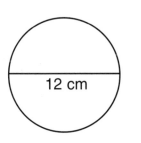 12 cm C = _____	2. 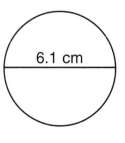 6.1 cm C = _____	3. 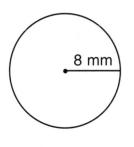 8 mm C = _____

4.

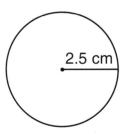 2.5 cm

C = _____

5. Mindy got 9 out of every 10 problems correct. If the test had 50 questions, how many problems did she answer correctly?

_____

Synonyms

Circle the synonym for the first word in each row.

1. zest	clean	enjoyment
2. yearn	crave	shudder
3. potent	value	demerit
4. valid	powerless	strong
5. unfit	like	unsuitable
6. tremble	shake	calm

 Writing Practice: What route do you take to get from your house to school every day? Write a set of directions.

298

Geometry

Solve the problems below.

1.

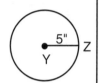

YZ is _____

a. 7"   c. diameter

b. radius   d. 10"

2.

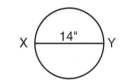

XY is _____

a. 7"   c. diameter

b. radius   d. 10"

---

3. diameter of #1 is _____

a. 7"   c. diameter

b. radius   d. 10"

---

4. radius of #2 is _____

a. 7"   c. diameter

b. radius   d. 10"

---

5. The five members of the wrestling team weigh 102 lbs., 110 lbs., 113 lbs., 114 lbs., and 126 lbs. What is their average weight?

_____

Punctuation

Circle the words that need hyphens. Add the hyphens.

picnic table   class president   merry go round   mortal like

best known   one half   father in law   twenty one

nose dive   mountain range   parking lot   open house

 Writing Practice: Write a story about a dog doing tricks.

Geometry

Calculate the volume for each problem. (Remember, V= l x w x h.) Then solve problem 5.

1. 5 in. long 2 in. wide 7 in. high V = _____	**2.** 10 cm long 4 cm wide 15 cm high V = _____	**3.** 31 ft. long 6 ft. wide 20 ft. high V = _____
4. 12 yd. long 13 yd. wide 14 yd. high V = _____	**5.** Eddie earns $5.37 an hour after school. He worked 17 hours last week. How much did he earn? _____	

Main Idea

Choose the sentence that would go in a paragraph with the main idea.

1. Yellowstone National Park is a place of beautiful scenery.
   a. We camped outside in the park.
   b. The trees were tall and green.

2. There were some interesting animals at the zoo.
   a. The bengal tiger roared loudly.
   b. I enjoyed walking through the zoo.

3. The Christmas Parade had colorful floats.
   a. It was so cold that we watched it on television.
   b. The best float had Santa Claus sitting on top.

4. Yahtzee® is a fun game to play.
   a. You roll the dice to get points.
   b. I beat my brother three times.

 Writing Practice: Write a persuasive paragraph explaining why you need a computer in your bedroom.

Geometry

Calculate the volume for each problem. (Remember, V = l x w x h)

| 1. 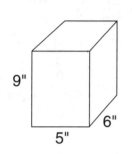 9" 6" 5" V = _____ | 2. 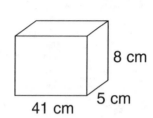 8 cm 41 cm 5 cm V = _____ | 3. S 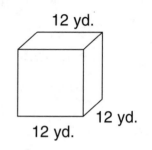 12 yd. 12 yd. 12 yd. V = _____ |

4.

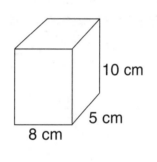

10 cm
5 cm
8 cm

V = _____

5. A cereal box is 6" by 3" by 9". What is the volume?

_____

Syllables

Divide these words into syllables. Be sure to include the accent marks.

1. danger _____

2. eagle _____

3. mystery _____

4. transparent _____

5. receiver _____

6. overpass _____

Writing Practice: Have you ever felt like you were in danger? Write a paragraph about what happened and how you felt.

Page 5

Sets

Look at the following set of whole numbers through ten {0, 1, 2, 3, 4, 5, 6, 7, 8, 9, 10}. Using this set, list the sets below. Then solve problem 5.

1. even numbers	2. odd numbers	3. numbers divisible by 5
(2, 4, 6, 8, 10)	(1, 3, 5, 7, 9)	(5, 10)

4. numbers divisible by three	5. Bobbie is going to a party. He has to leave by 5:00. Before he can go, he has to finish his chores (15 min.), walk his sister to her friend's house (5 min.), get air put in his bike tire (10 min.), and finish his homework (25 min.). If he gets home from school at 3:30, how much time is left to get dressed?
(3, 6, 9)	35 min.

Fact or Opinion

Write **F** if the statement is fact and **O** if the statement is opinion.

O 1. Piglets are cute baby pigs.
O 2. People may live in space someday.
F 3. An oyster has a shell.
O 4. There are aliens on Mars.
O 5. Libraries are fun to visit.
F 6. Water is necessary for humans to live.
O 7. Strawberries are delicious.
O 8. It is fun to play in the snow.

✍ **Writing Practice:** Write a story using the sentence starter below.
It was so unfair . . .

Page 6

Number Order

Solve the problems.

1. Write in order from least to greatest.	2. Write in order from least to greatest.	3. Write in order from greatest to least.
98,765 98,765	104.235 10.4235	989 999
987.65 987.65	10,423.5 104.235	898 989
9,876.5 9,876.5	1,042.35 1,042.35	999 899
98,765 98,765	10.4235 10,423.5	899 898

4. Write in order from greatest to least.	5. Noah brought 2 of most every kind of animal into the ark. If there were 189 kinds of animals, how many animals were in the ark?
2,003,005 2,003,005	
200,300.5 200,300.5	
20,030.05 20,030.05	
2,003.005 2,003.005	378 animals

Interjections

Write an interjection before each sentence.   (Answers will vary.)

1. _____! Watch out for that car!
2. _____! That hurt!
3. _____! We won the game!
4. _____! I hate squash!
5. _____! The football team lost!
6. _____! I won the contest!

Ouch! Wow! Yuck! Stop! Yeah! Look!

✍ **Writing Practice:** Write a story using the starter below.
We heard a noise and ran to the bush. There we saw . . .

Page 7

Number Order

Write in order from least to greatest for problems 1–4. Then solve problem 5.

1. 13,765 13,705 13,775 13,567	2. 206 260 252 210	3. 6,566 6,565 6,656 6,660
13,567 13,705	206 210	6,565 6,566
13,765 13,775	252 260	6,656 6,660

4. 1,042 1,240 1,402 1,024	5. Margaret played basketball for the school's team. During the first six games, she scored 11 points, 8 points, 24 points, 16 points, 9 points, and 15 points. How many points did she score in all six games?
1,024 1,042	
1,240 1,402	83 points

Predicate (Verb)

Write the tenses of the following verbs:

	Past	**Past Participle**
Example: write	wrote	written
1. sing	sang	sung
2. go	went	gone
3. blow	blew	blown
4. give	gave	given
5. do	did	done

✍ **Writing Practice:** Now choose one verb above and write a paragraph with all three tenses of the verb.

Page 8

Number Order and Writing Numbers

Follow the directions for each box.

1. Write in order from least to greatest.	2. Write in order from greatest to least.	3. Write the word name for this number.
47.03 4.037 470.3 47.30 4,730	12.340 1,230 123.40 1,420 120.34	4.037
4.037 47.03	1,420 1,230	four and
47.30 470.3	123.40 120.34	thirty-seven
4,730	12.340	thousandths

4. Write the word name for this number.	5. Read and solve the problem.
120.34	The students in Mr. Randall's class are going on a field trip. Six parents will be driving mini-vans. How many students will be riding in each van if there are 36 students?
one hundred twenty and thirty-four hundredths	6 students

Proofreading

Circle all letters that should be capitalized and add commas and periods where they belong.

1. We went to the grocery store for butter eggs and cheese.
2. I saw a big elephant at the St. Louis zoo.
3. I ate three pieces of sausage pepperoni and cheese pizza for lunch.
4. Cherry shouted, "the house is on fire!"
5. When I get home I'll have to wash the dishes make up my bed and sweep the kitchen floor.

✍ **Writing Practice:** You get to travel to a foreign country. Which country would you choose and why?

Page 9

Number Order

Write the numbers in order from least to greatest and then solve problem 5.

1. 201,800 208,100 202,788 202,877	2. 431,559 431.559 4,315.59 43,155.9	3. 5,643 5,346 5,436 5,634
201,800	431.559	5,346
202,788	4,315.59	5,436
202,877	43,155.9	5,634
208,100	431,599	5,643

4. 99,960 96,990 99,690 99,909	5. The Red Cross had a weekend blood drive. On Friday 120 people gave blood. On Saturday 191 gave blood, and on Sunday 85 people gave blood. By rounding each number to the nearest ten, estimate how many people gave blood during the weekend blood drive.
96,990	
99,690	
99,909	
99,960	400 people

Pronouns

Read the first sentence. Write a pronoun in the second sentence that describes the first sentence.

1. Brook is my neighbor. She has two brothers.
2. Stephan likes to play baseball. He plays every week.
3. Ted and Jo made a volcano. They made it for science.
4. Sammy is Joella's brother. He is three years older than Joella.
5. The tiger is dangerous. Don't go near it.
6. Most people don't like spiders or snakes. They are creepy animals.

✍ **Writing Practice:** Write a paragraph describing how you feel about insects.

Page 10

Standard Form

Write each in standard form for problems 1–4. Then solve problem 5.

1. 52 thousand 3 hundred	2. 4 thousand twenty-three	3. 1 hundred five
52,300	4,023	105

4. 4 hundred ninety-nine	5. There were 16 people in the gym, and seven were girls. How many were boys?
499	9 were boys

Plurals

Write the plural of these nouns.

1. goose geese
2. ox oxen
3. sheep sheep
4. city cities
5. book books
6. leaf leaves
7. cherry cherries
8. class classes

Now choose four plurals and write them in a complete sentence.
Answers will vary.

✍ **Writing Practice:** Write a descriptive paragraph by finishing the story.
I was walking down the street when suddenly I saw a bright light.

Standard Form
For problems 1–2, write the standard form in expanded form. For problems 3–4, write the expanded form into standard form. Then solve problem 5.

1. $492 =$ $400 + 90 + 2$	2. $1,021 =$ $1,000 + 000 + 20 + 1$	3. $1,000 + 900 + 2 = 1,902$
4. $20,000 + 8,000 + 300 + 10 + 9 = 28,319$		5. Laurie earned $25.68 for helping clean the garage. Lewis earned $2.45 more than Laurie for also washing the car. How much money did Lewis earn? 28.13

Abbreviations
Connect the titles of these names with the correct abbreviation.

Doctor — Dr.
Senator — Sen.
Governor — Gov.
Mister — Mr.
Reverend — Rev.
Junior — Jr.

✏ **Writing Practice:** Finish the sentence below. Then write a detailed description of how your costume would look. Then draw a picture of you in your costume.
On Halloween, I want to be a . . .

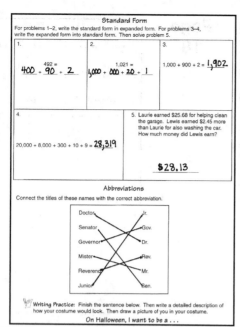

Writing Numbers
Write the following number words in numbers. Then solve problem 5.

1. eight million, two thousand, five hundred sixty-two	2. three million, four hundred thousand, seven hundred thirty	3. sixty-four million, four hundred twenty-one thousand, three hundred seven
$8,002,562$	$3,400,730$	$64,421,307$
4. seventy-seven thousand, seven		5. We walked $\frac{1}{10}$ of a mile to see the giraffe, $\frac{2}{10}$ of a mile to see the elephants, $\frac{4}{10}$ of a mile to see the bears, and $\frac{1}{10}$ of a mile to see the tigers. How far did we walk?
$77,007$		$\frac{8}{10}$ of a mile

Figurative Language
Write **L** if the statement is literal and **F** if the statement is figurative.

F 1. I'm so hungry I could eat a horse!
L 2. I'm exhausted!
F 3. Darkness swallowed the ghost town.
F 4. Boy, I'm late. Time surely does fly.
L 5. The flower floated on the water.
F 6. His eyes burned with fire.

✏ **Writing Practice:** Write a descriptive paragraph about spending the day at the zoo.

Writing Numbers
For problems 1 and 2, write the words in numbers. For problems 3 and 4, write the numbers in words. Then solve problem 5.

1. six million, one hundred four thousand, two hundred fifty-five	2. two hundred seventy-two thousand, six hundred ninety	3. 13,765 thirteen thousand, seven hundred sixty-five
$6,104,255$	$272,690$	
4. 1,206,400 one million, two hundred six thousand, four hundred		5. You and three friends are buying a present for your teacher and will need to pay equal amounts. The total is $20.44. How much will each pay? $5.11

Story Comprehension
Answer the questions about the story.

Amelia Earhart is known for being the first woman pilot to fly across the Atlantic Ocean. She made this famous flight in 1932. She received an award after this famous flight. The award was the Distinguished Flying Cross, and she was the first woman to have received the award. In 1937, she began a flight that would take her around the world. Her plane disappeared over the Pacific Ocean, and to this day, no one knows what happened to her.

1. What did Amelia Earhart do in 1932? She flew across the Atlantic Ocean.
2. What is the name of the award she received? She received the Distinguished Flying Cross.
3. What did Amelia Earhart attempt to do in 1937? She tried to fly across the world.
4. How did she die? No one knows how she died. She disappeared.

✏ **Writing Practice:** Write what you think the differences are in planes during Amelia Earhart's day and the jets that are used today.

Place Value
Look at the number **3,458**. Answer the questions about place value. Then solve number 5.

1. What place is the 5 in? 3,458 tens	2. What place is the 3 in? 3,458 thousands	3. What place is the 4 in? 3,458 hundreds
4. What is the number value of the 5? 3,458 50		5. Joe had 32 marbles and gave Anita and Kim 8 each. How many did he have for himself? 16 marbles

Predicate
Underline the predicate in each sentence.

1. The baseball team played on Saturday.
2. The students sang songs in choir.
3. Stars flicker and sparkle in the sky.
4. My favorite food is tacos.
5. Kim had to stay after school to finish her class work.

✏ **Writing Practice:** Write a paragraph with the following beginning phrase.
People like me because . . .

Place Value
For problems 1–2, write the numeral in word form. For problems 3–4, write the numbers in the boxes. Then solve problem 5.

1. 305 three hundred five	2. 2,295 two thousand, two hundred ninety-five	3. two hundred six $2\ 0\ 6$
4. eight thousand, one hundred forty-four $8,1\ 4\ 4$		5. Mrs. Green and Ms. Ward bought school supplies for $13.42. If they paid with $20.00, what would their change be? $6.58

Pronouns
Circle all pronouns in each sentence.

1. They asked if their teacher could give them some help.
2. The dog ate her hot dog after she dropped it on the floor.
3. Shoes were found in my locker, and they weren't mine.
4. My family likes to go shopping with our cousin.
5. We weren't sure if the present belonged to her.

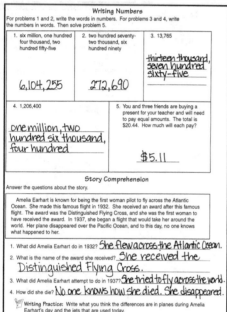

✏ **Writing Practice:** Write a paragraph about the best birthday party you ever had.

Place Value
For problems 1–4, find what number value is represented by the 7. Then solve problem 5.

1. 76 70	2. 927 7	3. 7,253 $7,000$
4. 6,745 700		5. Sherwon had 38 baseball cards. He gave 10 to Antwone. How many cards does Sherwon have left? 28 cards

Sentence Fragments
Finish each fragment to make complete sentences. (Answers will vary.)

1. Jose came to _____
2. Watch out for _____
3. _____ finished the race.
4. _____ comes down the road.
5. An ugly bug _____
6. _____ is pink with green stripes.

✏ **Writing Practice:** During holidays students get some extra days off from school. Write a paragraph about things you will do on your days off from school.

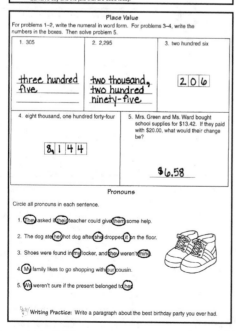

Page 17

Place Value

Fill in the blanks. Then solve problem 5.

1. In the number 3,745, the digit in the hundreds place is __7__	2. In the number 3,745, the digit in the thousands place is __3__	3. In the number 583,564, the number value of the 8 is __80,000__
4. In the number 583,564, the number value of the 6 is __60__	5. Sherrie had 12 pairs of earrings. Her sister borrowed 3 pairs. How many pairs of earrings did she have left? __9 pairs of earrings__	

Nouns

Circle all nouns in the following paragraph.

Thanksgiving

(Thanksgiving) is an American (holiday). It is observed on the fourth (Thursday) in (November). It all began many (years) ago when the (Indians) helped the (Pilgrims) who had come to (America). The (Indians) helped them plant (crops) and showed them how to survive in their new (land). They celebrated by eating a (feast) together. This is how (Thanksgiving) began.

✍ **Writing Practice:** Write a paragraph using the starting sentence below.
If I were an animal, I would be . . .

Page 18

Place Value

Look at the number 976,423 and answer the questions. Then solve problem 5.

1. What is the place value of 4?	2. What is the place value of 3?	3. What is the number value of 6?
976,423 __hundreds__	976,423 __ones__	976,423 __6,000__
4. What is the number value of 2?	5. Frankie talked on the phone for 20 minutes. Jerry talked on the phone $\frac{1}{2}$ of the time. How many minutes did Jerry talk on the phone?	
976,423 __20__	__10 minutes__	

Commas

Write a **C** for correct or a **N** for not correct beside each sentence.

N 1. Lindsay turn off your, CD player.
C 2. "I like to play my video games," said Patrick.
C 3. How old are you, Laura?
N 4. Robert lives in Knoxville Tennessee.
N 5. Joey said "Kevin you are a good bowler."
C 6. Kimberly's cousins are Megan, Christen, and Katie.
C 7. "Before we eat, Stephen, you need to set the table," said Jenny.
N 8. Stephanie have you helped your sister Suzanne?

✍ **Writing Practice:** Finish the statement below and write a paragraph on what makes you happy.
Happiness is . . .

Page 19

Place Value

Circle the answer to each problem. Then solve problem 5.

1. Which number is five thousand, seven hundred eighty-six?	2. Which is the number for ten thousand, five?	3. Which number is 900 + 9?
(a. 5,786) c. 50,768 b. 5,768 d. 50,786	a. 10,050 **(c. 10,005)** b. 1,050 d. 1,005	a. 9,909 **(c. 909)** b. 9,009 d. 990
4. Which number is 20,000 + 5,000 + 70 + 3? a. 25,703 c. 20,573 **(b. 25,073)** d. 25,730	5. Earth orbits the sun once in 365 days. How long would it take Earth to orbit the sun 25 times? __9,125 days__	

Punctuation

Choose the correct punctuation mark (. ? !) for each sentence.

1. Do not pick the daisies **.**
2. Where are the shovels **?**
3. Can you hear the woodpecker **?**
4. Ouch, these thorns are very sharp **!**
5. She is planting seeds **.**
6. What a beautiful day to work in the garden **!**

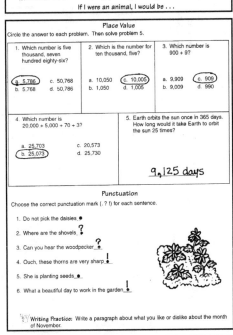

✍ **Writing Practice:** Write a paragraph about what you like or dislike about the month of November.

Page 20

Place Value

For problems 1–4, name the place value in the following number: 1,876,321. Then solve problem 5.

1. What is the place value of the 7?	2. What is the place value of the 6?	3. What is the place value of the 3?
1,876,321 __ten thousands__	1,876,321 __thousands__	1,876,321 __hundreds__
4. What is the place value of the 8? 1,876,321 __hundred thousands__	5. If three students paid $2.35 each for lunch and four students each paid $1.85 for lunch, how much did all the lunches cost? __$14.45__	

Prepositions

Fill in the blanks with a preposition from the box below. Use each word only once.

toward	before	to	into
with	down	around	from

1. I walked to school __with__ my sister.
2. We went __around__ the corner and __down__ the street.
3. As we walked __to__ the school, the bell rang.
4. My teacher walked __toward__ me and said, "Get a note __from__ the office."
5. They gave me a note, and I went __into__ my class __before__ the second bell.

✍ **Writing Practice:** Write a story using the sentence starter below.
The whole school could hear Matilda screaming . . .

Page 21

Place Value

For problems 1–2, write the numbers in the boxes. For problems 3–4, write the numeral in word form. Then solve problem 5.

1. fifteen thousand, seventy-two	2. three hundred thirty thousand, one hundred two	3. 888
1 5 . 0 7 2	3 3 0 . 1 0 2	eight hundred eighty-eight
4. 4.236 __four and two hundred thirty-six thousandths__	5. Using the number of boys and girls in your class, write a number sentence showing how many students are in your class. __Answers will vary.__	

Sentences

Rewrite the paragraph with complete sentences. Remember to add correct end marks and capital letters.

> During school today we had a test the test was in social studies we had to write the capital of each state I got two answers wrong the capital of Missouri is Springfield, not St. Louis, the capital of California is Sacramento, not Los Angeles.

__During school today we had a test. The test was in social studies. We had to write the capital of each state. I got two answers wrong. The capital of Missouri is Springfield, not St. Louis. The capital of California is Sacramento, not Los Angeles.__

✍ **Writing Practice:** Pretend you are a meteorologist for a television station. Write a weather forecast for the news by how it looks outside today.

Page 22

Place Value

Answer the questions.

1. Write 3,456,100 in expanded form.	2. Write 672,008 in expanded form.	3. Write 20,000 + 8,000 + 300 + 9 in standard form.
3,000,000 + 400,000 + 50,000 + 6,000 + 100	600,000 + 70,000 + 2,000 + 8	28,309
4. Write 4,000,000 + 100,000 + 20,000 + 9,000 + 80 + 1 in standard form. 4,129,081	5. Teresa bought a cheeseburger for $1.50, French fries for $0.50, and a soda for $0.75. How much did she pay for her meal? $2.75	

Comprehension

Answer questions about the following facts.

Facts About Fish

- All fish live in water.
- Most fish have scales.
- Some are catfish.
- Some fish live in fresh water.
- All fish are cold-blooded.
- Some fish live in salt water.

1. Is it true that all fish live in fresh water? __No__
2. Is it true that all fish have scales? __No__
3. Is it true that all catfish live in water? __Yes__
4. Is it true that catfish are cold-blooded? __Yes__

✍ **Writing Practice:** Write a paragraph using the sentence starter below.
Being a part of a family means . . .

#8333 Skill Builders: Ages 9-11

Page 23

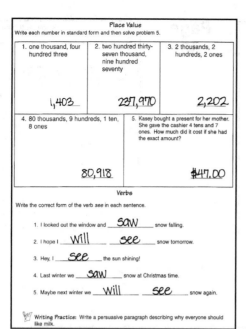

Place Value
Write each number in standard form and then solve problem 5.

1. one thousand, four hundred three	2. two hundred thirty-seven thousand, nine hundred seventy	3. 2 thousands, 2 hundreds, 2 ones
1,403	237,970	2,202

4. 80 thousands, 9 hundreds, 1 ten, 8 ones	5. Kasey bought a present for her mother. She gave the cashier 4 tens and 7 ones. How much did it cost if she had the exact amount?
80,918	$47.00

Verbs
Write the correct form of the verb *see* in each sentence.

1. I looked out the window and _saw_ snow falling.
2. I hope I _will see_ snow tomorrow.
3. Hey, I _see_ the sun shining!
4. Last winter we _saw_ snow at Christmas time.
5. Maybe next winter we _will see_ snow again.

Writing Practice: Write a persuasive paragraph describing why everyone should like milk.

Page 24

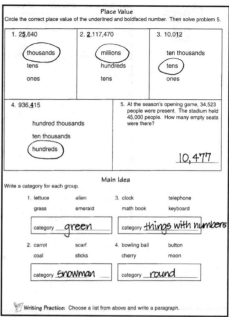

Place Value
Circle the correct place value of the underlined and boldfaced number. Then solve problem 5.

1. 25,640	2. 2,117,470	3. 10,012
(thousands) tens ones	(millions) hundreds tens	ten thousands (tens) ones

4. 936,415	5. At the season's opening game, 34,523 people were present. The stadium held 45,000 people. How many empty seats were there?
hundred thousands ten thousands (hundreds)	10,477

Main Idea
Write a category for each group.

1. lettuce alien   grass emerald
category _green_

3. clock telephone   math book keyboard
category _things with numbers_

2. carrot scarf   coal sticks
category _snowman_

4. bowling ball button   cherry moon
category _round_

Writing Practice: Choose a list from above and write a paragraph.

Page 25

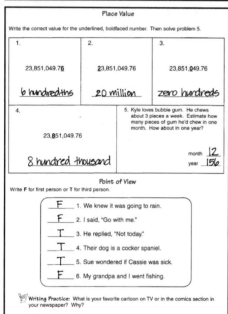

Place Value
Write the correct value for the underlined, boldfaced number. Then solve problem 5.

1. 23,851,049.76	2. 23,851,049.76	3. 23,851,049.76
6 hundredths	20 million	zero hundreds

4. 23,851,049.76	5. Kyle loves bubble gum. He chews about 3 pieces a week. Estimate how many pieces of gum he'd chew in one month. How about in one year?
8 hundred thousand	month 12 year 156

Point of View
Write F for first person or T for third person.

F 1. We knew it was going to rain.
F 2. I said, "Go with me."
T 3. He replied, "Not today."
T 4. Their dog is a cocker spaniel.
T 5. Sue wondered if Cassie was sick.
F 6. My grandpa and I went fishing.

Writing Practice: What is your favorite cartoon on TV or in the comics section in your newspaper? Why?

Page 26

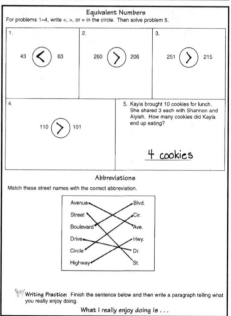

Equivalent Numbers
For problems 1–4, write <, >, or = in the circle. Then solve problem 5.

1. 43 < 63	2. 260 > 206	3. 251 > 215

4. 110 > 101	5. Kayla brought 10 cookies for lunch. She shared 3 each with Shannon and Alyieh. How many cookies did Kayla end up eating?
	4 cookies

Abbreviations
Match these street names with the correct abbreviation.

Avenue — Blvd.
Street — Cir.
Boulevard — Ave.
Drive — Hwy.
Circle — Dr.
Highway — St.

Writing Practice: Finish the sentence below and then write a paragraph telling what you really enjoy doing.
What I really enjoy doing is . . .

Page 27

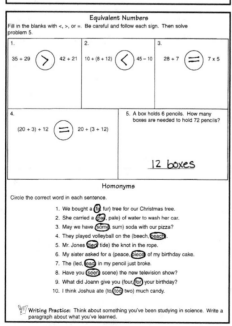

Equivalent Numbers
Fill in the blanks with <, >, or =. Be careful and follow each sign. Then solve problem 5.

1. 35 + 29 > 42 + 21	2. 10 + (8 + 12) < 45 − 10	3. 28 + 7 = 7 x 5

4. (20 + 3) + 12 = 20 + (3 + 12)	5. A box holds 6 pencils. How many boxes are needed to hold 72 pencils?
	12 boxes

Homonyms
Circle the correct word in each sentence.

1. We bought a (fir, fur) tree for our Christmas tree.
2. She carried a (pail, pale) of water to wash her car.
3. May we have (some, sum) soda with our pizza?
4. They played volleyball on the (beech, beach).
5. Mr. Jones (tied, tide) the knot in the rope.
6. My sister asked for a (peace, piece) of my birthday cake.
7. The (led, lead) in my pencil just broke.
8. Have you (seen, scene) the new television show?
9. What did Joann give you (four, for) your birthday?
10. I think Joshua ate (to, too, two) much candy.

Writing Practice: Think about something you've been studying in science. Write a paragraph about what you've learned.

Page 28

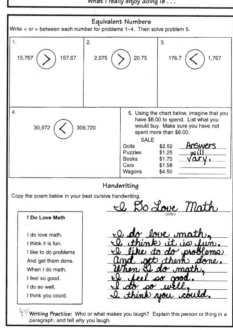

Equivalent Numbers
Write < or > between each number for problems 1–4. Then solve problem 5.

1. 15,767 > 157.67	2. 2,075 > 20.75	3. 176.7 < 1,767

4. 30,972 < 309,720	5. Using the chart below, imagine that you have $8.00 to spend. List what you would buy. Make sure you have not spent more than $8.00.
	SALE Dolls $2.52 Puzzles $1.25 Books $1.75 Cars $1.58 Wagons $4.50 — Answers will vary.

Handwriting
Copy the poem below in your best cursive handwriting.

I Do Love Math

I do love math,
I think it is fun.
I like to do problems
And get them done.
When I do math,
I feel so good.
I do so well,
I think you could.

I Do Love Math (title)
I do love math,
I think it is fun.
I like to do problems
and get them done.
When I do math,
I feel so good.
I do so well,
I think you could.

Writing Practice: Who or what makes you laugh? Explain this person or thing in a paragraph, and tell why you laugh.

Page 29

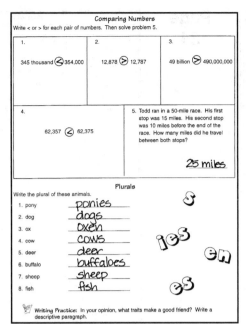

Comparing Numbers
Write < or > for each pair of numbers. Then solve problem 5.

1.	2.	3.
345 thousand $<$ 354,000	12,878 $>$ 12,787	49 billion $>$ 490,000,000

4.	5. Todd ran in a 50-mile race. His first stop was 15 miles. His second stop was 10 miles before the end of the race. How many miles did he travel between both stops?
62,357 $<$ 62,375	25 miles

Plurals
Write the plural of these animals.

1. pony — ponies
2. dog — dogs
3. ox — oxen
4. cow — cows
5. deer — deer
6. buffalo — buffaloes
7. sheep — sheep
8. fish — fish

s   ies   en   es

Writing Practice: In your opinion, what traits make a good friend? Write a descriptive paragraph.

Page 30

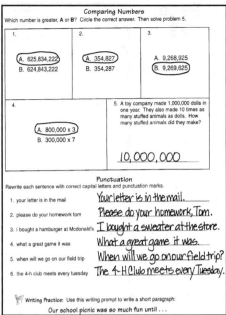

Comparing Numbers
Which number is greater, A or B? Circle the correct answer. Then solve problem 5.

1.	2.	3.
A. 625,834,222 (circled) B. 624,843,222	A. 354,827 (circled) B. 354,287	A. 9,268,925 B. 9,269,625 (circled)

4.	5. A toy company made 1,000,000 dolls in one year. They also made 10 times as many stuffed animals as dolls. How many stuffed animals did they make?
A. 800,000 x 3 (circled) B. 300,000 x 7	10,000,000

Punctuation
Rewrite each sentence with correct capital letters and punctuation marks.

1. your letter is in the mail — Your letter is in the mail.
2. please do your homework tom — Please do your homework, Tom.
3. i bought a hamburger at Mcdonald's — I bought a sweater at the store.
4. what a great game it was — What a great game it was.
5. when will we go on our field trip — When will we go on our field trip?
6. the 4-h club meets every tuesday — The 4-H Club meets every Tuesday.

Writing Practice: Use this writing prompt to write a short paragraph:
Our school picnic was so much fun until . . .

Page 31

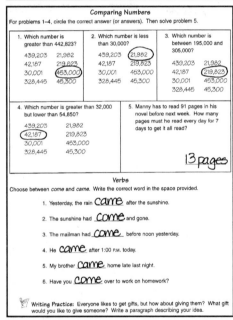

Comparing Numbers
For problems 1–4, circle the correct answer (or answers). Then solve problem 5.

1. Which number is greater than 442,823?
439,203   21,982
42,187   219,823
30,001   453,000 (circled)
328,445   45,300

2. Which number is less than 30,000?
439,203   21,982 (circled)
42,187   219,823
30,001   453,000
328,445   45,300

3. Which number is between 195,000 and 305,000?
439,203   21,982
42,187   219,823 (circled)
30,001   453,000
328,445   45,300

4. Which number is greater than 32,000 but lower than 54,850?
439,203   21,982
42,187 (circled)   219,823
30,001   453,000
328,445   45,300

5. Manny has to read 91 pages in his novel before next week. How many pages must he read every day for 7 days to get it all read?

13 pages

Verbs
Choose between *come* and *came*. Write the correct word in the space provided.

1. Yesterday, the rain **came** after the sunshine.
2. The sunshine had **come** and gone.
3. The mailman had **come** before noon yesterday.
4. He **came** after 1:00 P.M. today.
5. My brother **came** home late last night.
6. Have you **come** over to work on homework?

Writing Practice: Everyone likes to get gifts, but how about giving them? What gift would you like to give someone? Write a paragraph describing your idea.

Page 32

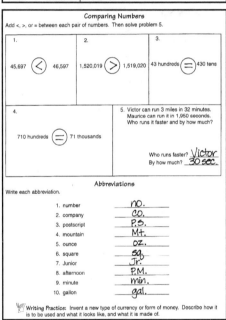

Comparing Numbers
Add <, >, or = between each pair of numbers. Then solve problem 5.

1.	2.	3.
45,697 $<$ 46,597	1,520,019 $>$ 1,519,020	43 hundreds $=$ 430 tens

4.	5. Victor can run 3 miles in 32 minutes. Maurice can run it in 1,950 seconds. Who runs it faster and by how much?
710 hundreds $=$ 71 thousands	Who runs faster? Victor By how much? 30 sec.

Abbreviations
Write each abbreviation.

1. number — no.
2. company — co.
3. postscript — P.S.
4. mountain — Mt.
5. ounce — oz.
6. square — sq.
7. Junior — Jr.
8. afternoon — P.M.
9. minute — min.
10. gallon — gal.

Writing Practice: Invent a new type of currency or form of money. Describe how it is to be used and what it looks like, and what it is made of.

Page 33

Rounding
Round to the nearest 10. Then solve problem 5.

1. 42	2. 78	3. 55
40	80	60

4. 186	5. Daniel saw 16 trees, 12 bushes, 23 flowers, and 2 lizards on his walk in the woods. How many items did Daniel see?
190	53 items

Compound Words
Find these compound words in the puzzle.

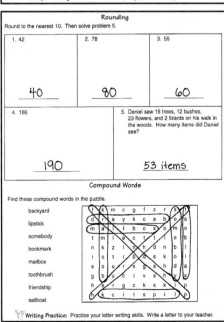

backyard
lipstick
somebody
bookmark
mailbox
toothbrush
friendship
sailboat

Writing Practice: Practice your letter writing skills. Write a letter to your teacher.

Page 34

Rounding
Round to the nearest 10 for problems 1–4. Then solve number 5.

1. 26	2. 79	3. 452
30	80	450

4. 1,658	5. Ellen made an 89, 92, 97, 88, and 100 on her spelling tests. What is her average of all 5 grades?
1,660	93.2

Adjectives
Choose the correct adjective in each sentence.

1. That is the (badest, worst) accident I've ever seen.
2. She is the (goodest, best) student in the class.
3. Marty has the (silliest, sillyest) sense of humor.
4. Who is (smartest, smarter), Joanna or Ellen?
5. Which sister is (shorter, shortest), Joy or Jill?
6. I have the (higher, highest) grades in my math class.
7. Max is (funnier, funniest) than his brother Malcolm.
8. We should be (carefuller, more careful) when playing close to the street.

Writing Practice: Finish this story.
Joan wanted to give her mom a Christmas present, but she didn't have any money. So she decided to . . .

Page 35

Rounding

For problems 1–4, round each number to the nearest ten. Then solve problem 5.

1.	2.	3.
123 = **120**	565 = **570**	791 = **790**

4.	5. A long distance phone call costs $0.25 the first 3 minutes and $0.40 for any additional minutes. How much would it cost for a 10-minute phone call?
637 = **640**	**$ 3.05**

Plurals

Circle the correct plural.

1. **bridge** (a. bridges) b. bridgies
2. **boss** a. boss's (b. bosses)
3. **speech** a. speechs (b. speeches)
4. **chicken** (a. chickens) b. chickenes
5. **box** a. boxs (b. boxes)
6. **kiss** a. kiss's (b. kisses)
7. **bush** a. bushses (b. bushes)
8. **tomato** a. tomatos (b. tomatoes)

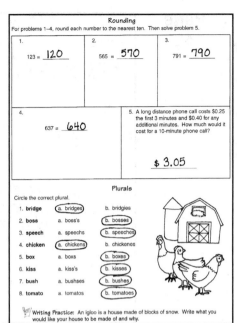

✍ *Writing Practice:* An igloo is a house made of blocks of snow. Write what you would like your house to be made of and why.

Page 36

Rounding

Round to the nearest 100. Then solve problem 5.

1. 864	2. 729	3. 671
900	**700**	**700**

4. 5,329	5. Greta is 6 years younger than her brother. Her brother is 13. How old is Greta?
5,300	**7 years old**

Contractions

Circle the correct contraction for each sentence.

1. We (won't), willn't) arrive at school late.
2. The food (wasn't), was'nt) cooked properly.
3. They (hav'nt, haven't) done their chores this week.
4. (I'ave, I've) seen a meteor fall from the sky.
5. It looks like (it's, its') going to rain.

✍ *Writing Practice:* Write about your favorite foods. What are they, and why do you like them? Then draw a picture of them.

Page 37

Rounding

Round to the nearest hundred. Then solve problem 5.

1. 123	2. 789	3. 2,713
100	**800**	**2,700**

4. 22,503	5. Count the number of students in your classroom. Add 10 to the total. Then multiply by 2. Subtract the number of students in your room. What number did you end up with? _____ What would you have to do next to get the number you started with?
22,500	**Subtract 20.**

Plurals

Circle the correct plural form.

1. woman (womans, (women), womens)
2. child (childs, child's, (children))
3. box ((boxes), boxs, box's)
4. deer (deers, deer's, (deer))
5. city (citys, (cities), cityes)
6. brush (brushs, (brushes), brushses)

✍ *Writing Practice:* Explain in a paragraph why you would or would not like to get married someday.

Page 38

Rounding

Round to the place value that is underlined. Then solve number 5.

1. 6,789	2. 5,329	3. 982
6,800	**5,330**	**980**

4. 23,087	5. Roberto lives 134 miles from the nearest mountain. Round this distance to the nearest 10 miles.
23,000	**130 miles**

Suffixes

Underline each word that contains a suffix.

comfortable	foolish	uncover
unwrap	prepaid	teacher
argument	singer	election
laziness	finalist	jumping
prearrange	careless	beautiful

✍ *Writing Practice:* Write a story about the wildest dream you've ever had.

Page 39

Rounding

Round to the nearest place. Then solve problem 5.

1. tens place	2. hundreds place	3. ones place
176 = **180**	349 = **300**	$3.69 = **$4.00**

4. thousands place	5. Jeff needs 15 quarts of potting soil. He can only find 4-quart bags. How many 4-quart bags will he need? **4** How much will not be used? **1 quart**
8,764 = **9,000**	

Predicate (Verb)

Fill in the blank with the correct tense of *run*.

1. I **ran** yesterday.
2. I will **run** on Friday.
3. I have **run** in a race before.
4. Seth will **run** in a marathon next week.
5. He **ran** in a marathon last year.
6. They have **run** many miles to get in shape.

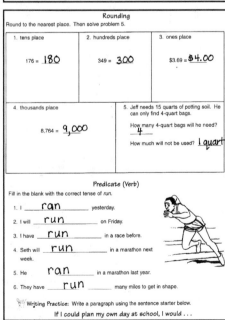

✍ *Writing Practice:* Write a paragraph using the sentence starter below.
If I could plan my own day at school, I would . . .

Page 40

Rounding

For problems 1–4, round **428,146** to the nearest value shown. Then solve problem 5.

1. nearest hundred	2. nearest thousand	3. nearest ten
428,100	**428,000**	**428,150**

4. nearest hundred thousand	5. The population of a southern city was 61,822. What rounded number would be used if a brochure about the city was printed?
400,000	**62,000**

Subjects

Circle the simple subject in each sentence.

1. Only (Lena) had her homework.
2. (Ivan) said, "That homework was difficult."
3. The sick (children) stayed home from school.
4. (You) play the piano well.
5. Our (uncle) came to visit us.
6. Can (we) play a game of jacks?

✍ *Writing Practice:* Describe your favorite television show.

Page 41

Rounding

Solve the problems below.

1. Round 71,845 to the nearest hundred.	2. Round 459,056 to the nearest ten.	3. Round 6,752,653 to the nearest million.
71,800	459,060	7,000,000

4. Round 495,056 to the nearest hundred thousand.	5. Mr. Paul bought 20 assignment books for his classroom. They cost $0.49 each. Can he pay for them with a $10 bill? How do you know? Write a number sentence to show the answer.
500,000	20 × $.49 = $9.80

Clauses

Underline the clause in each sentence.

1. While Toby waited for the school bus, he read a book.

2. The baby yawned when she was ready for a nap.

3. We will have P. E. outside unless it rains today.

4. Until the clock strikes noon, we will work on science.

5. He received a good grade on his test although he missed three problems.

✍ **Writing Practice:** Write a paragraph about how you could be famous one day.

Page 42

Rounding

Round to the nearest hundred and thousand and then solve problem 5.

1. 23,329	2. 3,574	3. 4,725,210
hundred: 23,300	hundred: 3,600	hundred: 4,725,200
thousand: 23,000	thousand: 4,000	thousand: 4,725,000

4. 165,372	5. Andy's family drove a total of 1,793 miles during their two-week vacation. About how many miles did they travel each day?
hundred: 165,400	
thousand: 165,000	128 miles

Alphabetical Order

Write the names of these Civil Rights leaders in alphabetical order by last name.

Martin Luther King, Jr.
Mary McCloud Bethune
Harriet Tubman
Rosa Parks
A. Philip Randolph
Thurgood Marshall
Oliver Brown
Frederick Douglass
Jesse Jackson
Sojourner Truth

Mary McCloud Bethune
Olivier Brown
Frederick Douglass
Jesse Jackson
Martin Luther King, Jr.
Thurgood Marshall
Rosa Parks
A. Philip Randolph
Sojourner Truth
Harriet Tubman

✍ **Writing Practice:** Write a paragraph about what you could do to help people get along with each other.

Page 43

Rounding

Round each number to the nearest thousand. Then solve problem 5.

1. 703	2. 28,619	3. 14,005,221
1,000	29,000	14,005,000

4. 340,530	5. Irene made a 97, 73, 82, and 91 on her tests in biology. How much higher was her best score than her lowest?
341,000	24 points

Sentences

Rewrite these fragments as complete sentences.

1. burning leaves

2. ran to the door

3. caught in the escalator

4. the famous man

5. a noise outside

6. with his homework

✍ **Writing Practice:** April 1 is April Fool's Day. Describe a time when someone really fooled you.

Page 44

Rounding

Choose the correctly rounded number. Then solve problem 5.

1. 2,631 to nearest 10	2. 27,982,703 to nearest million	3. $15.45 to nearest dollar
(a. 2,630) b. 2,600	a. 27,000,000 (b. 28,000,000)	a. $16.00 (b. $15.00)

4. 4,103,067 to nearest thousand	5. Andrew's mother bought groceries for a party. Estimate how much she spent if she bought the following: chips $1.69, soda $1.09, cookies $2.39, and cupcakes $3.89.
a. 4,100,000 (b. 4,103,000)	$9.00

Author's Purpose

Using the choices from the box below, select the author's purpose.

_a_ 1. The most common last name is Smith.

_d_ 2. He ran the last part of his race crying with pain, yet he still finished.

_a_ 3. There will be new rules for the cafeteria!

_b_ 4. Buy "Super X Cereal" and start your day out right!

_a_ 5. The blue whale is the largest of all whales.

_b_ 6. But Wilbur said, "I don't want to die. Save me Charlotte!"

a. give information   b. persuade   c. entertain   d. arouse emotions

✍ **Writing Practice:** Who do you think was the most important person in history? Why?

Page 45

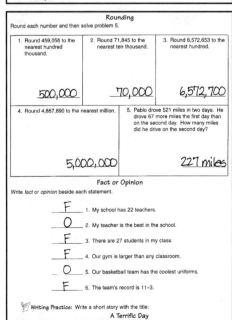

Rounding

Round each number and then solve problem 5.

1. Round 459,056 to the nearest hundred thousand.	2. Round 71,845 to the nearest ten thousand.	3. Round 6,572,653 to the nearest hundred.
500,000	70,000	6,572,700

4. Round 4,867,890 to the nearest million.	5. Pablo drove 521 miles in two days. He drove 67 more miles the first day than on the second day. How many miles did he drive on the second day?
5,000,000	227 miles

Fact or Opinion

Write *fact* or *opinion* beside each statement.

F 1. My school has 22 teachers.

O 2. My teacher is the best in the school.

F 3. There are 27 students in my class.

F 4. Our gym is larger than any classroom.

O 5. Our basketball team has the coolest uniforms.

F 6. The team's record is 11–3.

✍ **Writing Practice:** Write a short story with the title:
A Terrific Day

Page 46

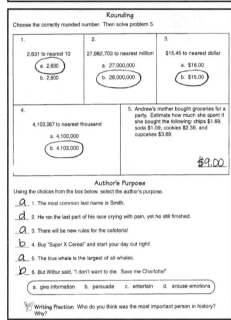

Estimation

Estimate by rounding, then write your estimated sum or difference. Then solve problem 5.

1. Round to the nearest hundred.	2. Round to the nearest hundred.	3. Round to the nearest thousand.
123 + 456	798 − 144	6,198 + 2,781
100 + 500 = 600	800 − 100 = 700	6,000 + 3,000 = 9,000

4. Round to the nearest thousand.	5. If Caleb read 12 pages on Monday, 56 pages on Tuesday, and 9 pages on Wednesday, how many pages did he read in all?
5,110 − 1,529	
5,000 − 2,000 = 3,000	77 pages

Adverbs

Fill in the blank with the correct adverb.

1. He walked slowly to the car.

2. We have to get up early tomorrow.

3. The team quickly ran around the field.

4. My sister sings beautifully.

5. His friend is very considerate of others.

| tomorrow |
| beautifully |
| slowly |
| quickly |
| very |

✍ **Writing Practice:** You've won a contest and you are on your way to the moon. Write a paragraph about your adventures.

Page 47

Estimation

Do not work each problem. Estimate the answers. Write it in the blank. Then solve problem 5.

1. Estimate to the nearest hundred.	2. Estimate to the nearest hundred.	3. Estimate to the nearest ten.
436 + 157	713 − 324	29 x 65
600	400	2,100

4. Estimate to the nearest ten.	5. Daphne had 75 tulip bulbs to plant. She planted 5 bulbs in a row. How many rows did she plant?
24)442	
22	15 rows

Kind of Sentences

Fill in the blanks with the words: *declarative, interrogative, imperative,* or *exclamatory.*

1. Have you ever been on a farm? — interrogative
2. You get to see all kinds of animals on a farm. — declarative
3. "I like pigs the best," said Leeann. — declarative
4. Don't step in the mud. — imperative
5. What a beautiful countryside! — exclamatory
6. Did you know that people work hard on a farm? — interrogative
7. They grow many fruits and vegetables that we eat. — declarative
8. "I love fresh corn!" exclaimed Markel. — exclamatory
9. "Don't make a pig out of yourself," said Markel's mother. — imperative
10. May we come back and visit again? — interrogative

Writing Practice: Write a persuasive paragraph to convince your teacher that you are serious about school.

Page 48

Estimation

Estimate each answer.

1. About how much more money would you need to buy a sweater that cost $29.95 if you have $15.00?	2. You want to buy paper and 2 pencils for $1.89 and you have $5.00. About how much would your change be?	3. What is the estimated total of students in your class if there are 18 girls and 13 boys?
$15.00	$3.00	30 students

4. How many movie tickets could you buy with a ten dollar bill if each ticket cost $4.00?	5. Sue bought 10 stamps that cost 32¢ each. Estimate how much she paid for her stamps.
2 tickets	$3.00

Punctuation

Add punctuation marks where needed in the following paragraph.

My mother took me to a picnic on Memorial Day. There were so many people there so we had to park far away. We ate the following foods: hot dogs, hamburgers, potato salad, and baked beans. Then it started to rain, so we had to go home.

Writing Practice: What do you think life would be like if people were invisible?

Page 49

Estimation

For problems 1–4, choose which answer is closest to what you have estimated. Then solve problem 5.

1. How many bites does it take to eat a banana?	2. How much does your book bag weigh?	3. How many students are in your grade?
a. 10	a. 10 lbs.	a. 50
b. 20	b. 20 lbs.	b. 100
c. 30	c. 30 lbs.	c. 150

(Answers will vary.)

4. How tall is your math teacher?	5. Cleo bought lunch at the mall. She had $13.00 in her purse. If a sandwich cost $4.00, a soda cost $1.50, and a piece of cake cost $2.00, how much change will she receive?
a. 5 ft.	
b. 6 ft.	
c. 7 ft.	$5.50

Prepositions

Circle the prepositions in each sentence.

1. The blanket is laying (over) the chair.
2. The pencil is (under) the oak stool.
3. Please get me the cleaner (above) the shelf.
4. Maggie is sitting (beside) David.
5. Place the napkins (on) the table.
6. The dog went (under) the ball.
7. We live (by) the noisiest street.
8. The glass cleaner is (below) the laundry soap.

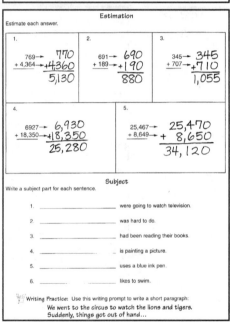

Writing Practice: Sometimes pets act like members of the family. Do you have a pet like that? If you do, write about how your pet acts. If you don't have a pet, write a story about a pet.

Page 50

Estimation

Estimate each answer.

1.	2.	3.
769 → 770 + 4,364 → +4,360 5,130	691 → 690 + 189 → 190 880	345 → 345 + 707 → +710 1,055

4.	5.
6927 → 6,930 + 18,350 → +18,350 25,280	25,467 → 25,470 + 8,649 → + 8,650 34,120

Subject

Write a subject part for each sentence.

1. _____ were going to watch television.
2. _____ was hard to do.
3. _____ had been reading their books.
4. _____ is painting a picture.
5. _____ uses a blue ink pen.
6. _____ likes to swim.

Writing Practice: Use this writing prompt to write a short paragraph:
We went to the circus to watch the lions and tigers. Suddenly, things got out of hand…

Page 51

Estimation

Estimate by rounding to the nearest thousand. Then solve problem 5.

1.	2.	3.
12,378 − 9,629	4,862 − 2,153	34,692 − 18,023
est. 2,000	est. 3,000	est. 17,000

5.	5. In 1840, 458 patents were given to inventors, but 4 years earlier only 103 were given. How many more were given in 1840 than in 1836?
6,823 + 8,346	
est. 15,000	355

Clauses

Underline the dependent clause in each sentence.

1. When he was a young boy, he moved to Wyoming.
2. Until baseball season is here, Joshua plays basketball.
3. He watched quietly as the paramedic helped his brother.
4. Because their car broke down, he had to walk to school.
5. I waited for an hour before the bus came.
6. I jumped back when the door slowly opened.

Writing Practice: Imagine that you are an astronomer and discover a new planet. Describe what the physical features of the planet are and what life on it is like.

Page 52

Addition

Write corresponding numbers to the alphabet under each letter. (Example: A = 1, B = 2, C = 3, etc.) Add up the numbers in these words. Then solve problem 5.

1. paper	2. glue	3. pencil
56	45	59

4. notebook	5. Which word added up was the largest number?
97	notebook

Following Directions

Follow the steps. Begin by putting your pencil on the center square. Circle each letter you stop at. Write it in the space provided.

1. Go 1 block West
2. Go 2 blocks North
3. Go 3 blocks East
4. Go 4 blocks South
5. Go 1 block West
6. Go 4 blocks North
7. Go 1 block West

E	R	S	O	I
T	P	A	H	A
K	F	★	M	B
Q	C	G	L	D
S	K	J	N	E

What do all people need? F R I E N D S

Writing Practice: If you had x-ray vision, what would you use it for? Write a paragraph telling about this special gift.

Page 53

Addition
Solve each problem below.

1.	2.	3.
69 + 96 **165**	459 + 391 **850**	6,765 + 4,364 **11,129**

4.	5. An ice cream store had 2 pints of ice cream for $5.00. How many pints would you get for $20.00?
47,889 + 52,093 **99,982**	**8 pints**

Friendly Letters
Match the part of the friendly letter with its name.

- **b** 1. Dear Julie,   a. heading
- **c** 2. the thoughts and ideas of your letter   b. greeting
- **a** 3. January 1, 2001   c. body
- **e** 4. the name of person writing the letter   d. closing
- **d** 5. Your friend,   e. signature

Writing Practice: Write a friendly letter to a friend or a relative about something interesting happening in your life.

Page 54

Addition
Add the numbers in each column. Then solve problem 5.

1.	2.	3.
98 76 54 +32 **260**	145 163 237 +846 **1,391**	2,965 4,526 2,632 +5,038 **15,161**

4.	5. Doreen went shopping and spent all of her money. Her total purchases were $87.35. How much change did she receive? What else do you need to know about this problem? a. what she bought (b) how much money she gave the cashier c. you have all you need to know
10,132 12,573 35,742 +54,624 **113,071**	

Adverbs
Write a word before each -ly to make a sentence using adverbs. **(Answers will vary.)**

1. _____ly he sang to the baby.
2. I listened _____ly to the teacher.
3. She worked _____ly on her assignment.
4. They _____ly joined in the search for the missing wallet.
5. The band played _____ly.
6. That is a _____ly nice picture you painted.

Writing Practice: When you are feeling unhappy, what do you do? Write about how you begin to feel happy again.

Page 55

Addition
Solve the problems.

1.	2.	3.
7,283 3,854 +9,103 **20,240**	987 986 +985 **2,958**	682 607 +643 **1,932**

4.	5. Kenisha bought 2 folders for 29 cents each, 2 pencils for 12 cents each, and notebook paper for 39 cents. She had $5.00. What would be her change?
2,218 3,210 +4,216 **9,644**	**$3.79**

Predicate (Verb)
Write a sentence with each verb.

1. has taken _____ **Answers**
2. bought_____ **will**
3. has flown_____ **vary.**
4. went _____
5. have seen _____
6. walked _____
7. was going _____
8. is _____

Writing Practice: Write a paragraph using the sentence starter below.

Playing in the snow is fun because . . .

Page 56

Addition
Solve each problem below.

1.	2.	3.
723 588 +396 **1,707**	71,259 55,169 +543 **126,971**	4,635,640 3,550,518 +1,756,170 **9,942,328**

4.	5. Kevin and Kimberly are going to Spain to visit their aunt. They estimate their cost at $690.00 each. They've saved only half. How much have they each saved?
215,705 376,156 +89,912 **681,773**	**$345.00**

Pronouns
Choose the correct reflexive pronoun that makes each sentence complete.

- **d** 1. Dan taught ____ how to ride a bike.   a. ourselves
- **a** 2. We made _____ sick from eating too much candy.   b. myself
- **f** 3. The students are setting high goals for _____.   c. yourself
- **c** 4. "Help _____ to a cookie after dinner," said Mom.   d. himself
- **b** 5. I couldn't help _____ from falling asleep.   e. itself
- **e** 6. The tree seemed to lean _____ toward the sky.   f. themselves

Writing Practice: Choose an object in the room. Write five clues that would help someone discover what it is.

Page 57

Addition
Find the minuend of each subtraction problem by using the numbers already given. Then solve problem 5.

1.	2.	3.
189,046 −73,281 115,765	**26,202** −48 26,154	**118,225** −45,439 72,786

4.	5. After spending $342.80 for a television, D. J. had $186.20 left. How much did she have before she bought the television?
7,547 −1,764 5,783	**$529.00**

Nouns
Fill in each blank with a common (C) or proper (P) noun.

1. _____ was born in the _____ of May.
 (P)   (C)
2. The _____ visited the _____ Zoo.
 (C)   (P)
3. On _____ we will take a spelling _____.
 (P)   (C)
4. _____ sold magazines to his _____.
 (P)   (C)
5. Our _____ is named _____ School.
 (C)   (P)
6. We drove through the _____ in the beautiful state of _____.
 (C)   (P)

Writing Practice: Describe what your life would be like if you lived underwater.

Page 58

Addition
Solve each problem below.

1.	2.	3.
26,407 389 1,683 +42 **28,521**	705 3,060 129 +5,783 **9,677**	5,863 19,700 85,708 +635 **111,906**

4.	5. During the month of November, Shawn spent $42.00 for lunches, $14.00 for movies, and $67.23 for clothes. How much did he spend in all?
595 1,460 3,790 +295 **6,140**	**$123.23**

Figurative Language
Tell what you think each figurative statement really means.

1. He's all ears! **He is listening intently.**
2. Get off my back! **Leave me alone!**
3. Lend me your ear. **Listen to me.**
4. Give me a hand. **Help me.**
5. Who let the cat out of the bag? **Who told the secret?**
6. I've got my eye on you. **I'm watching you.**

Writing Practice: Write a "how-to" paragraph on how to make a ham sandwich.

Page 59

Addition and Average

Add the scores of each bowler. Write the bowler who had the highest total of pins. Then solve problem 5.

1. Jeb's Scores	2. Parth's Scores	3. Micah's Scores
120	132	90
114	98	144
105	111	122
Total = 339	Total = 341	Total = 356

4. Who was the winner?

Micah

5. Kevin bowled 3 games in a tournament. What is the average of his score?

Game	Score
1	158
2	172
3	211

Average = 180.3

Capitalization

Circle the words that should be capitalized.

1. (I) live on (bryan) (street)
2. (I) have lived there since last (february)
3. (we) moved in our new house on a (saturday)
4. (we) used to live near (salt) (lake) (city)
5. (I) was born in (chicago) on (january) 10.
6. (on) my birthday (I) am going to see (niagara) (falls)
7. (m) mother speaks (spanish)
8. (she) was born in (mexico)

L T W I B F S N C M

Writing Practice: Write a paragraph about a favorite book or story. Describe why it is your favorite.

Page 60

Subtraction

Solve each problem.

1.	2.	3.
841 − 30 = 811	644 − 132 = 512	891 − 105 = 786

4.	5. Jim has to leave for school at 7:30 A.M. It is 6:45 A.M. How long does he have before he leaves for school?
85 − 18 = 67	45 minutes

Sequencing

Put these sentences in order by looking at the time-order words.

2 When we got there, we checked into the hotel and unpacked our bags.
5 There we rode rides and saw Mickey Mouse.
3 Then we went for a swim.
1 My family and I went to Florida.
6 Finally, we left all tired and worn out.
4 Next, we changed clothes and left for Disney World.

Writing Practice: Write a paragraph using the sentence starter below.

Rainy days make me feel . . .

Page 61

Subtraction

Solve each problem below.

1.	2.	3.
82 − 36 = 46	503 − 88 = 415	2,000 − 392 = 1,608

4.	5. A passenger car on a train can carry 67 passengers. How many passengers can a train with 12 passenger cars carry?
30,415 − 4,776 = 25,639	804 passengers

Pronouns

Rewrite the underlined words with a pronoun.

1. The girl and her friend played on a soccer team. — They
2. Jonah said, "Jonah like to eat corn on the cob." — I
3. My mother used to live in South Carolina. — She
4. Why don't the children play outside? — they
5. The rabbit ate the rabbit's food. — its
6. Katie and I share the same birthday. — We
7. The next day Emilio and Caren walked home together. — they
8. Rubert found a watch in his backyard. — He

Writing Practice: Describe an eventful day at school and the different things that you did.

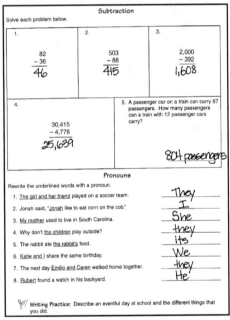

Page 62

Subtraction

Solve each problem below.

1.	2.	3.
32,000 − 8,671 = 23,329	1,000,000 − 537,112 = 462,888	9,000 − 5,523 = 3,477

4.	5. A whale eats an average of 800 pounds of fish a day. How many would he eat in one week? One month?
7,040,200 − 64,344 = 6,975,856	week 5,600 lbs. month 22,400 lbs.

Dictionary Skills

Write each vocabulary word with its definition. Use the dictionary, if needed.

1. leave ship or aircraft — d i s e m b a r k
2. unhappy — d i s c o n s o l a t e
3. break up — d i s b a n d
4. offend — d i s g u s t
5. show unjust favor — d i s c r i m i n a t e
6. release — d i s c h a r g e

disband	disembark	disgust
disconsolate	discharge	discriminate

Writing Practice: October 15 is National Grouch Day. Write a list of 5 things that make you grouchy. Then write 5 things to do that will help you to not be grouchy.

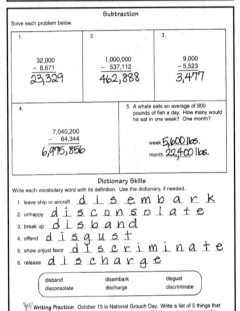

Page 63

Subtraction

Subtract the number at the top from each number listed below. Then solve problem 5.

1. subtract 32	2. subtract 21	3. subtract 19
44 → 12	67 → 46	48 → 29
58 → 26	42 → 21	39 → 20
63 → 31	29 → 8	27 → 8
33 → 1	90 → 69	19 → 0

4. subtract 8	5. California has about 65 times more pets than the state of Georgia. If Georgia has 283,000 pets, how many does California have?
91 → 83	
87 → 79	
73 → 65	18,395,000
60 → 52	

Prefixes

Write what each word means by looking at the meanings of the following prefixes.

uni = one	tri = three	inter = between	pre = before
bi = two	semi = half	intra = within	sub = under

1. unicycle — cycle with one wheel
2. bicentennial — celebration every two hundred years
3. triangle — figure with three angles
4. semicircle — half a circle
5. interstate — roads between states
6. intravenous — within the veins
7. prepay — pay before
8. subway — roadway under the ground

Writing Practice: Write a newspaper article for your school newspaper convincing students and teachers to recycle.

Page 64

Subtraction

Write the missing addend to complete each problem.

1.	2.	3.
20,482 + 34,687 = 55,169	$67.31 + 41.59 = $108.90	73,281 + 15,765 = 89,046

4.	5. Mrs. Patten ordered 73 fiction, 51 nonfiction, and 38 biographies for the library. How many books did she order?
3,807 + 4,524 = 8,331	162 books

Fact or Opinion

Write **F** if the statement is a fact or **O** if the statement is an opinion.

O 1. Every child should have a pet dog.
F 2. We should all brush our teeth to keep them healthy.
F 3. November has 30 days.
O 4. Ice cream is the most popular dessert.
O 5. Peanut butter and jelly sandwiches are delicious.
F 6. School is a place where children learn.

Writing Practice: You've been given an unusual gift from your aunt. What is it? Write her a thank you note.

Page 65

Subtraction
Solve each problem.

1.	2.	3.
2,000 − 1,385 **615**	$10.00 − $ 9.43 **$0.57**	$56.00 − $19.93 **$36.07**

4.	5. On July 4th the high temperature in Sacramento was 93°. The low temperature that evening was 67°. What was the change in temperature for that day?
7,000 − 4,928 **2,072**	**26°**

Adjectives
Circle the adjectives that describe a Christmas tree.

star · (green)
(shiny) · stand
present · (big)
(beautiful) · (bright)
ornament · (round)
lights · branches
(sharp) · under
(tall) · (decorative)

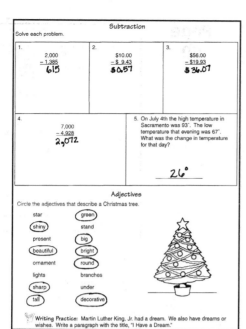

Writing Practice: Martin Luther King, Jr. had a dream. We also have dreams or wishes. Write a paragraph with the title, "I Have a Dream."

Page 66

Subtraction
Solve each problem.

1.	2.	3.
$40.40 − $12.98 **$27.42**	1,620 − 1,598 **22**	$30.05 − $ 8.67 **$21.38**

4.	5. Mrs. Morgan bought her students Christmas gifts that totaled $16.98. What is her change if she pays with $20.00?
3,000 − 1,542 **1,458**	**$3.02**

Cause and Effect
Tell which part of the sentence is the cause and which is the effect. Write **C** if it is the cause; write **E** if it is the effect.

1. **C** Because of playing in the rain, I got a bad cold **E**
2. **E** To make good grades, I study hard and do my homework **C**
3. **E** We went to the zoo because our class won a contest **C**
4. **C** I went to bed early so I could get up in time for school **E**
5. **C** Since Tory and Alfonzo are good friends, they play at each other's house **E**
6. **E** I have to write Don a letter, because he moved to Illinois **C**

Writing Practice: If you could meet any famous person, who would it be, and why? Write a paragraph explaining your answer.

Page 67

Addition and Subtraction
For problems 1–4, write each problem in words and solve. Then solve problem 5.

1.	2.	3.
27 + 46 **73**	106 − 85 **21**	99 + 23 **122**
twenty-seven plus forty-six	one hundred six minus eighty-five	ninety-nine plus twenty-three

4.	5. Jason collected books. He had 13 mysteries, 5 insect books, 7 joke books, and 21 picture books. How many books did he have in all?
243 − 19 **224** two hundred forty-three minus nineteen	**46 books**

Subject
Underline the subject in each sentence.

1. The <u>children</u> ate pizza for lunch.
2. <u>June and Susan</u> traveled to Florida.
3. The <u>boy and his dog</u> played with the ball.
4. Good <u>stories</u> are found in books.
5. The little <u>girl</u> talked to the clown.

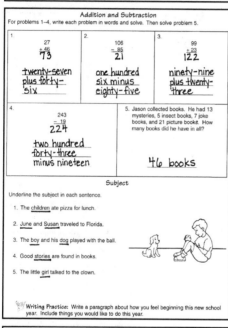

Writing Practice: Write a paragraph about how you feel beginning this new school year. Include things you would like to do this year.

Page 68

Addition and Subtraction
Solve the problems.

1.	2.	3.
472 + 29 **501**	482 + 19 **501**	921 − 19 **902**

4.	5. Tonya bought a cheeseburger for $1.50, French fries for $0.50, and a soda for $0.50. How much did she pay for her meal?
839 − 228 **611**	**$2.50** How much change would she get back if she paid with a $5.00 bill? **$2.50**

Adjectives
Write an adjective in each blank. **(Answers will vary.)**

1. A _____ girl walked down the street.
2. Mom bought us _____ pads of paper.
3. The _____ car had a flat tire.
4. The children built a _____ snowman.
5. The _____ grapes tasted sweet.

Writing Practice: Which sport do you like to play? Write a persuasive paragraph telling why your sport is the best.

Page 69

Addition and Subtraction
Solve the problems. Be careful to follow the signs.

1.	2.	3.
346 + 421 **767**	259 + 630 **889**	987 − 183 **804**

4.	5. One shark ate 64 fish. Another shark ate 21 fish. How many fish were eaten in all?
906 − 412 **494**	**85 fish**

Pronouns
Fill in the blanks with the correct pronoun. Capitalize when necessary.

| it | my | our | her | we | I | they |

1. **My** sister, Ana, and **her** friend went to the mall.
2. **They** shopped for two hours.
3. Ana and **I** went back the next day.
4. **We** bought **our** mother a birthday present.
5. Mom said she liked **it** very much.

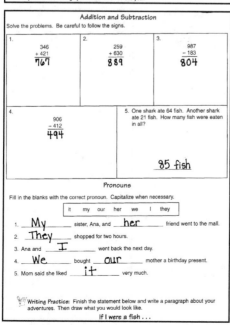

Writing Practice: Finish the statement below and write a paragraph about your adventures. Then draw what you would look like.
If I were a fish . . .

Page 70

Addition and Subtraction
Subtract and then check by addition. Then solve problem 5.

1.	2.	3.
423 − 187 **236**	804 − 355 **449**	1,201 − 987 **214**

4.	5. The sports store is having a 50% off sale. If T-shirts cost $8.00, shorts cost $5.00, and tennis shoes cost $24.00, how much will each item be at 50% off?
4,000 − 1,284 **2,716**	**T-shirts = $4.00** **shorts = $2.50** **tennis shoes = $12.00**

Verbs
Replace each underlined verb with a more vivid verb.

1. Mom <u>made</u> a cake.   **Answers**
2. Steven <u>made</u> a race car.   **will**
3. I <u>went</u> to the store.   **vary.**
4. Dad <u>went</u> next door.
5. The girl <u>came</u> to school.
6. He <u>came</u> to the party.

Writing Practice: Write a paragraph using the sentence starter below.
One of the best things I can do is . . .

Page 71

Addition and Subtraction
Use the map provided to answer the questions.

1. What is the difference in miles between Memphis and Chattanooga and between Memphis and Nashville?

50 miles

2. Which city is the closest from Nashville—Chattanooga or Knoxville? By how much?

Chattanooga 125 miles

3. What is the distance from Knoxville to Nashville to Memphis?

650 miles

4. Would it be closer to travel to the Tri-Cities from Memphis by way of Nashville, or Chattanooga and Knoxville?

Nashville

Study Skills
Determine if you would find the following information in an atlas, thesaurus, or almanac.

1. Which country is north of Spain? — **atlas**
2. What is a synonym for the word program? — **thesaurus**
3. Which continent is an island? — **atlas**
4. Which state has more tornadoes than any other? — **almanac**
5. Which state population is larger—Georgia or Alabama? — **almanac**

Writing Practice: What is the best thing your parents have ever done for you? Write a paragraph about it.

Page 72

Multiplication
Fill in the squares by multiplying the numbers.

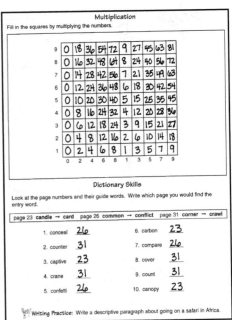

Dictionary Skills
Look at the page numbers and their guide words. Write which page you would find the entry word.

page 23 candle → card   page 26 common → conflict   page 31 corner → crawl

1. conceal — **26**
2. counter — **31**
3. captive — **23**
4. crane — **31**
5. confetti — **26**
6. carbon — **23**
7. compare — **26**
8. cover — **31**
9. count — **31**
10. canopy — **23**

Writing Practice: Write a descriptive paragraph about going on a safari in Africa.

Page 73

Multiplication
Solve each problem.

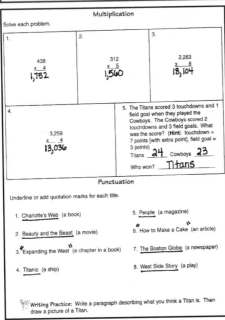

1. 438 × 4 = **1,752**
2. 312 × 5 = **1,560**
3. 2,263 × 8 = **18,104**
4. 3,259 × 4 = **13,036**
5. The Titans scored 3 touchdowns and 1 field goal when they played the Cowboys. The Cowboys scored 2 touchdowns and 3 field goals. What was the score? (Hint: touchdown = 7 points [with extra point], field goal = 3 points)
Titans **24** Cowboys **23**
Who won? **Titans**

Punctuation
Underline or add quotation marks for each title.

1. Charlotte's Web (a book)
2. Beauty and the Beast (a movie)
3. "Expanding the West" (a chapter in a book)
4. Titanic (a ship)
5. People (a magazine)
6. "How to Make a Cake" (an article)
7. The Boston Globe (a newspaper)
8. West Side Story (a play)

Writing Practice: Write a paragraph describing what you think a Titan is. Then draw a picture of a Titan.

Page 74

Multiplication
Solve each problem.

1. 42 × 8 = **336**
2. 124 × 3 = **372**
3. 235 × 4 = **940**
4. 2,346 × 2 = **4,692**
5. Kym watched television for 2 hours on Friday, 3 hours on Saturday, and on Sunday twice as much as on Friday. How many hours did she watch over the three days?

9 hours

Nouns
Write these nouns under the correct heading.

Spain, tears, girl, book, Houston, love, student, cat, desk, cousin, state, happiness

Person	Place	Thing	Idea
girl	Spain	tears	love
student	Houston	book	happiness
cousin	state	cat	
		desk	

Writing Practice: September is "All-American Breakfast Month." Write a paragraph about your favorite breakfast.

Page 75

Multiplication
Solve each problem.

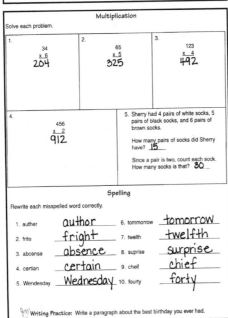

1. 34 × 6 = **204**
2. 65 × 5 = **325**
3. 123 × 4 = **492**
4. 456 × 2 = **912**
5. Sherry had 4 pairs of white socks, 5 pairs of black socks, and 6 pairs of brown socks.
How many pairs of socks did Sherry have? **15**
Since a pair is two, count each sock. How many socks is that? **30**

Spelling
Rewrite each misspelled word correctly.

1. auther — **author**
2. frite — **fright**
3. abcence — **absence**
4. certian — **certain**
5. Wendesday — **Wednesday**
6. tommorrow — **tomorrow**
7. twelth — **twelfth**
8. suprise — **surprise**
9. cheif — **chief**
10. fourty — **forty**

Writing Practice: Write a paragraph about the best birthday you ever had.

Page 76

Multiplication
Solve each problem.

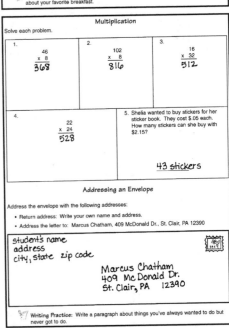

1. 46 × 8 = **368**
2. 102 × 8 = **816**
3. 16 × 32 = **512**
4. 22 × 24 = **528**
5. Shelia wanted to buy stickers for her sticker book. They cost $.05 each. How many stickers can she buy with $2.15?

43 stickers

Addressing an Envelope
Address the envelope with the following addresses:
• Return address: Write your own name and address.
• Address the letter to: Marcus Chatham, 409 McDonald Dr., St. Clair, PA 12390

student's name
address
city, state   zip code

Marcus Chatham
409 McDonald Dr.
St. Clair, PA   12390

Writing Practice: Write a paragraph about things you've always wanted to do but never got to do.

Multiplication
Solve each problem.

1. 23 × 27 = **621**	2. 98 × 23 = **2,254**	3. 46 × 25 = **1,150**
4. 43 × 18 = **774**	5. Tim and Jill ordered French fries. There were 36 fries in the packet. If Tim ate 13 and Jill ate 11, how many more fries would each of them eat if they ate the same number of additional fries? **6 fries each**	

Verbs
Circle each action verb below.

shirt, **punches**, hat, child, **leaped**, **sing**

cape, **run**, **reads**, shoes, **kicks**, suit

wishes, eye, dishes, **washes**, **flew**, sky

✍ Writing Practice: Write a paragraph using the sentence starter below.

My goal for the New Year is . . .

Multiplication
Solve each problem.

1. 340 × 2 = **680**	2. 176 × 4 = **704**	3. 226 × 3 = **678**
4. $1.92 × 5 = **$9.60**	5. Carlos has $10.00 to spend on a gift for his brother. He buys a football for $3.99 and also buys a helmet. If his change is $1.02, how much did the helmet cost? **$4.99**	

Verb Tense
Write the correct form of the verb in each sentence. The verb follows the sentence.

1. Nathan and Natalie **walk** to school together. *(walk)*
2. "Something **smells** funny," I said as we got to school. *(smell)*
3. The science teacher was **doing** an experiment. *(do)*
4. Our teacher **said** to get out our homework. *(say)*
5. I couldn't find my homework so I **looked** in my desk. *(look)*
6. She said I could **give** it to her after math class. *(give)*
7. Renee **stood** up and said, "I found it. It fell on the floor." *(stand)*
8. On the way home, a bee **stung** me. *(sting)*
9. It hurt so badly that I **screamed** "Ouch!" *(scream)*
10. Mom put an ice pack on it, and it **felt** better. *(feel)*

✍ Writing Practice: Write a paragraph using the sentence starter below.

If I could travel anywhere in the world, it would be to . . .

Multiplication
Solve the problems.

1. 82 × 13 = **1,066**	2. 46 × 25 = **1,150**	3. 307 × 14 = **4,298**
4. 224 × 63 = **14,112**	5. Mrs. Stolz has 13 boxes of pencils. Each box has 24 pencils in it. How many pencils does she have in all? **312 pencils**	

Plurals or Possessives
Choose the correct word to complete each sentence.

1. This recipe is for chocolate _____.
   a. cookie's   b. cookies'   **c. cookies**
2. It was _____ job to help with the dishes.
   a. Dads   **b. Dad's**   c. Dads'
3. James and Melissa saw the _____ kittens first.
   a. cat's   b. cats   c. cats'
4. Mr. Adams is a wonderful teacher who _____ fifth grade.
   a. teach's   **b. teaches**   c. teaches'
5. The _____ coats were hung in their lockers.
   a. students'   b. student's   c. students

✍ Writing Practice: Write a story about a job you would like to do when you get older. Tell why you chose that job.

Multiplication
Solve each problem.

1. 974 × 63 = **61,362**	2. 290 × 76 = **22,040**	3. 794 × 13 = **10,322**
4. 69 × 42 = **2,898**	5. Jenny bought a car for $17,936.29. Miguel bought a car for $25,000.00. How much more did Miguel spend than Jenny? **$7,063.71**	

Adjectives
Fill in the blanks with an adjective. **(Answers will vary.)**

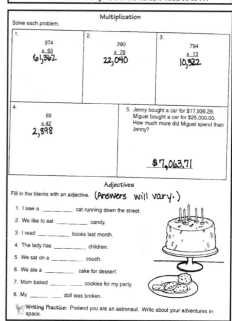

1. I saw a _____ cat running down the street.
2. We like to eat _____ candy.
3. I read _____ books last month.
4. The lady has _____ children.
5. We sat on a _____ couch.
6. We ate a _____ cake for dessert.
7. Mom baked _____ cookies for my party.
8. My _____ doll was broken.

✍ Writing Practice: Pretend you are an astronaut. Write about your adventures in space.

Multiplication
Use the information about the different symbols provided on the chart to solve each problem.

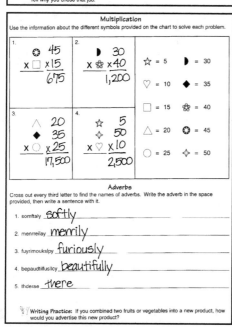

1. ☀ 45 × □ × 15 = **675**
2. ☽ 30 × ✿ × 40 = **1,200**
3. △ 20, 35 ◆ × ○ × 25 = **17,500**
4. ☆ 5, ✦ 50 × ♡ × 10 = **2,500**

☆ = 5   ☽ = 30
♡ = 10   ◆ = 35
□ = 15   ✿ = 40
△ = 20   ☀ = 45
○ = 25   ✦ = 50

Adverbs
Cross out every third letter to find the names of adverbs. Write the adverb in the space provided, then write a sentence with it.

1. somftaly **softly**
2. menrreilay **merrily**
3. fuyrimoukslpy **furiously**
4. bepaudtilfusllcy **beautifully**
5. thderae **there**

✍ Writing Practice: If you combined two fruits or vegetables into a new product, how would you advertise this new product?

Multiplication
Multiply the number in the center by each point. Write the answer by the point. Then solve problem 5.

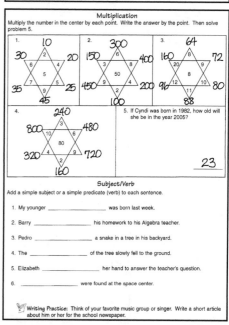

5. If Cyndi was born in 1982, how old will she be in the year 2005? **23**

Subject/Verb
Add a simple subject or a simple predicate (verb) to each sentence.

1. My younger _____ was born last week.
2. Barry _____ his homework to his Algebra teacher.
3. Pedro _____ a snake in a tree in his backyard.
4. The _____ of the tree slowly fell to the ground.
5. Elizabeth _____ her hand to answer the teacher's question.
6. _____ were found at the space center.

✍ Writing Practice: Think of your favorite music group or singer. Write a short article about him or her for the school newspaper.

Multiplication
Find the median for each set of numbers and then solve problem 5.

1. 17, 24, 34, 28, 16	2. 215, 219, 225, 200, 231	3. 48, 68, 51, 65, 55
24	219	55

4. $3.63, $4.74, $3.59, $4.62, $3.48	5. Mrs. Forrest gave a questionnaire to her math class of 12 boys and 13 girls. 7 boys and 7 girls returned their questionnaires. How many will she still need to get back from the boys? from the girls?
$3.63	boys 5 girls 6

Word Order
Rewrite each sentence correctly.

1. the temperature in the woods were below freezing and i got two cold
The temperature in the woods was below freezing and I got too cold.

2. the story about dr. terry were interesting
The story about Dr. Terry was interesting.

3. last tuesday i go to see the movie the patriot
Last Tuesday, I went to see the movie, "The Patriot."

4. canada be on the border of the united states
Canada is on the border of the United States.

5. do you like to ate shrimp
Do you like to eat shrimp?

Writing Practice: Write a story for a newspaper with the title "Whale Survives Oil Spill."

Multiplication
Circle each correct problem. Then solve problem 5.

1.	2.	3.
49 x 9 = 421	(338 x 7 = 2,366)	742 x 36 = 25,712

4.	5. A dog fell in a 12-foot well. Everyday, he climbed up 3 feet and slipped back 2 feet. How many days did it take him to reach the top?
(482 x 65 = 31,330)	10 days

Adjectives
Write two adjectives to describe the noun. Be sure they begin with the same letter as the noun.

1. children

4. leaf

2. pie

5. sister

3. book

6. dog

Writing Practice: If you were a fashion designer, what kind of clothing and shoes would you design? Write a short descriptive paragraph about your fashion collection.

Multiplication
Solve each problem below.

1.	2.	3.
1,962 x 53	638 x 86	302 x 95
103,986	54,868	28,690

4.	5. Kari had $34.98 left of her birthday money. She saw a sweater for $15.88 and a pair of shoes for $24.69. How much more money does she need to buy both items?
3,509 x 72 252,648	$5.59

Comprehension
Answer the questions after reading the paragraph.

The Nobel Prize is awarded annually for outstanding works in science, literature, and world peace. It was named after Alfred Nobel, a Swedish chemist. He was best known for his invention of dynamite. When he died, he left almost 10 million dollars to fund future awards. Americans like Woodrow Wilson and Martin Luther King, Jr. have won the Nobel Prize.

1. Who is the Nobel Prize named after? Alfred Nobel

2. What did he invent? dynamite

3. Name the three fields that the Nobel Prize is awarded. science, literature, and world peace

4. What was the money that Nobel left used for? to fund future awards

Writing Practice: Pretend you are awarded the Nobel Prize. Write a paragraph about why you won the prize.

Multiplication
Fill in the missing factors for each set of multiplication problems. Then solve problem 5.

1.	2.	3.
5 x 6 = 30 6 x 8 = 48 7 x 9 = 63	10 x 2 = 20 9 x 9 = 81 3 x 5 = 15	4 x 8 = 32 4 x 9 = 36 5 x 5 = 25

4.	5. Jessica saved $92 last month and $120 this month. She spent $125 on clothes. How much does she have left?
2 x 12 = 24 15 x 3 = 45 9 x 11 = 99	$87.00

Word Order
Rearrange the words in each sentence to make a complete sentence.

1. speaker We a special in had library. the
We had a special speaker in the library.

2. Theodor She a read story to Geisel. our about class
She read a story about Theodor Geisel to our class.

3. Geisel Seuss. is Theodor known as also
Theodor Geisel is also known as. Dr. Seuss.

4. 1904. in born was He
He was born in 1904.

5. favorite he book is and Green My Eggs Ham. wrote
My favorite book he wrote is Green Eggs and Ham.

6. writing wonder why I he use his name when real didn't books?
I wonder why he didn't use his real name when writing books.

Writing Practice: You have been given the chance to create and publish your own magazine. What kind of articles and stories would it feature? What kind of magazine would it be?

Multiplication
For problems 1–4, find the LCM (lowest common multiple) of the numbers listed below. Then solve problem 5.

1. 2, 3	2. 8, 12	3. 5, 15
6	24	15

4. 4, 9	5. Marty lives 18 miles from her school. By rounding to the nearest ten, about how many miles is that?
36	20 miles

Verb Usage
Underline the base words.

1. dis<u>obey</u>
2. <u>teach</u>er
3. <u>unlike</u>
4. <u>tricycle</u>
5. <u>sickness</u>
6. <u>lovely</u>
7. <u>beginning</u>
8. <u>discover</u>
9. <u>misfortune</u>
10. <u>helpful</u>
11. <u>mindful</u>
12. <u>jumping</u>
13. <u>misplace</u>
14. <u>disassemble</u>
15. <u>reporting</u>

Writing Practice: Write a paragraph using the sentence starter below.

I looked everywhere, but I couldn't find my . . .

Multiplication
Solve each problem below.

1.	2.	3.
464 x 183	814 x 572	8,723 x 602
84,912	465,608	5,251,246

4.	5. There are five chairs in the front row. Each successive row has two more chairs. How many chairs are in the sixth row?
3,435 x 242 831,270	15

Homographs
Write sentences showing the different meanings of each pair of words.

1. fine

2. fine

3. wound

4. wound

5. shed

6. shed

Writing Practice: What was the happiest moment of your life?

Page 89

Multiplication
Solve each problem below.

1.	2.	3.
6,728 x 123 **827,544**	59 x 38 **2,242**	3,604 x 49 **176,596**

4.	5. The local middle school sponsored a skating party for its students in 5th and 6th grades. The cost per child was $6.00. How much did the school pay if 213 students went?
234 x 153 **35,802**	**$1,278**

Real/Unreal
Write **R** if real or **U** if unreal.

U 1. book about Harry Potter
U 2. Dorothy in the *Wizard of Oz*
R 3. Martin Luther King, Jr.
U 4. novel read in English class
U 5. Wilbur said, "Charlotte, you have to save me."
R 6. book about kinds of animals

Writing Practice: Use this writing prompt to write a short paragraph:
Something important I learned this year was...

Page 90

Multiplication and Fractions
Use multiplication to solve the problems below.

1.	2.	3.
$\frac{2}{3}$ x 20 = **13$\frac{1}{3}$**	15 x $\frac{4}{5}$ = **12**	6.48 x .23 = **1.4904**

4.	5. Sean is $\frac{1}{3}$ as old as his brother. His brother is 21. How old is Sean?
3.729 x 45 = **167.805**	**7**

Direct Object
Underline the direct object in each sentence.

1. Robin hit a <u>homerun</u> during the ballgame.
2. He brought a <u>friend</u> to the game.
3. We liked the <u>trip</u> to the museum.
4. They played some <u>music</u> by Bach.
5. Pete wrote a <u>story</u> about caves.
6. Bats eat <u>insects</u> flying around at night.

Writing Practice: What type of music do you like to listen to? Why?

Page 91

Multiplication and Division
Solve each problem.

1.	2.	3.
234 x 91 **21,294**	6,124 x 52 **318,448**	**127 r 1** 6)763

4.	5. Dad needed to buy four tires for the car. He could buy them for $28.99 each or four for $108.00. Which way would cost the least?
4,327 r 1 3)12,982	**Buy four together.**

Figurative Language
Match the statement with the correct kind of figurative language.

b. 1. He's fast as lightning!   a. personification
d. 2. He's a pig!   b. simile
a. 3. The tree wanted to rest.   c. alliteration
e. 4. The wind blew with a whoosh!   d. metaphor
c. 5. She sings the song sweetly.   e. onomatopoeia

Writing Practice: You've been given a pen pal. Write a letter to your pen pal describing yourself and telling him or her about yourself.

Page 92

Multiplication and Division
Solve each problem.

1.	2.	3.
22.35 x 22 **491.7**	1,244 x 12 **14,928**	**37.25** 2)74.50

4.	5. Donny needs 42 birthday invitations. The invitations are sold in packages of 5. How many packages will Donny need to buy? **9**
777 r 1 2)1,555	How do you know? **9 x 5 = 45** **45 invitations is enough.**

Dictionary Skills
The pronunciation of words are given in the dictionary. Write what letter is silent in each word. You may use a dictionary, if needed. For numbers 11–15, create your own words and write the silent letter.

1. autumn **n**
2. knots **k**
3. climbing **b**
4. Wednesday **d**
5. thumbs **b**
6. know **k**
7. shake **e**
8. gnome **g, e**
9. mechanic **h**
10. maze **e**
11. **Answers**
12. **will**
13. **vary.**
14.
15.

Writing Practice: Write a story and use words that have silent letters in them. After you have finished writing, circle the silent letters.

Page 93

Division
Divide and then solve problem 5.

1.	2.	3.
28 ÷ 7 = **4**	64 ÷ 8 = **8**	72 ÷ 9 = **8**

4.	5. Juanita wanted to divide the cookies she made between her and her 3 friends. She made 2 dozen cookies. How many cookies did each girl get?
42 ÷ 6 = **7**	**6 cookies**

Adverbs
Unscramble these adverbs.

1. stfa **fast**
2. ryelal **really**
3. nyoilis **noisily**
4. yadot **today**
5. dably **badly**
6. lelw **well**
7. vyer **very**
8. lyetuiq **quietly**

Writing Practice: Write a persuasive paragraph telling someone why the state you live in is the best state there is.

Page 94

Division
Solve each problem.

1.	2.	3.
7 2)14	**7 r 1** 5)36	**12** 3)36

4.	5. Four buses were driven to school. There were 52 students on each bus. How many students were on all four buses?
8 r 4 6)52	**208 students**

Homographs
Write two sentences with each homograph showing different meanings. Then think of one more homograph and write two sentences with it.

1. rose
2. leaves
3.

Answers will vary.

Writing Practice: Write a story about visiting a farm and seeing farm animals up close.

Page 95

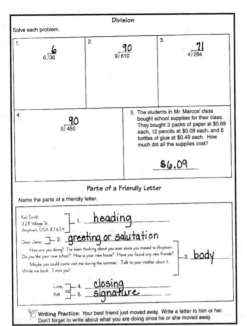

Division
Solve each problem.

1. $6\overline{)36} = 6$

2. $9\overline{)810} = 90$

3. $4\overline{)284} = 71$

4. $5\overline{)450} = 90$

5. The students in Mr. Marcos' class bought school supplies for their class. They bought 3 packs of paper at $0.69 each, 12 pencils at $0.09 each, and 6 bottles of glue at $0.49 each. How much did all the supplies cost?

$6.09

Parts of a Friendly Letter
Name the parts of a friendly letter.

Keli Smith
328 Village St.
Anytown, USA 87654
1. heading

Dear Jane, 2. greeting or salutation

How are you doing? I've been thinking about you ever since you moved to Anytown. Do you like your new school? How is your new house? Have you found any new friends? Maybe you could come visit me during the summer. Talk to your mother about it. Write me back. I miss you!
3. body

Love, 4. closing
Keli 5. signature

Writing Practice: Your best friend just moved away. Write a letter to him or her. Don't forget to write about what you are doing since he or she moved away.

Page 96

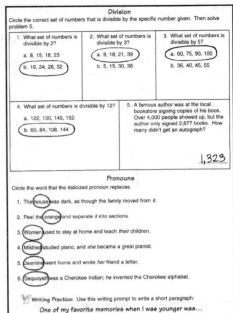

Division
Circle the correct set of numbers that is divisible by the specific number given. Then solve problem 5.

1. What set of numbers is divisible by 2?
   a. 8, 15, 18, 23
   b. 16, 24, 28, 32 (circled)

2. What set of numbers is divisible by 3?
   a. 9, 18, 21, 39 (circled)
   b. 5, 15, 30, 36

3. What set of numbers is divisible by 5?
   a. 60, 75, 90, 100 (circled)
   b. 36, 40, 45, 55

4. What set of numbers is divisible by 12?
   a. 122, 130, 145, 152
   b. 60, 84, 108, 144 (circled)

5. A famous author was at the local bookstore signing copies of his book. Over 4,000 people showed up, but the author only signed 2,677 books. How many didn't get an autograph?

1,323

Pronouns
Circle the word that the italicized pronoun replaces.

1. The house was dark, as though the family moved from *it*.

2. Peel the orange and separate *it* into sections.

3. Women used to stay at home and teach *their* children.

4. Mildred studied piano, and *she* became a great pianist.

5. Jasmine went home and wrote *her* friend a letter.

6. Sequoyah was a Cherokee Indian; *he* invented the Cherokee alphabet.

Writing Practice: Use this writing prompt to write a short paragraph:
One of my favorite memories when I was younger was...

Page 97

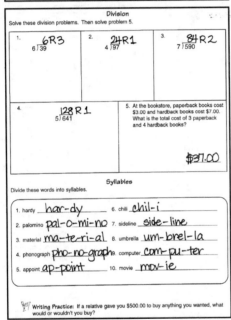

Division
Solve these division problems. Then solve problem 5.

1. $6\overline{)39} = 6R3$

2. $4\overline{)97} = 24R1$

3. $7\overline{)590} = 84R2$

4. $5\overline{)641} = 128R1$

5. At the bookstore, paperback books cost $3.00 and hardback books cost $7.00. What is the total cost of 3 paperback and 4 hardback books?

$37.00

Syllables
Divide these words into syllables.

1. hardy — har-dy
2. palomino — pal-o-mi-no
3. material — ma-te-ri-al
4. phonograph — pho-no-graph
5. appoint — ap-point
6. chili — chil-i
7. sideline — side-line
8. umbrella — um-brel-la
9. computer — com-pu-ter
10. movie — mov-ie

Writing Practice: If a relative gave you $500.00 to buy anything you wanted, what would or wouldn't you buy?

Page 98

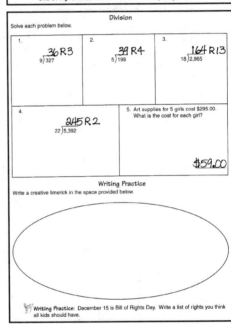

Division
Solve each problem below.

1. $9\overline{)327} = 36R3$

2. $5\overline{)199} = 39R4$

3. $18\overline{)2,965} = 164R13$

4. $22\overline{)5,392} = 245R2$

5. Art supplies for 5 girls cost $295.00. What is the cost for each girl?

$59.00

Writing Practice
Write a creative limerick in the space provided below.

Writing Practice: December 15 is Bill of Rights Day. Write a list of rights you think all kids should have.

Page 99

Division
Solve each problem.

1. $8\overline{)8,923} = 1,115 \text{ r } 3$

2. $5\overline{)45.95} = 9.19$

3. $12\overline{)24,840} = 2,070$

4. $11\overline{)776,655} = 70,605$

5. Shawn read 78 pages in the novel *The Giver*. If there are 321 pages, how many more pages does he have to read?

243 pages

Vocabulary
Match the word with the definition.

b. 1. moving air
c. 2. water falling to the earth in drops
g. 3. study of weather
f. 4. cloud close to the ground
d. 5. frozen rain
h. 6. sound that follows lightning
e. 7. instrument used to measure air pressure
a. 8. invisible mixture of gases surrounding the earth

a. air
b. wind
c. rain
d. sleet
e. barometer
f. fog
g. meteorology
h. thunder

Writing Practice: Have you ever wanted to be a famous athlete? What sport would you be famous for? Write about how you would become famous.

Page 100

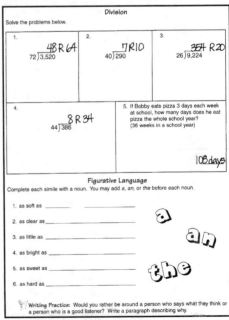

Division
Solve the problems below.

1. $72\overline{)3,520} = 48R64$

2. $40\overline{)290} = 7R10$

3. $26\overline{)9,224} = 354R20$

4. $44\overline{)386} = 8R34$

5. If Bobby eats pizza 3 days each week at school, how many days does he eat pizza the whole school year? (36 weeks in a school year)

108 days

Figurative Language
Complete each simile with a noun. You may add *a*, *an*, or *the* before each noun.

1. as soft as _____
2. as clear as _____
3. as little as _____
4. as bright as _____
5. as sweet as _____
6. as hard as _____

a   an   the

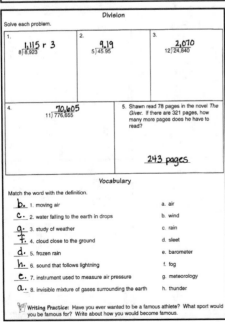

Writing Practice: Would you rather be around a person who says what they think or a person who is a good listener? Write a paragraph describing why.

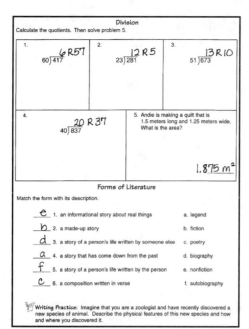

Division

Calculate the quotients. Then solve problem 5.

1. 60)417 6 R57	2. 23)281 12 R5	3. 51)673 13 R10

4. 40)837 20 R37	5. Andie is making a quilt that is 1.5 meters long and 1.25 meters wide. What is the area? 1.875 m²

Forms of Literature

Match the form with its description.

e 1. an informational story about real things — a. legend
b 2. a made-up story — b. fiction
d 3. a story of a person's life written by someone else — c. poetry
a 4. a story that has come down from the past — d. biography
f 5. a story of a person's life written by the person — e. nonfiction
c 6. a composition written in verse — f. autobiography

✍ **Writing Practice:** Imagine that you are a zoologist and have recently discovered a new species of animal. Describe the physical features of this new species and how and where you discovered it.

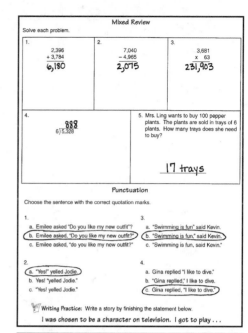

Mixed Review

Solve each problem.

1. 2,396 + 3,784 6,180	2. 7,040 − 4,965 2,075	3. 3,681 x 63 231,903

4. 6)5,328 888	5. Mrs. Ling wants to buy 100 pepper plants. The plants are sold in trays of 6 plants. How many trays does she need to buy? 17 trays

Punctuation

Choose the sentence with the correct quotation marks.

1.
a. Emilee asked "Do you like my new outfit"?
b. Emilee asked, "Do you like my new outfit?" ⭕
c. Emilee asked, "do you like my new outfit?"

2.
a. "Yes!" yelled Jodie. ⭕
b. Yes! yelled Jodie.
c. "Yes! yelled Jodie.

3.
a. "Swimming is fun" said Kevin.
b. "Swimming is fun," said Kevin. ⭕
c. "Swimming is fun, said Kevin."

4.
a. Gina replied "I like to dive."
b. "Gina replied," I like to dive.
c. Gina replied, "I like to dive." ⭕

✍ **Writing Practice:** Write a story by finishing the statement below.
I was chosen to be a character on television. I got to play . . .

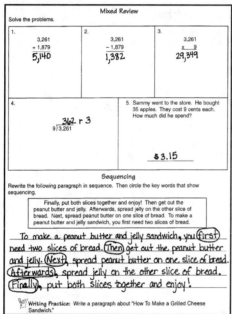

Mixed Review

Solve the problems.

1. 3,261 + 1,879 5,140	2. 3,261 − 1,879 1,382	3. 3,261 x 9 29,349

4. 9)3,261 362 r 3	5. Sammy went to the store. He bought 35 apples. They cost 9 cents each. How much did he spend? $3.15

Sequencing

Rewrite the following paragraph in sequence. Then circle the key words that show sequencing.

Finally, put both slices together and enjoy! Then get out the peanut butter and jelly. Afterwards, spread jelly on the other slice of bread. Next, spread peanut butter on one slice of bread. To make a peanut butter and jelly sandwich, you first need two slices of bread.

To make a peanut butter and jelly sandwich, you (first) need two slices of bread. (Then) get out the peanut butter and jelly. (Next), spread peanut butter on one slice of bread. (Afterwards), spread jelly on the other slice of bread. (Finally), put both slices together and enjoy!

✍ **Writing Practice:** Write a paragraph about "How To Make a Grilled Cheese Sandwich."

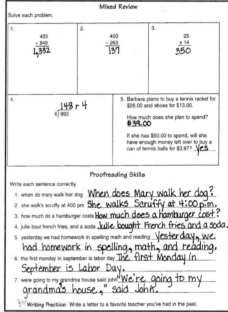

Mixed Review

Solve each problem.

1. 483 + 849 1,332	2. 400 − 263 137	3. 25 x 14 350

4. 6)892 148 r 4	5. Barbara plans to buy a tennis racket for $26.00 and shoes for $13.00. How much does she plan to spend? $39.00 If she has $50.00 to spend, will she have enough money left over to buy a can of tennis balls for $3.97? Yes

Proofreading Skills

Write each sentence correctly.

1. when do mary walk her dog When does Mary walk her dog?
2. she walk's scruffy at 400 pm She walks Scruffy at 4:00 p.m.
3. how much do a hamburger costs How much does a hamburger cost?
4. julie bout french fries, and a soda Julie bought French fries and a soda.
5. yesterday we had homework in spelling math and reading Yesterday, we had homework in spelling, math, and reading.
6. the first monday in september is labor day The first Monday in September is Labor Day.
7. were going to my grandma house said john "We're going to my grandma's house," said John.

✍ **Writing Practice:** Write a letter to a favorite teacher you've had in the past.

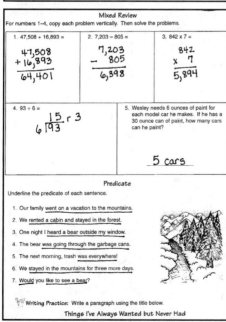

Mixed Review

For numbers 1–4, copy each problem vertically. Then solve the problems.

1. 47,508 + 16,893 = 47,508 + 16,893 64,401	2. 7,203 − 805 = 7,203 − 805 6,398	3. 842 x 7 = 842 x 7 5,894

4. 93 ÷ 6 = 6)93 15 r 3	5. Wesley needs 6 ounces of paint for each model car he makes. If he has a 30 ounce can of paint, how many cars can he paint? 5 cars

Predicate

Underline the predicate of each sentence.

1. Our family went on a vacation to the mountains.
2. We rented a cabin and stayed in the forest.
3. One night I heard a bear outside my window.
4. The bear was going through the garbage cans.
5. The next morning, trash was everywhere!
6. We stayed in the mountains for three more days.
7. Would you like to see a bear?

✍ **Writing Practice:** Write a paragraph using the title below.
Things I've Always Wanted but Never Had

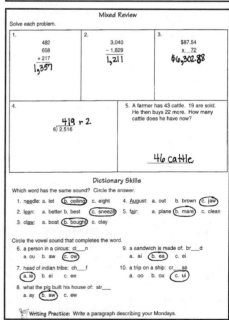

Mixed Review

Solve each problem.

1. 482 658 + 217 1,357	2. 3,040 − 1,829 1,211	3. $87.54 x 72 $6,302.88

4. 6)2,516 419 r 2	5. A farmer has 43 cattle. 19 are sold. He then buys 22 more. How many cattle does he have now? 46 cattle

Dictionary Skills

Which word has the same sound? Circle the answer.

1. needle: a. lot b. ceiling ⭕ c. eight
2. lean: a. better b. best c. sneeze ⭕
3. claw: a. boat b. bought ⭕ c. clay
4. August: a. out b. brown c. jaw ⭕
5. fair: a. plane b. mare ⭕ c. clean

Circle the vowel sound that completes the word.

6. a person in a circus: cl__n
   a. ou b. aw c. ow ⭕
7. head of indian tribe: ch__f
   a. ie ⭕ b. ei c. ee
8. what the pig built his house of: str___
   a. ay b. aw ⭕ c. ew
9. a sandwich is made of: br___d
   a. ai b. ea ⭕ c. ei
10. a trip on a ship: cr__se
    a. oo b. ou c. ui ⭕

✍ **Writing Practice:** Write a paragraph describing your Mondays.

Page 107

Mixed Review

Solve each problem.

1.	2.	3.
906,370 3,912 + 658 **910,940**	1.27 x 29 **36.83**	6,175 − 967 **5,208**

4.	5. Bertha has 37 marbles. Her friend, Anthony has 41 marbles. They decide to put all the marbles together and then divide them up evenly. How many marbles would each person get?
58 r 3 8)467	**39 marbles**

Nouns

Circle all words in the fish that are nouns.

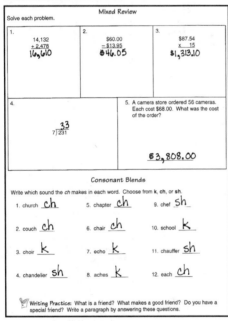

shark, octopus, treasure, salty, seaweed, sandy, boat, large, plankton, ocean, colorful, deep, gills, shiny

✍ *Writing Practice:* Write a story using eight of the words above.

Page 108

Mixed Review

Solve the problems.

1. 7,245 ÷ 6 =	2. 8,042 − 2,679 =	3. 1,023 x 42 =
1,207 r 3	**5,363**	**42,966**

4. 23 + 46 + 179 + 245 =	5. Johnnie wanted to watch the Olympics at 7:00 P.M. It was only 2:23 P.M. How much time did he have before the Olympics would come on television?
493	**4 hrs. 37 min.**

Prepositions

Find these prepositions in the puzzle.

after
among
beside
between
by
for
from
in
to
with

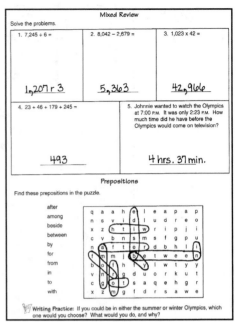

✍ *Writing Practice:* If you could be in either the summer or winter Olympics, which one would you choose? What would you do, and why?

Page 109

Mixed Review

Solve each problem.

1.	2.	3.
14,132 + 2,478 **16,610**	$60.00 − $13.95 **$46.05**	$87.54 x 15 **$1,313.10**

4.	5. A camera store ordered 56 cameras. Each cost $68.00. What was the cost of the order?
33 7)231	**$3,808.00**

Consonant Blends

Write which sound the *ch* makes in each word. Choose from **k**, **ch**, or **sh**.

1. church **ch**
2. couch **ch**
3. choir **k**
4. chandelier **sh**
5. chapter **ch**
6. chair **ch**
7. echo **k**
8. aches **k**
9. chef **sh**
10. school **k**
11. chauffer **sh**
12. each **ch**

✍ *Writing Practice:* What is a friend? What makes a good friend? Do you have a special friend? Write a paragraph by answering these questions.

Page 110

Mixed Review

Solve each problem.

1.	2.	3.
468 + 129 **597**	700 − 124 **576**	325 x 32 **10,400**

4.	5. The library has about 140 mystery books, rounded to the nearest ten. What is the least number of mystery books in the library?
73 5)365	**135**

Capitalization

Circle all letters that should be capitalized in the following titles. Then rewrite them correctly.

1. "the big snow" — **"The Big Snow"**
2. "clifford gets a job" — **"Clifford Gets a Job"**
3. "all in the morning" — **"All In the Morning"**
4. "i can read about birds" — **"I Can Read about Birds"**
5. "the prince and the pauper" — **"The Prince and the Pauper"**
6. "georgie to the rescue" — **"Georgie to the Rescue"**
7. "the story about ping" — **"The Story about Ping"**
8. "a weed is a flower" — **"A Weed Is a Flower"**

Writing Practice: Write a paragraph using the sentence starter below.

I really get angry when . . .

Page 111

Mixed Review

Solve each problem.

1.	2.	3. Which of these symbols should go in the box to get the smallest answer? 100 ☐ 20 = a. + c. x b. − **d. ÷**
43 x 28 **1,204**	181 x 22 **3,982**	

4. Which one would show the largest answer? a. + **c. x** b. − d. +	5. Marilynn has 5 pencils, Alfred has 7 pencils, Jasmine has 8 pencils, and Ryan has 2 pencils. How many pencils do they all have together? **22 pencils** How many more pencils do Marilynn and Alfred have than Jasmine and Ryan? **2 pencils**

Subject

Find the subject in this mixed-up sentence. Circle the subject.

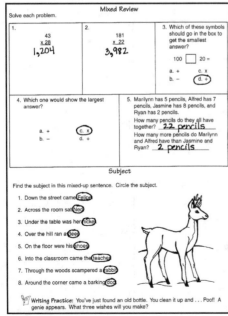

1. Down the street came (Felix).
2. Across the room sat (Ned).
3. Under the table was her (ticket).
4. Over the hill ran a (deer).
5. On the floor were his (shoes).
6. Into the classroom came the (teacher).
7. Through the woods scampered a (rabbit).
8. Around the corner came a barking (dog).

✍ *Writing Practice:* You've just found an old bottle. You clean it up and . . . Poof! A genie appears. What three wishes will you make?

Page 112

Mixed Review

Solve each problem.

1. 481 + 369 = **850**	2. 4,800 − 1,469 = **3,331**	3. 482 x 23 = **11,086**

4. 879 ÷ 4 = **219 r 3**	5. A suitcase fell off a 40-story building. Someone caught it on the 16th floor. How many stories did it fall? **24** How many stories were left before it would have hit the ground? **16**

Abbreviations

Write the abbreviations to these units of measurement.

1. ounce **oz.**
2. inch **in.**
3. milligram **mg**
4. yard **yd.**
5. centimeter **cm**
6. quart **qt.**
7. gallon **gal.**
8. pint **pt.**
9. mile **mi.**

Next, write the words for which these abbreviations stand.

10. P.M. **post meridian**
11. A.M. **ante meridian**
12. sec. **second**
13. min. **minute**
14. hr. **hour**
15. B.C. **before Christ**
16. A.D. **Anno Domini**
17. c. **cup/circa/century**
18. ml **milliliter**

✍ *Writing Practice:* Write a poem using the title, "If."

Page 113

Mixed Review

Solve each problem.

1.	2.	3.
426 + 879 **1,305**	3,024 − 1,883 **1,141**	552 x 6 **3,312**

4.	5. Isaiah planted 4 rows of beans. Each row had 23 bean plants. How many bean plants are there in all?
7 7)49	**92 bean plants**

Dictionary Skills

Circle all words you would find on a dictionary page with these guide words.

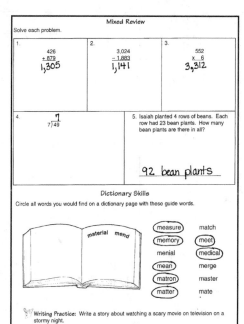

material   mend

(measure)   match
(memory)   (meet)
menial   (medical)
(mean)   merge
(matron)   master
(matter)   mate

✍ **Writing Practice:** Write a story about watching a scary movie on television on a stormy night.

Page 114

Mixed Review

Solve the problems below.

1.	2.	3.
243 + 76 **319**	500 − 23 **477**	325 x 4 **1,300**

4.	5. Mrs. Spadafino drives 20 miles to school. Mrs. Hutchison drives 13 miles, Mrs. Martin drives 8 miles, and Mrs. Olive drives 6 miles. How many total miles do they drive?
632 + 378 **1,010**	**47 miles**

Kinds of Sentences

Write the correct letter beside each sentence.

I. 1. Pass the butter, please.   D. Declarative

D. 2. There was a shooting star out last night.   E. Exclamatory

E. 3. What a beautiful sunrise this morning!   I. Imperative

Q. 4. Did you see a movie on Saturday?   Q. Interrogative

✍ **Writing Practice:** Write a paragraph about your favorite place to eat. Tell why you like it and what you like to eat there.

Page 115

Mixed Review

Solve each problem.

1.	2.	3.
241 362 + 103 **706**	2,000 − 1,782 **218**	4,553 x 4 **18,212**

4.	5. Joe and Jeff entered the 100 yard dash in the school race. Joe practiced 1 hour a day for 5 weeks, and Jeff practiced 2 hours a day for 3 weeks. Who spent more time practicing for the race?
71 r 1 7)498	**Jeff**

Nouns

Circle the nouns in the following paragraph.

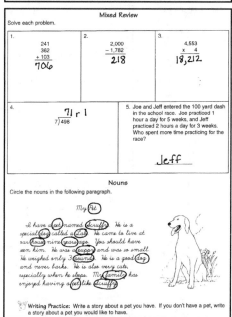

My (Pet)

I have a (pet) named (Scruffy). He is a special (dog) called a (lab). He came to live at our (house) nine (years) ago. You should have seen him. He was a (puppy) and was so small. He weighed only 3 (pounds). He is a good (dog) and never barks. He is also very cute, especially when he sleeps. My (family) has enjoyed having a (pet) like (Scruffy).

✍ **Writing Practice:** Write a story about a pet you have. If you don't have a pet, write a story about a pet you would like to have.

Page 116

Mixed Review

Solve each problem.

1.	2.	3.
37,777 + 25,666 **63,443**	6,001 − 2,594 **3,407**	67 x 49 **3,283**

4.	5. Mrs. Lewis' class is going on a field trip. There are 20 students going, and 4 children can ride in each car. How many cars will be needed?
12 8)96	**5 cars**

Possessive Nouns

Circle the group of words with the correct possessive form.

1. A. the girls doll
   (B. the girl's doll)
   C. the girls's doll

2. (A. Maria's desk)
   B. Marias' desk
   C. Marias desk

3. A. my moms car
   (B. my mom's car)
   C. my moms's car

4. (A. the children's pets)
   B. the childrens pets
   C. the childrens' pets

✍ **Writing Practice:** Write a scary story beginning with the phrase below.

I could not believe my eyes . . .

Page 117

Mixed Review

Solve each problem.

1.	2.	3.
746 832 + 295 **1,873**	6,035 − 2,475 **3,560**	1,271 x 9 **11,439**

4.	5. Jan sold 120 boxes of Girl Scout Cookies. Sharyn sold 109 boxes, and Alex sold 283. How many boxes did they sell in all? **512 boxes** How many more boxes did Alex sell than both Jan and Sharyn together? **54 boxes**
36 4)144	

Possessive or Contraction

Write a sentence showing the correct usage of each word.

1. its _____ Answers
2. it's _____ will
3. their _____ vary.
4. they're _____
5. your _____
6. you're _____

✍ **Writing Practice:** Write a paragraph using the title below.

What I Learned from a Grandparent

Page 118

Mixed Review

Solve each problem below.

1.	2.	3.
1,382 9,217 + 463 **11,062**	11,846 − 7,271 **4,575**	3,240 x 81 **262,440**

4.	5. Gina had $1,000 in a savings account. In six months, she received $25 interest. How much would she have earned with $5,000 in her savings account?
43 R3 17)734	**$125.00**

Sentences/Conjunctions

Combine the sentences by using a conjunction (and, but, or, nor, for, yet).

1. I like to watch television. I don't watch it too much.
I like to watch television, but I don't watch it too much.

2. I watch movies. I watch sports.
I watch movies, and I watch sports.

3. Don went to camp in Missouri. He really wants to go to Florida.
Don went to camp in Missouri, but he really wants to go to Florida.

4. JoAnn came to help us move. We had lots of heavy boxes.
JoAnn came to help us move, for we had lots of heavy boxes.

5. Bones are easily broken. They are not easily mended.
Bones are easily broken, but they are not easily mended.

6. You can play. You can sit on the bleachers.
You can play, or you can sit on the bleachers.

✍ **Writing Practice:** Have you ever had or wanted to have a slumber party? What did/would you do during the party?

Mixed Review

Solve each problem below.

1. $(35 \div 5) + 6 = 13$	2. $(12 - 8) \times 4 = 16$	3. $15 - (21 \div 3) = 8$

4. $8 \times (4 \times 2) = 64$	5. What is the perimeter of a soccer field 110 yds. by 80 yds.? What is the area? perimeter = 380 yds. area = 8,800 yds.^{2}

Conjunctions

Circle the conjunction in each sentence.

1. Jose (and) Maria are exchange students from Mexico.
2. They enjoy American food (but) they like Mexican food the best.
3. Maria's mom used to make tortillas (or) tacos everyday for lunch.
4. Now she cooks hamburgers (or) hot dogs some days.
5. They like school (but) have difficulty with the English language.
6. Math (and) science are most interesting to them.

✏ **Writing Practice:** Use this writing prompt to write a short paragraph:

The sky was a clear blue, and the clouds above looked like...

Mixed Review

For problems 1–4, fill in the blanks. Then solve problem 5.

1. One-fourth of 28 is 7.	2. Three weeks and 4 days would be 25 days in all.	3. Four cartons of eggs (Each carton equals a dozen.) is 48 eggs in all.

4. There are 90 degrees in a right angle.	5. Our club collected money to buy a gift for a sick classmate. In all, we collected 82 quarters, 90 dimes, 45 nickels, and 79 pennies. How much money was collected in all? $32.54

Homonyms

Write *your* or *you're* in the blanks. Capitalize when necessary.

1. Your cake was delicious.
2. You're my closest friend.
3. I need your advice.
4. What is your name?
5. You're from Minnesota.
6. You're invited to my party.
7. You're late for school.
8. Your cat licked my hand.

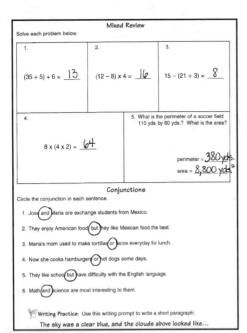

✏ **Writing Practice:** Write a persuasive paragraph telling why you agree or disagree with having no smoking in public places.

Mixed Review

For problems 1–4, fill in the blanks. Then solve problem 5.

1. The average of 6, 18, and 12 is 12.	2. In October, there are four full weeks and 3 days.	3. The time between 10:25 A.M. and 11:10 A.M. is 45 minutes.

4. One-third of the number 12 is 4.	5. In the classroom, there are 24 students. $\frac{1}{3}$ are reading, $\frac{1}{2}$ are doing math, and the rest are working on spelling. How many are working on spelling? 4 students

Rhyming Words

Fill in the blanks of this poem with a word that rhymes. (Answers may vary.)

Groundhog Day

This furry friend might come out once a year
To keep his shadow if the day is clear.
And on this very special Groundhog Day
If his shadow is seen, winter will stay,
For six more long weeks we'll have to keep warm,
But if it's cloudy, his shadow's not there
There'll soon be warm weather and days will be fair
So please, Mr. Sun, just this one day,
Find a big dark cloud—and stay away!
—Unknown

✏ **Writing Practice:** Write a story about a surprising turn of events when the groundhog sees his shadow.

Mixed Review

Solve each problem.

1. $(40 + 3) - (20 + 12) = 11$	2. $(60 + 8) - (34 + 8) = 26$	3. $(6 \times 9) - (9 \times 4) = 18$

4. $(8 \times 8) - (7 \times 7) = 15$	5. 28 fifth graders were asked about their favorite ice cream. 14 said chocolate, and the others said vanilla. What percentage likes chocolate? 50%

Prefixes

Answer each question about prefixes.

1. If **mis** means *wrong*, what does:
   a. mistreat mean? treats wrong
   b. misread mean? reads wrong
2. If **re** means *do again*, what does:
   a. repaint mean? paint again
   b. retell mean? tell again
3. If **un** means *not*, what does:
   a. untied mean? not tied
   b. uncover mean? not covered

✏ **Writing Practice:** Write a story with the title below.

The Case of the Missing Clock

Mathematical Terms

Circle the correct mathematical term for the underlined numbers. Then solve problem 5.

1. $10 - 8 = \underline{2}$ a. product b. sum (c. difference) d. quotient	2. $23 + 23 = \underline{46}$ a. product (b. sum) c. difference d. quotient	3. $20 \div 5 = \underline{4}$ a. product b. sum c. difference (d. quotient)

4. $3 \times 5 = \underline{15}$ (a. product) b. sum c. difference d. quotient	5. Cleveland has 104,238 in population, Columbus has 679,234 in population, and Dayton has 414,757 in population. What is the total population of all three cities? 1,198,229 people

Homonyms

Eight homonyms are used incorrectly in this story. Circle each of them and write the correct word in the blanks below.

It was a beautiful (blue) sky. We were playing football with (four) friends. Stephan (threw) the ball at me. It (should) have dropped, but I fell forward to get it. Suddenly, I screamed! I had fallen on a (bee). I ran home and my (feet) began to hurt. Later that (night) I went to bed with my leg hurting from the bee sting.

blue · our · threw · would
bee · so · feet · night

✏ **Writing Practice:** Write a story using the sentence starter below.

We heard a "thump" outside the window . . .

Mathematical Terms

Circle the correct term to the underlined part of each number sentence. Then solve problem 5.

1. $\underline{81}$ divided by 9 = 9 a. subtrahend b. addends c. multiplier (d. dividend)	2. $6 \times \underline{6} = 36$ a. subtrahend b. addends (c. multiplier) d. dividend	3. $\underline{33} - 11 = 22$ (a. subtrahend) b. addends c. multiplier d. dividend

4. $\underline{10} + 10 = 20$ a. subtrahend (b. addends) c. multiplier d. dividend	5. It takes 24 inches of string to wrap a package. How much string will be needed to wrap 25 packages? 600 inches

Verb Usage

Circle the correct verb in each sentence.

1. The sun has (rise, rose, (risen)) brightly this morning.
2. The Founder's Day program has (begin, began, (begun)) late.
3. The swim team has (swim, swam, (swum)) five laps.
4. The walnuts have (fall, fell, (fallen)) off the trees.
5. Watermelon was (grow, grew, (grown)) on my uncle's farm.
6. My mother and I will (go), went, gone) to the basketball game tonight.
7. The window pane was (break, broke, (broken)) by a rock.
8. The principal has (tell, (told), telled) us the announcements.
9. Where was Kate (hid, hide, (hidden))?
10. The *Titanic* was (sink, sank, (sunk)) many years ago.

✏ **Writing Practice:** Write a story using the following words: *shrub, caterpillar, leaf, change, butterfly, crawl, sleepy, home.*

Money

Count the total change. Write it on the blank provided.

1. **$5.73**	2. **$2.19**	3. **$13.20**
3 dollars		12 dollars
3 half dollars	2 quarters	4 quarters
3 quarters	12 dimes	2 dimes
3 dimes	5 nickels	
3 nickels	24 pennies	
3 pennies		

4. **$6.55**	5. Terrell saved 12 quarters, 6 dimes, 14 nickels, and 13 pennies. Shamika saved 10 quarters, 8 dimes, 12 nickels, and 20 pennies. Who saved the most money?
5 dollars	
5 quarters	
5 nickels	
5 pennies	**Terrell**

Dictionary Skills

Look up these words to find their origin.

1. parrot — **French**
2. raccoon — **Native American**
3. chocolate — **Spanish**
4. automobile — **Greek**
5. piano — **Italian**
6. chimpanzee — **African**
7. pajamas — **Indian**
8. tea — **Chinese**
9. pretzel — **German**
10. cookie — **Dutch**

Writing Practice: A *fable* is a story that teaches a lesson, and animals are usually the characters. Write your own fable about a chicken and a cow.

Money

Write what type of bills and coins equal each money value.

1. $17.53	2. $107.65	3. $75.25
Answers will vary.	Answers will vary.	Answers will vary.

4. $63.71	5. Erica bought cereal for $2.39, juice for $1.59, and flour for $1.25. How much did she spend?
Answers will vary.	**$5.23**

Prefix/Suffix

Add a *prefix* to each word and then write a sentence with each word.

1. ____clear
2. ____do — **Answers will vary.**
3. ____order
4. ____trust

Add a *suffix* to each word and then write a sentence with each word.

5. care____
6. kind____ — **Answers will vary.**
7. sail____
8. help____

Writing Practice: You are sleeping soundly when the phone rings and wakes you up. Write a story about what happens.

Money

Solve each word problem using money.

1. Jerome spent between $12.00 and $13.00. Which two food items did he buy?	2. Lacey went to the bookstore for her teacher. The teacher gave her $1.00. Mrs. Woodson gave Lacey the following change: a quarter, 2 nickels, and 3 pennies. Which item did Lacey buy?
(a.) steak $5.50	a. pencil $0.25
b. hot dog $2.75	(b.) notebook $0.62
(c.) shrimp $7.00	c. eraser $0.10
d. French fries $1.50	d. ruler $0.68

3. The fourth grade hired a bus to take a trip to Mammoth Cave. It cost $15.00. Each student paid $0.50. How many students rode the bus?	4. The second graders collected money for charity. They collected 50 quarters, 65 dimes, 105 nickels, and 245 pennies. How much money did they collect?
30 students	**$26.70**

Antonyms/Synonyms

If the words are antonyms, write **A** in the space. If the words are synonyms, write **S** in the space.

A 1. difficult/easy	**A** 6. shouted/whispered
A 2. brave/coward	**S** 7. cent/penny
A 3. empty/full	**A** 8. swift/slow
S 4. finish/end	**A** 9. friend/foe
S 5. residence/home	**S** 10. liberty/freedom

Writing Practice: It rains so hard one afternoon that your bus gets stuck in the mud. Write a story about the unusual bus ride.

Money

Calculate the correct change. Then solve problem 5.

1. pizza	$1.50	2. pencil	$0.25	3. shampoo	$1.89
soda	$0.75	paper	$1.89	conditioner	$2.09
cookies	$0.35	notebook	$7.69	comb/brush	$1.49
money given	**$10.00**	**money given**	**$20.00**	**money given**	**$10.02**
change	**$7.40**	change	**$10.17**	change	**$4.55**

4. magazine	$2.50	5. Mr. Douglas needs $500.00 for a down payment on his car. He earns $275.00 a week and has saved $426.00. How much does he still need to save?
lip gloss	$1.68	
gel pens	$4.72	
money given	**$20.00**	
change	**$11.10**	**$74.00**

Main Idea

Fill in the web with details to go along with the main idea.

Writing Practice: Now write a paragraph about winter using the details you wrote in the above web.

Addition with Money

Solve each problem.

1. $654.88 + $98.92 =	2. $9,832.11 + $903.45 =	3. $54.00 + $87.38 =
$753.80	**$10,735.56**	**$141.38**

4. $99.99 + $11.11 =	5. Amanda bought 5 shirts in the mall for $9.99 each. How much did she spend in all?
$111.10	**$49.95**

Parts of Speech

Match each part of speech with its definition.

b. 1. noun	a. describe noun or pronoun
e. 2. pronoun	b. names a person, place, thing, or idea
d. 3. verb	c. connects words
a. 4. adjective	d. express action or state of being
g. 5. adverb	e. takes the place of a noun
h. 6. preposition	f. shows emotion or surprise
f. 7. interjection	g. describes a verb
c. 8. conjunction	h. relates a noun to another word

Writing Practice: You're walking on the beach and you look down and see a bottle. It has a message inside. Write about what it says.

Addition with Money

Solve each problem.

1. $20.00 + $2.43	2. $6.02 + $3.45	3. $3.94 + $3.08
$22.43	**$9.47**	**$7.02**

4. $70.00 + $29.95	5. If you bought snacks that totaled $6.89, how much change would you get if you paid with $10.00?
$99.95	**$3.11**

Plurals

Write the plural of the nouns below. Then write a sentence containing the plural word.

1. boy — **boys** — Answers will vary.
2. dish — **dishes**
3. song — **songs**
4. fox — **foxes**
5. knife — **knives**
6. ship — **ships**

Writing Practice: Write a paragraph about fun things you can do outside during the fall season. Then circle all plural words.

Page 131

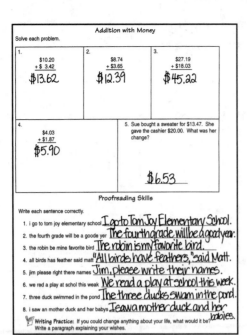

Addition with Money
Solve each problem.

1. $10.20 + $3.42 = $13.62
2. $8.74 + $3.65 = $12.39
3. $27.19 + $18.03 = $45.22
4. $4.03 + $1.87 = $5.90
5. Sue bought a sweater for $13.47. She gave the cashier $20.00. What was her change?
$6.53

Proofreading Skills
Write each sentence correctly.

1. i go to tom joy elementary school — I go to Tom Joy Elementary School.
2. the fourth grade will be a goode yer — The fourth grade will be a good year.
3. the robin is mine favorite bird — The robin is my favorite bird.
4. all birds has feather said matt — "All birds have feathers," said Matt.
5. jim please right there names — Jim, please write their names.
6. we red a play at schol this weak — We read a play at school this week.
7. three duck swimmed in the pond — The three ducks swam in the pond.
8. i saw a mother duck and her babys — I saw a mother duck and her babies.

✍ **Writing Practice:** If you could change anything about your life, what would it be? Write a paragraph explaining your wishes.

Page 132

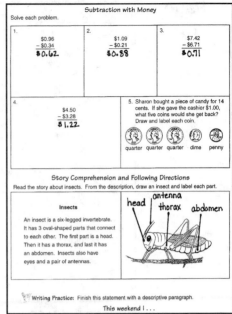

Subtraction with Money
Solve each problem.

1. $0.96 − $0.34 = $0.62
2. $1.09 − $0.21 = $0.88
3. $7.42 − $6.71 = $0.71
4. $4.50 − $3.28 = $1.22
5. Sharon bought a piece of candy for 14 cents. If she gave the cashier $1.00, what five coins would she get back? Draw and label each coin.
quarter quarter quarter dime penny

Story Comprehension and Following Directions
Read the story about insects. From the description, draw an insect and label each part.

Insects

An insect is a six-legged invertebrate. It has 3 oval-shaped parts that connect to each other. The first part is a head. Then it has a thorax, and last it has an abdomen. Insects also have eyes and a pair of antennas.

head antenna thorax abdomen

✍ **Writing Practice:** Finish this statement with a descriptive paragraph.
This weekend I . . .

Page 133

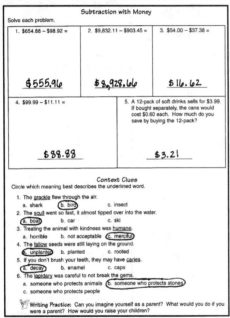

Subtraction with Money
Solve each problem.

1. $654.88 − $98.92 = $555.96
2. $9,832.11 − $903.45 = $8,928.66
3. $54.00 − $37.38 = $16.62
4. $99.99 − $11.11 = $88.88
5. A 12-pack of soft drinks sells for $3.99. If bought separately, the cans would cost $0.60 each. How much do you save by buying the 12-pack?
$3.21

Context Clues
Circle which meaning best describes the underlined word.

1. The grackle flew through the air.
   a. shark **b. bird** c. insect
2. The scull went so fast, it almost tipped over into the water.
   a. boat b. car c. ski
3. Treating the animal with kindness was humane.
   a. horrible b. not acceptable **c. merciful**
4. The fallow seeds were still laying on the ground.
   a. unplanted b. planted c. rooted
5. If you don't brush your teeth, they may have caries.
   a. decay b. enamel c. caps
6. The lapidary was careful to not break the gems.
   a. someone who protects animals **b. someone who protects stones**
   c. someone who protects people

✍ **Writing Practice:** Can you imagine yourself as a parent? What would you do if you were a parent? How would you raise your children?

Page 134

Subtraction with Money
Solve each problem below.

1. $4.60 − $1.80 = $2.80
2. $0.90 − $0.42 = $0.48
3. $542.46 − $267.95 = $274.51
4. $13.82 − $9.40 = $4.42
5. The distance around a field is 59.81 meters. The total length of three sides is 37.05 meters. What is the length of the other side?
22.76 m

Sequencing
Put the steps of this recipe in order from 1 to 8.

Ham Omelet

2 Then chop up the ham into small pieces.
8 Serve with orange juice and toast.
1 Before you start, break the eggs in a bowl.
6 Flip one side over the other side.
3 Whip the eggs with a wire whisk.
5 Add the chopped ham in the skillet.
7 Turn with a spatula to lightly brown the other side.
4 Pour the eggs in the skillet.

✍ **Writing Practice:** Write a short descriptive paragraph about the current President of the United States and what this person has accomplished.

Page 135

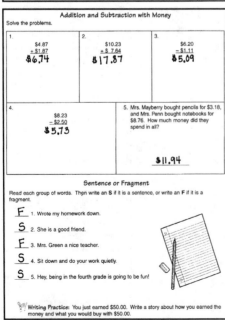

Addition and Subtraction with Money
Solve the problems.

1. $4.87 + $1.87 = $6.74
2. $10.23 + $7.64 = $17.87
3. $6.20 − $1.11 = $5.09
4. $8.23 − $2.50 = $5.73
5. Mrs. Mayberry bought pencils for $3.18, and Mrs. Penn bought notebooks for $8.76. How much money did they spend in all?
$11.94

Sentence or Fragment
Read each group of words. Then write an **S** if it is a sentence, or write an **F** if it is a fragment.

F 1. Wrote my homework down.
S 2. She is a good friend.
F 3. Mrs. Green a nice teacher.
S 4. Sit down and do your work quietly.
S 5. Hey, being in the fourth grade is going to be fun!

✍ **Writing Practice:** You just earned $50.00. Write a story about how you earned the money and what you would buy with $50.00.

Page 136

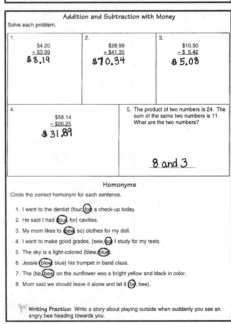

Addition and Subtraction with Money
Solve each problem.

1. $4.20 + $3.99 = $8.19
2. $28.99 + $41.35 = $70.34
3. $10.50 − $5.42 = $5.08
4. $58.14 − $26.25 = $31.89
5. The product of two numbers is 24. The sum of the same two numbers is 11. What are the two numbers?
8 and 3

Homonyms
Circle the correct homonym for each sentence.

1. I went to the dentist (four, **for**) a check-up today.
2. He said I had (**four**, for) cavities.
3. My mom likes to (**sew**, so) clothes for my doll.
4. I want to make good grades, (sew, **so**) I study for my tests.
5. The sky is a light-colored (blew, **blue**).
6. Jessie (**blew**, blue) his trumpet in band class.
7. The (be, **bee**) on the sunflower was a bright yellow and black in color.
8. Mom said we should leave it alone and let it (**be**, bee).

✍ **Writing Practice:** Write a story about playing outside when suddenly you see an angry bee heading towards you.

Page 137

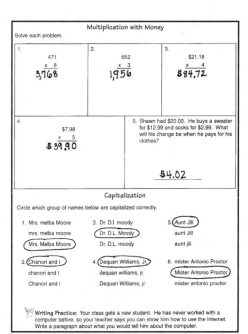

Multiplication with Money
Solve each problem.

1.	2.	3.
471 × 8 = 3,768	652 × 3 = 1,956	$21.18 × 4 = $84.72

4.	5. Shawn had $20.00. He buys a sweater for $12.99 and socks for $2.99. What will his change be when he pays for his clothes?
$7.98 × 5 = $39.90	$4.02

Capitalization
Circle which group of names below are capitalized correctly.

1. Mrs. melba Moore / mrs. melba moore / **Mrs. Melba Moore** (circled)
2. **Chanori and I** (circled) / chanori and I / Chanori and i
3. Dr. D.I. moody / **Dr. D.L. Moody** (circled) / Dr. D.L. moody
4. **Dequan Williams, Jr.** (circled) / dequan williams, jr. / Dequan Williams, jr.
5. **Aunt Jill** (circled) / aunt Jill / aunt jili
6. mister Antonio Proctor / **Mister Antonio Proctor** (circled) / mister antonio proctor

Writing Practice: Your class gets a new student. He has never worked with a computer before, so your teacher says you can show him how to use the Internet. Write a paragraph about what you would tell him about the computer.

Page 138

Multiplication with Money
Solve each problem.

1.	2.	3.
$45.21 × 21 = $949.41	$3.82 × 14 = $53.48	$5.25 × 30 = $157.50

4.	5. During Columbus' last voyage, only 116 men survived. One hundred forty men began the voyage. How many did not survive?
$92.98 × 8 = $743.84	24 died

Contractions
Rewrite the underlined words with a contraction.

There's — 1. There is time to read before going to bed.
That's — 2. That is the first one I have read in a while.
I'd — 3. I would like to read a mystery novel.
can't — 4. I cannot read for very long.
shouldn't — 5. The book should not take but a few days to read.
doesn't — 6. It does not look too hard.
I'll — 7. I will get a new book when I finish.

Writing Practice: Write a paragraph using the sentence starter below.
My goals for the new year are . . .

Page 139

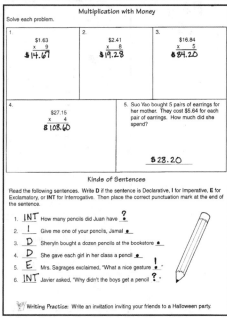

Multiplication with Money
Solve each problem.

1.	2.	3.
$1.63 × 9 = $14.67	$2.41 × 8 = $19.28	$16.84 × 5 = $84.20

4.	5. Suo Yao bought 5 pairs of earrings for her mother. They cost $5.64 for each pair of earrings. How much did she spend?
$27.15 × 4 = $108.60	$28.20

Kinds of Sentences
Read the following sentences. Write **D** if the sentence is Declarative, **I** for Imperative, **E** for Exclamatory, or **INT** for Interrogative. Then place the correct punctuation mark at the end of the sentence.

1. INT How many pencils did Juan have **?**
2. I Give me one of your pencils, Jamal **.**
3. D Sheryln bought a dozen pencils at the bookstore **.**
4. D She gave each girl in her class a pencil **.**
5. E Mrs. Sagrages exclaimed, "What a nice gesture **.** **!**
6. INT Javier asked, "Why didn't the boys get a pencil **?**

Writing Practice: Write an invitation inviting your friends to a Halloween party.

Page 140

Division with Money
Solve each problem. Round to the nearest penny.

1.	2.	3.
$5.99 2)$11.97	$8.66 4)$34.63	$16.35 3)$49.06

4.	5. Sandra was given $12.00 for lunch at school for 5 days. How much can Sandra spend each day?
$21.90 4)$87.61	$2.40

Homonyms
Write a sentence using each homonym. (Answers will vary.)

1. hear _____
   here _____
2. sail _____
   sale _____
3. do _____
   dew _____
4. ate _____
   eight _____

Writing Practice: Write a paragraph using the sentence starter below.
I couldn't believe I got caught . . .

Page 141

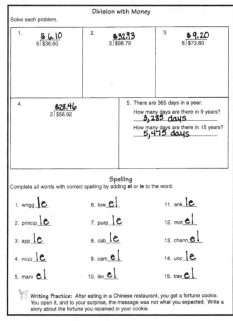

Division with Money
Solve each problem.

1.	2.	3.
$6.10 6)$36.60	$32.93 3)$98.79	$9.20 8)$73.60

4.	5. There are 365 days in a year.
$28.46 2)$56.92	How many days are there in 9 years? 3,285 days / How many days are there in 15 years? 5,475 days

Spelling
Complete all words with correct spelling by adding **el** or **le** to the word.

1. wrigg **le**
2. princip **le**
3. app **le**
4. nozz **le**
5. marv **el**
6. tow **el**
7. purp **le**
8. cab **le**
9. cam **el**
10. lev **el**
11. ank **le**
12. mot **el**
13. chann **el**
14. unc **le**
15. trav **el**

Writing Practice: After eating in a Chinese restaurant, you get a fortune cookie. You open it, and to your surprise, the message was not what you expected. Write a story about the fortune you received in your cookie.

Page 142

Multiplication and Division with Money
Solve each problem.

1.	2.	3.
$1.29 × 3 = $3.87	$3.42 × 6 = $20.52	$0.60 6)$3.60

4.	5. There were 28 people in Ruth's class. There were 12 boys. How many were girls?
$0.60 7)$4.20	16 girls

Subjects and Predicates
Circle the subject and underline the predicate in each sentence.

1. My friends and I went trick-or-treating.
2. I was a spooky ghost.
3. Our neighbors gave us lots of candy.
4. Jordan tripped over his costume.
5. We ran and jumped all the way down the street.
6. Halloween is a time to have fun with your friends.

Writing Practice: Write an informative paragraph for the school newspaper about the school dance in two weeks.

Page 143

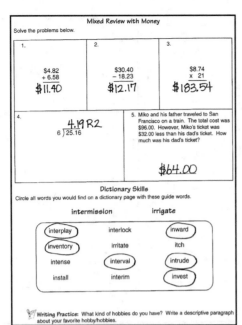

Mixed Review with Money
Solve the problems below.

1.	2.	3.
$4.82 + 6.58 **$11.40**	$30.40 − 18.23 **$12.17**	$8.74 x 21 **$183.54**

4.	5.
4.19 R2 6) 25.16	Miko and his father traveled to San Francisco on a train. The total cost was $96.00. However, Miko's ticket was $32.00 less than his dad's ticket. How much was his dad's ticket? **$64.00**

Dictionary Skills
Circle all words you would find on a dictionary page with these guide words.

intermission   irrigate

(interplay)   interlock   (inward)
(inventory)   irritate   itch
intense   (interval)   (intrude)
install   interim   (invest)

✍ **Writing Practice:** What kind of hobbies do you have? Write a descriptive paragraph about your favorite hobby/hobbies.

Page 144

Problem-Solving with Money
Look at the menu. Four families from the neighborhood ordered fast food one evening. Compute the cost of each family's meal, using the menu.

1. Family 1 ordered 2 hot dogs, 2 French fries, 1 potato salad, and 2 sodas.	2. Family 2 ordered 1 hamburger, 3 pizzas, 1 milkshake, and 3 sodas.	3. Family 3 ordered 2 corn dogs, 1 pizza, 2 potato chips, and 3 milkshakes.
Total = **$6.40**	Total = **$8.65**	Total = **$8.95**

4. Family 4 ordered 1 of each item on the menu. Total = **$10.60**	**Fast Food Menu** hot dog $1.25 hamburger $1.50 pizza $1.50 corn dog $1.25 French fries $1.00 potato salad $0.90 potato chips $0.75 soft drink $0.50 milkshake $1.15 ice cream cone $0.80

Pronouns
Write the pronoun above the underlined word.

1. Marques ran fast. **He** Marques won the race.
2. The boys like to play baseball. **They** The boys play it every Saturday.
3. Mom went to the grocery store. **She** Mom bought food for our lunches.
4. Barbara and I are friends. **We** Barbara and I like to talk on the phone.

Circle the possessive pronoun in each sentence.

5. "That's (my) book," said Emily.
6. Did the baby play with (her) ball?
7. The blue backpack is (mine).
8. The dog ate (its) bone.

✍ **Writing Practice:** Write a paragraph using the sentence starter below.
The art of being friendly . . .

Page 145

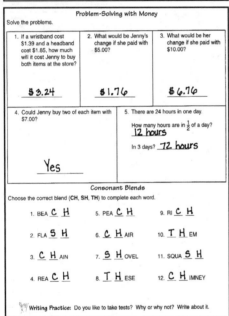

Problem-Solving with Money
Solve the problems.

1. If a wristband cost $1.39 and a headband cost $1.85, how much will it cost Jenny to buy both items at the store? **$3.24**	2. What would be Jenny's change if she paid with $5.00? **$1.76**	3. What would be her change if she paid with $10.00? **$6.76**

4. Could Jenny buy two of each item with $7.00? **Yes**	5. There are 24 hours in one day. How many hours are in ½ of a day? **12 hours** In 3 days? **72 hours**

Consonant Blends
Choose the correct blend (CH, SH, TH) to complete each word.

1. BEA **C H**   5. PEA **C H**   9. RI **C H**
2. FLA **S H**   6. **C H** AIR   10. **T H** EM
3. **C H** AIN   7. **S H** OVEL   11. SQUA **S H**
4. REA **C H**   8. **T H** ESE   12. **C H** IMNEY

✍ **Writing Practice:** Do you like to take tests? Why or why not? Write about it.

Page 146

Problem-Solving with Money
You've just inherited one million dollars, but there's one catch. You have to spend all of it or you lose it. Answer the questions. Choose from the items listed in the box below.

1. List the 4 items that you would buy. **Answers will vary.**	2. What is the total cost of all 4 items? **Answers will vary.**	3. How much money do you have left? **Answers will vary.**

house	$250,000.00	ten-speed bicycle	$250.00
sports car	$25,000.00	trip to Disney World	$1,200.00
swimming pool	$15,000.00	fast-food restaurant	$56,000.00
boat	$31,000.00	roller skating rink	$100,000.00

Suffixes
Write what each word means by looking at the meanings of the following suffixes.

(-er) one who does something	(-ee) one who receives something	(-meter) device for measuring
(-ation) act of	(-less) without	(-y) having
(-ous) having	(-ful) full of	

1. teacher _**one who teaches**_
2. thermometer _**device for measuring temperature**_
3. employee _**one who is employed for wages**_
4. transportation _**act of transporting**_
5. careless _**without care**_
6. chilly _**having chills**_
7. joyous _**having joy**_
8. beautiful _**full of beauty**_

✍ **Writing Practice:** Write a paragraph using the sentence starter below.
One of the strangest sights I ever saw was . . .

Page 147

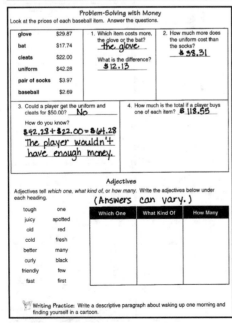

Problem-Solving with Money
Look at the prices of each baseball item. Answer the questions.

glove	$29.87
bat	$17.74
cleats	$22.00
uniform	$42.28
pair of socks	$3.97
baseball	$2.69

1. Which item costs more, the glove or the bat? **the glove** What is the difference? **$12.13**	2. How much more does the uniform cost than the socks? **$38.31**

3. Could a player get the uniform and cleats for $50.00? **No** How do you know? **$42.28 + $22.00 = $64.28** **The player wouldn't have enough money.**	4. How much is the total if a player buys one of each item? **$118.55**

Adjectives
Adjectives tell which one, what kind of, or how many. Write the adjectives below under each heading. **(Answers can vary.)**

tough	one
juicy	spotted
old	red
cold	fresh
better	many
curly	black
friendly	few
fast	first

Which One	What Kind Of	How Many

✍ **Writing Practice:** Write a descriptive paragraph about waking up one morning and finding yourself in a cartoon.

Page 148

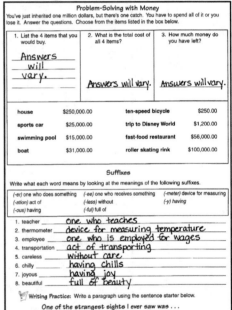

Problem-Solving with Money
List the fewest coins and paper money you would receive as change in the following problems and then solve problem 5.

1. If a customer spent $0.84 and paid with a dollar bill, how much change will the customer receive? **1 penny, 1 nickel, and 1 dime**	2. If a customer spent $1.73 and paid with two dollar bills, how much change will the customer receive? **2 pennies and 1 quarter**	3. If a customer spent $3.22 and paid with a five dollar bill, how much change will the customer receive? **3 pennies, 3 quarters, and 1 dollar**

4. If a customer spent $16.55 and paid with a twenty dollar bill, how much change will the customer receive? **2 dimes + 1 quarter + 3 dollars**	5. George spent 1 dollar, 2 quarters, 3 dimes, and 1 nickel on candy. His friend spent 1 dollar, 3 quarters, and 1 nickel. How much did each spend and who spent more? George **$1.85** George's friend **$1.80** Who spent more? **George**

Adverbs
Choose the right adverb to complete each sentence.

1. The play ended _**suddenly**_ .   carefully
2. They acted _**badly**_ in the mall.   quickly
3. Jorge plays football very _**well**_ .   badly
4. She _**carefully**_ hiked up the mountain.   suddenly
5. The sunset was _**clearly**_ seen.   well
6. Mrs. Johnson walked _**quickly**_ to her car. clearly

✍ **Writing Practice:** Write a paragraph about how you feel you're doing in school this year.

Problem-Solving with Money

Use the information in the chart to answer the questions.

		Christmas Sale
1. How much would it cost for 2 small ornaments and 1 large ornament?	2. Would it cost more for 1 regular set of lights or 2 boxes of cards?	*ornaments*
		small 2/$3.00
		large 2/$5.00
$5.50	**lights**	*lights*
3. Will $5.00 be enough to purchase 1 roll of wrapping paper, 3 bags of bows, and 1 small ornament?	4. What would the total cost be if you purchased 1 of each item?	regular $4.89
		icicle $5.89
		cards $2.25 box
		wrapping paper $1.99/roll
no	**$19.61**	*bows in bag* $0.59/bag
		2 bags/$1.00

Verbs

Underline any verb and helping verb in each sentence.

1. It seemed colder yesterday.
2. We were walking down the street.
3. Bob was going to play football.
4. It began to snow heavily.
5. It was so cold, so I went inside.
6. Maybe tomorrow it will be warmer.

Writing Practice: Write a persuasive paragraph explaining your position on students going to school for nine months versus year-round school.

Addition with Decimals

Solve each problem below.

1.	2.	3.
46.8 + 9.6 **56.4**	8.982 + 24.83 **33.812**	0.84 + 0.67 **1.51**

4.	5. The cost of 2 books is $10.50. One cost $2.50 more than the other. What is the cost of each book?
36.341 + 22.8 **59.141**	Book 1 **$4.00** Book 2 **$6.50**

Nouns

Underline 11 common nouns in the paragraph about whales.

Whales are one of the most intelligent animals. They are mammals, which mean they give birth to live young and use lungs to breathe. They migrate thousands of miles each year. When there isn't much food, they can live off their blubber.

Writing Practice: October is National Clock Month. Write about a time you lost track of time and were late for an important event/appointment.

Addition with Decimals

Add each group of numbers with decimals. Then solve problem 5.

1. 15,873 + 5.32 =	2. 15.873 + 53.2 =	3. 1,587.3 + .532 =
15,878.32	**69.073**	**1,587.832**

4.	5. There are 24 hours in one day. How many hours are there in one week? **168 hours**
1.5873 + 532 = **533.5873**	How many hours are in 12 weeks? **2,016 hours**

Predicate (Verb)

Choose the correct verb for each sentence.

1. **Let** the students play kickball. (Let, Leave)
2. Please don't **sit** on the floor. (sit, set)
3. We **taught** our bird to talk. (taught, learned)
4. Where **were** you yesterday? (was, were)
5. There **are** two bikes in the yard. (is, are)
6. Where have you **taken** my picture? (took, taken)
7. We **ate** our lunch in our classroom. (ate, eaten)
8. **May** I go to the mall with you? (may, can)

Writing Practice: Write a paragraph using the sentence starter below.

I have some good memories about . . .

Addition with Decimals

Add. Then solve problem 5.

1. 2.9461 + 56.03 =	2. 294.61 + 560.3 =	3. 2,946.1 + 5,603 =
58.9761	**854.91**	**8,549.1**

4. 29.461 + 5.603 =	5. The Hundred Years War was fought from 1337 to 1453. How many total years did the war go on?
35.064	**116 years**

Main Idea

Circle the topic that doesn't belong under the main idea. For problem 4, write four topics under the main idea.

1. Animals in the zoo
   a. bears
   b. dogs *(circled)*
   c. tigers
   d. monkeys

2. Favorite hobbies
   a. stamp collecting
   b. collecting dolls
   c. reading books
   d. doing homework *(circled)*

3. Why school is important
   a. learn how to clean your room *(circled)*
   b. learn new things
   c. learn to use the library
   d. learn to get along with others

4. You can learn a lot in social studies.
   a. **Answers**
   b. **will**
   c. **vary.**
   d.

Writing Practice: Write a story with the writing starter below.

It was a wonderful surprise . . .

Multiplication with Decimals

Solve each problem.

1.	2.	3.
0.06 x 0.6 = **0.036**	0.4 x 30.2 = **12.08**	5 x 0.05 = **0.25**

4.	5. 25 students were asked how often they read a book. 10 said they read at least 5 days a week. What percentage of the students read at least 5 days a week?
6.0 x 0.7 = **4.2**	**40%**

Analogies

Complete each analogy.

1. Wings are to butterflies, as fins are to **fish**.
2. Chimney is to house, as **peak** is to mountain.
3. Mother is to child, as cow is to **calf**.
4. Pen is to chicken, as **stable** is to horse.
5. 5 is to pentagon, as 8 is to **octagon**.
6. Grapes are to jelly, as apples are to **applesauce**.
7. Antlers are to deer, as **horns** are to unicorns.
8. Pencils are to writing instruments, as **(Answers can vary.)** are to tools.

Writing Practice: Picture yourself 10 years from now. What do you think you'll be doing? Write about it.

Multiplication with Decimals

Solve each problem.

1.	2.	3.
9.34 x 10 **93.4**	0.5 x 1,000 **500**	.98 x 100 **98**

4.	5. Nicole earned $8.50. She spent $3.75 at the store and saved $3.00 in her piggy bank. How much money does she have left to spend?
76.4 x 10 **764**	**$1.75**

Sentences

Write four sentences about any fairy tale using each kind of sentence.

1. Declarative
2. Imperative
3. Interrogative
4. Exclamatory

Writing Practice: Write a letter to a new pen pal describing yourself.

Multiplication with Decimals
Solve each problem below.

1.	2.	3.
4.2 x 0.6 **2.52**	0.73 x 4 **2.92**	1.6 x 3.7 **5.92**

4.	5. What is the mode of Sarah's history grades if she had the following grades? Sarah's history grades: 77, 58, 82, 95, 65, 100, 96, 95
1.06 x 5 **5.30**	**95**

Punctuation
Add commas where needed.

1. My sister, brother, and cousin went to camp with me.
2. Jim, my uncle, took us last week.
3. Emily said, "Let's go back next year."
4. I want this book, but I will have to read it later.
5. We went to the library, to the grocery store, and then back home.
6. The poodle, which is noted for its small size, can be a great pet.

Writing Practice: Use this writing prompt to write a short paragraph:
My favorite belonging is…

Multiplication with Decimals
Solve the problems below.

1.	2.	3.
39.37 x .21 **8.2677**	11.89 x .33 **3.9237**	91.44 x .16 **14.6304**

4.	5. Kareem is two years older than his brother, Javier, but is 5 years younger than his sister, Janis. If Janis is 19, how old are Kareem and Javier?
40.47 x .25 **10.1175**	Kareem is **14 years old** Javier is **12 years old**

Alphabetical Order
Write these mathematical terms in alphabetical order.

perimeter	**decimals**
ratio	**division**
multiply	**geometry**
percent	**multiply**
division	**percent**
place value	**perimeter**
decimals	**place value**
geometry	**ratio**

Writing Practice: What is your favorite food dish? Why? What is your least favorite food dish? Why?

Rounding Decimals
Round to the nearest whole number and then solve problem 5.

1.	2.	3.
6.29 = **6**	1.7 = **2**	0.96 = **1**

4.	5. Sarah, Ricardo, and Dominique rode their bikes. Sarah rode 2.1 miles, Ricardo rode 3.7 miles, and Dominique rode 5.5 miles. About how many miles did they ride altogether? Find the answer by rounding each decimal to the nearest whole number.
21.39 = **21**	**12 miles**

Context Clues
Decide on the meaning of the underlined word in the sentences below. Circle its meaning below each sentence.

1. I used my dad's shears to cut a rope.
   a. knife   **b. scissors**   c. brush
2. His statement was muddled and could not be understood.
   a. knowing   b. stubborn   **c. confusing**
3. Carlos deleted his letter from the computer.
   a. removed   b. added   c. changed
4. Eagles are scarce because there are not many around.
   a. plentiful   b. common   **c. uncommon**
5. In the early morning, fog makes it looks hazy.
   a. cloudy   b. clear   c. sunny
6. The stick jabbed me in the side when I fell down.
   a. cut   **b. poked**   c. scraped

Writing Practice: Write a short story about two friends running against each other in a race.

Rounding Decimals
Round to the nearest whole number. Then solve problem 5.

1.	2.	3.
4.3 = **4**	9.78 = **10**	85.03 = **85**

4.	5. Merlin walked 2.3 miles, Arnold walked 7.5 miles, William walked 3.1 miles, and Franklin walked 8.7 miles. Round each to the nearest whole number. How many miles did they walk in all?
7.1 = **7**	**22 miles**

Verbs
Fill in the chart with the correct form of the verb.

Present	Past	Past Participle
sing	**sang**	sung
ring	rang	rung
read	read	**read**
think	**thought**	thought
walk	walked	walked
take	**took**	taken
sit	sat	**sat**
blow	**blew**	blown

Writing Practice: Write a story using the sentence starter below.
In the middle of the night, I was thirsty. When I got up, I couldn't believe my eyes . . .

Mixed Review with Decimals
Solve each problem.

1.	2.	3.
97,035.6 + 33,461.2 **130,496.8**	39.87 x .23 **9.1701**	6.470 + 3.998 **10.468**

4.	5. Janice spent $12.46 at the store on Friday and $72.90 on Saturday.
2.34 x 56 **1.3104**	How much money did Janice spend in both days? **$85.36** How much more money did she spend on Saturday than on Friday? **$60.44**

Adjectives
Write an adjective (a descriptive word) in front of each noun.
(Answers will vary.)

1. _____ stone
2. _____ shoes
3. _____ movie
4. _____ baseball game
5. _____ tree
6. _____ flower
7. _____ elephant
8. _____ classroom
9. _____ pizza
10. _____ cake

Writing Practice: You are the President of the United States for one day. Write a paragraph and tell about what you did and what decisions you made for the country.

Mixed Review with Decimals
Solve each problem.

1.	2.	3.
27.83 + 9.75 **37.58**	96.70 − 54.82 **41.88**	43.03 x 6 **258.18**

4.	5. Miguel and his three friends found $33.60 on the ground in his yard. If they decide to split the money between each of them, how much would each person get?
2.6 8) 20.8	**$8.40**

Possessives
Rewrite each group of words to make them show ownership.

1. the shoes of Josh — **Josh's shoes**
2. the desks of the students — **students' desks**
3. the wings of the geese — **geese's wings**
4. the toys of the baby — **baby's toys**
5. the homework of Julie — **Julie's homework**
6. the coats of the girls — **girls' coats**
7. the flowers of the florist — **florist's flowers**
8. the leaves of the tree — **tree's leaves**

Writing Practice: Write a paragraph using the sentence starter below.
If I had a million dollars, I would . . .

Mixed Review with Decimals
Solve each problem below.

1.	2.	3.
3,461.8 + 88.75 **3,550.55**	2.4 − 1.63 **0.77**	6.03 x 8.4 **50.652**

4.	5. Write any number down. Add 10. Multiply by 4. Add 200. Divide by 4. Subtract the number you write down. What answer did you get? Everyone's answer should be the same.
13.5 2.3)31.05	**60**

Context Clues
Write the meaning of each underlined word by seeing how it is used in each sentence.

1. He bellowed with a loud voice. **shouted**
2. I was flabbergasted at the outcome of the game. **surprised**
3. Bradley grimaced with pain after he broke his foot. **winced**
4. The massive ship held 2,500 passengers. **very big or large**
5. Mom was bewildered when her watch wouldn't work. **confused**
6. The replica of the original flag was almost exact. **copy**

✍ **Writing Practice:** You get home from school, and you can't find your keys. No one is home. Write about what you would do.

Division with Decimals
Solve each problem.

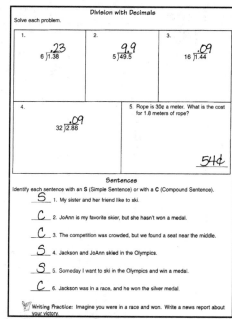

1.	2.	3.
.23 6)1.38	**9.9** 5)49.5	**.09** 16)1.44

4.	5. Rope is 30¢ a meter. What is the cost for 1.8 meters of rope?
.09 32)2.88	**54¢**

Sentences
Identify each sentence with an **S** (Simple Sentence) or with a **C** (Compound Sentence).

S 1. My sister and her friend like to ski.
C 2. JoAnn is my favorite skier, but she hasn't won a medal.
C 3. The competition was crowded, but we found a seat near the middle.
S 4. Jackson and JoAnn skied in the Olympics.
S 5. Someday I want to ski in the Olympics and win a medal.
C 6. Jackson was in a race, and he won the silver medal.

✍ **Writing Practice:** Imagine you were in a race and won. Write a news report about your victory.

Division with Decimals
Solve each problem below.

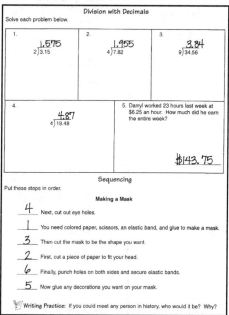

1.	2.	3.
1.575 2)3.15	**1.955** 4)7.82	**3.84** 9)34.56

4.	5. Darryl worked 23 hours last week at $6.25 an hour. How much did he earn the entire week?
4.87 4)19.48	**$143.75**

Sequencing
Put these steps in order.

Making a Mask

4 Next, cut out eye holes.
1 You need colored paper, scissors, an elastic band, and glue to make a mask.
3 Then cut the mask to be the shape you want.
2 First, cut a piece of paper to fit your head.
6 Finally, punch holes on both sides and secure elastic bands.
5 Now glue any decorations you want on your mask.

✍ **Writing Practice:** If you could meet any person in history, who would it be? Why?

Division with Decimals
Solve the problems below.

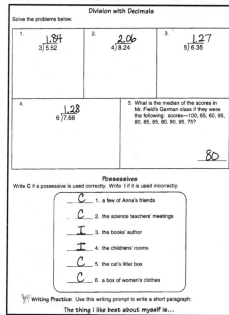

1.	2.	3.
1.84 3)5.52	**2.06** 4)8.24	**1.27** 5)6.35

4.	5. What is the median of the scores in Mr. Field's German class if they were the following: scores—100, 65, 60, 95, 80, 85, 65, 80, 90, 95, 75?
1.28 6)7.68	**80**

Possessives
Write **C** if a possessive is used correctly. Write **I** if it is used incorrectly.

C 1. a few of Anna's friends
C 2. the science teachers' meetings
I 3. the books' author
I 4. the childrens' rooms
C 5. the cat's litter box
C 6. a box of women's clothes

✍ **Writing Practice:** Use this writing prompt to write a short paragraph:
The thing I like best about myself is…

Division with Decimals
Solve each problem below.

1.	2.	3.
45.6 ÷ 100 = **0.456**	0.98 ÷ 10 = **0.098**	556 ÷ 100 = **5.56**

4.	5. The original price of a CD is $13.00. If it is on sale at $1.29 off, what is the price now?
32.92 ÷ 100 = **0.3292**	**$11.71**

Punctuation and Capitalization
Choose the correctly punctuated words.

1. a. J. K. rowling
   b. J K Rowling
   c. J. K. Rowling
2. a. Dr. T C Trane
   b. Dr. T. C. Trane
   c. Dr. t c Trane
3. a. Mesa verde Park
   b. Mesa Verde Park
   c. Mesa Verde park
4. **a. James Lee, Jr.**
   b. James Lee, jr.
   c. James Lee jr.
5. a. Turner St
   b. turner st.
   c. Turner St.
6. **a. Mrs. Bette L. Scott**
   b. Mrs. Bette L Scott
   c. Mrs Bette L. Scott

✍ **Writing Practice:** Write the safety rules for leaving your classroom and the school during a fire drill or actual fire.

Decimals and Fractions
Write the following decimals as a fraction. Then solve problem 5.

1.	2.	3.
0.67 = **$\frac{67}{100}$**	0.9 = **$\frac{9}{10}$**	0.212 = **$\frac{212}{1,000}$** or **$\frac{53}{250}$**

4.	5. A grasshopper can jump 3 feet high and 20 times its length. If a grasshopper is 3.5 inches long, how far can it jump?
0.49 = **$\frac{49}{100}$**	**70 inches**

Abbreviations
Unscramble the name of the state. Then match it to its abbreviation.

Nickname		State	Abbreviations
1. Heart of Dixie	(AAAAMBL)	**Alabama**	**AL**
2. Last Frontier	(AAAKSL)	**Alaska**	**AK**
3. Grand Canyon State	(AANROZI)	**Arizona**	**AZ**
4. Land of Opportunity	(AAASKRNS)	**Arkansas**	**AR**
5. Gem State	(IOHAD)	**Idaho**	**ID**
6. Land of Lincoln	(IIILSLNO)	**Illinois**	**IL**
7. Hoosier State	(IIAANND)	**Indiana**	**IN**
8. Hawkeye State	(IAOW)	**Iowa**	**IA**

Abbreviations
IA
ID
IN
IL
AZ
AR
AL
AK

✍ **Writing Practice:** Hawaii is the only state that is a group of islands. Write a story about being alone on an island.

Page 167

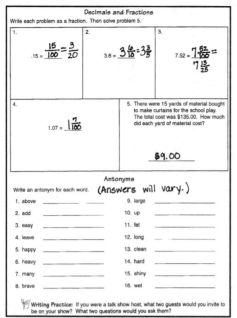

Decimals and Fractions

Write each problem as a fraction. Then solve problem 5.

1. $.15 = \dfrac{15}{100} = \dfrac{3}{20}$

2. $3.6 = 3\dfrac{6}{10} = 3\dfrac{3}{5}$

3. $7.52 = 7\dfrac{52}{100} = 7\dfrac{13}{25}$

4. $1.07 = 1\dfrac{7}{100}$

5. There were 15 yards of material bought to make curtains for the school play. The total cost was $135.00. How much did each yard of material cost?

$9.00

Antonyms

Write an antonym for each word. (Answers will vary.)

1. above _____   9. large _____
2. add _____   10. up _____
3. easy _____   11. fat _____
4. leave _____   12. long _____
5. happy _____   13. clean _____
6. heavy _____   14. hard _____
7. many _____   15. shiny _____
8. brave _____   16. wet _____

Writing Practice: If you were a talk show host, what two guests would you invite to be on your show? What two questions would you ask them?

Page 168

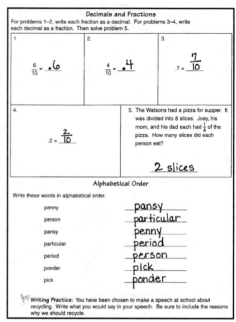

Decimals and Fractions

For problems 1–2, write each fraction as a decimal. For problems 3–4, write each decimal as a fraction. Then solve problem 5.

1. $\dfrac{6}{10} = .6$

2. $\dfrac{4}{10} = .4$

3. $.7 = \dfrac{7}{10}$

4. $.2 = \dfrac{2}{10}$

5. The Watsons had a pizza for supper. It was divided into 8 slices. Joey, his mom, and his dad each had $\frac{1}{4}$ of the pizza. How many slices did each person eat?

2 slices

Alphabetical Order

Write these words in alphabetical order.

penny → pansy
person → particular
pansy → penny
particular → period
period → person
ponder → pick
pick → ponder

Writing Practice: You have been chosen to make a speech at school about recycling. Write what you would say in your speech. Be sure to include the reasons why we should recycle.

Page 169

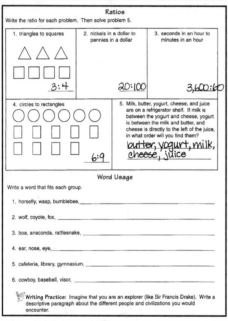

Ratios

Write the ratio for each problem. Then solve problem 5.

1. triangles to squares — 3:4

2. nickels in a dollar to pennies in a dollar — 20:100

3. seconds in an hour to minutes in an hour — 3,600:60

4. circles to rectangles — 6:9

5. Milk, butter, yogurt, cheese, and juice are on a refrigerator shelf. If milk is between the yogurt and cheese, yogurt is between the milk and butter, and cheese is directly to the left of the juice, in what order will you find them?

butter, yogurt, milk, cheese, juice

Word Usage

Write a word that fits each group.

1. horsefly, wasp, bumblebee, _____
2. wolf, coyote, fox, _____
3. boa, anaconda, rattlesnake, _____
4. ear, nose, eye, _____
5. cafeteria, library, gymnasium, _____
6. cowboy, baseball, visor, _____

Writing Practice: Imagine that you are an explorer (like Sir Francis Drake). Write a descriptive paragraph about the different people and civilizations you would encounter.

Page 170

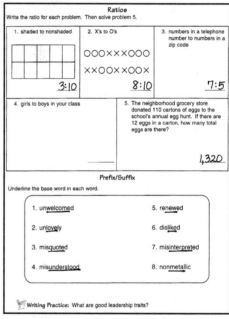

Ratios

Write the ratio for each problem. Then solve problem 5.

1. shaded to nonshaded — 3:10

2. X's to O's — 8:10

3. numbers in a telephone number to numbers in a zip code — 7:5

4. girls to boys in your class

5. The neighborhood grocery store donated 110 cartons of eggs to the school's annual egg hunt. If there are 12 eggs in a carton, how many total eggs are there?

1,320

Prefix/Suffix

Underline the base word in each word.

1. un<u>welcome</u>d   5. re<u>new</u>ed
2. un<u>love</u>ly   6. dis<u>like</u>d
3. mis<u>quote</u>d   7. mis<u>interpret</u>ed
4. mis<u>understood</u>   8. non<u>metallic</u>

Writing Practice: What are good leadership traits?

Page 171

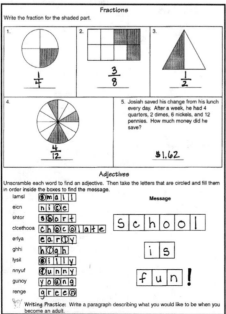

Fractions

Write the fraction for the shaded part.

1. $\dfrac{1}{4}$

2. $\dfrac{3}{8}$

3. $\dfrac{1}{2}$

4. $\dfrac{4}{12}$

5. Josiah saved his change from his lunch every day. After a week, he had 4 quarters, 2 dimes, 6 nickels, and 12 pennies. How much money did he save?

$1.62

Adjectives

Unscramble each word to find an adjective. Then take the letters that are circled and fill them in order inside the boxes to find the message.

lamsl — s m a l l
eicn — n i c e
shtor — s h o r t
clcethooa — c h o c o l a t e
erlya — e a r l y
ghhi — h i g h
lysil — s i l l y
nnyuf — f u n n y
gunoy — y o u n g
renge — g r e e n

Message: S c h o o l i s f u n !

Writing Practice: Write a paragraph describing what you would like to be when you become an adult.

Page 172

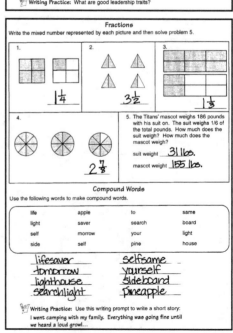

Fractions

Write the mixed number represented by each picture and then solve problem 5.

1. $1\dfrac{1}{4}$

2. $3\dfrac{1}{2}$

3. $1\dfrac{1}{3}$

4. $2\dfrac{7}{8}$

5. The Titans' mascot weighs 186 pounds with his suit on. The suit weighs 1/6 of the total pounds. How much does the suit weigh? How much does the mascot weigh?

suit weight: 31 lbs.
mascot weight: 155 lbs.

Compound Words

Use the following words to make compound words.

life, apple, to, same, light, saver, search, board, self, morrow, your, light, side, self, pine, house

lifesaver   selfsame
tomorrow   yourself
lighthouse   sideboard
searchlight   pineapple

Writing Practice: Use this writing prompt to write a short story:
I went camping with my family. Everything was going fine until we heard a loud growl.

Fractions
Write the correct fraction expressed by the shaded part. Then solve problem 5.

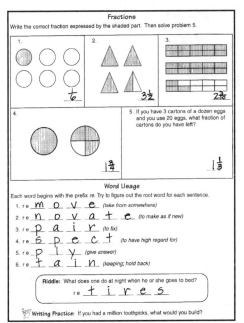

1. $\frac{}{6}$

2. $3\frac{1}{2}$

3. $2\frac{}{10}$

4. $\frac{3}{7}$

5. If you have 3 cartons of a dozen eggs and you use 20 eggs, what fraction of cartons do you have left?

$1\frac{1}{3}$

Word Usage
Each word begins with the prefix *re*. Try to figure out the root word for each sentence.

1. re __m o v e__ *(take from somewhere)*
2. re __n o v a t e__ *(to make as if new)*
3. re __p a i r__ *(to fix)*
4. re __s p e c t__ *(to have high regard for)*
5. re __p l y__ *(give answer)*
6. re __t a i n__ *(keeping; hold back)*

> **Riddle:** What does one do at night when he or she goes to bed?
> re __t i r e s__

🖉 **Writing Practice:** If you had a million toothpicks, what would you build?

Fractions
Write <, >, or = between each fraction and then solve problem 5.

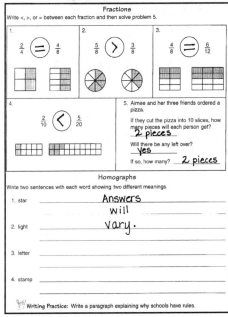

1. $\frac{2}{4} = \frac{4}{8}$

2. $\frac{5}{8} > \frac{3}{8}$

3. $\frac{4}{8} = \frac{6}{12}$

4. $\frac{2}{10} < \frac{5}{20}$

5. Aimee and her three friends ordered a pizza.

If they cut the pizza into 10 slices, how many pieces will each person get?

__2 pieces__

Will there be any left over?

__yes__

If so, how many? __2 pieces__

Homographs
Write two sentences with each word showing two different meanings.

1. star __Answers__
2. light __will vary.__
3. letter
4. stamp

🖉 **Writing Practice:** Write a paragraph explaining why schools have rules.

Equivalent Fractions
Fill in the missing number and then solve problem 5.

1. $\frac{3}{12} = \frac{1}{4}$

2. $\frac{2}{3} = \frac{6}{9}$

3. $\frac{1}{2} = \frac{8}{16}$

4. $\frac{4}{16} = \frac{1}{4}$

5. Justin's word in a word game made 12 points, but then it was doubled. Quentin's word made 20 points, but then it was tripled. What is Justin's and Quentin's score now?

Justin's score = __24__

Quentin's score = __60__

Common/Proper Nouns
Fill in the blanks with nouns. (Answers will vary.)

Common	Proper
city	
	Tennessee
river	
	Jupiter
boy	
	Dr. Simpson

🖉 **Writing Practice:** Write a short story about living in the Mohave Desert. Circle each common noun and underline each proper noun.

Equivalent Fractions
For problems 1–4, write <, >, or = in each blank. Then solve problem 5.

1. $\frac{1}{2} < \frac{3}{4}$

2. $\frac{2}{3} = \frac{4}{6}$

3. $\frac{1}{4} < \frac{1}{3}$

4. $\frac{2}{3} < \frac{4}{5}$

5. How much did a team pay for jerseys if each jersey cost $9.00 and the team bought 3 dozen?

$324.00

Adjectives
Write the article *a* or *an* before each noun.

1. __a__ house
2. __an__ hour
3. __an__ orange
4. __an__ aunt
5. __a__ job
6. __an__ eye
7. __a__ gorilla
8. __an__ arm
9. __a__ man
10. __an__ old man
11. __an__ elephant
12. __a__ candy
13. __an__ apple
14. __a__ table
15. __a__ chair

🖉 **Writing Practice:** Write a story using the title below.

My Saddest Day

Equivalent Fractions
Fill in the blanks with the missing number. Then solve problem 5.

1. $\frac{1}{4} = \frac{4}{16}$

2. $\frac{3}{5} = \frac{12}{20}$

3. $\frac{5}{4} = \frac{20}{16}$

4. $\frac{2}{3} = \frac{8}{12}$

5. Brittani had 13 goldfish. Her mother bought her 6 more. The next day she found 2 dead. Then a week later one fish had 12 babies. How many goldfish does she now have?

__29 goldfish__

Prefixes
Circle each word with a prefix.

happiness	(unclear)	(redone)
jumping	helpless	(preseason)
careful	mender	(disadvantage)
(misinterpret)	capable	(mistake)

🖉 **Writing Practice:** Write a paragraph using the sentence starter below.

When I get home from school, I . . .

Equivalent Fractions
Circle the correct answer for each unknown. Then solve problem 5.

1. $\frac{4}{5} = \frac{?}{10}$

5 6 7 (8)

2. $\frac{?}{8} = \frac{28}{32}$

5 6 (7) 8

3. $\frac{2}{3} = \frac{14}{?}$

20 (21) 22 23

4. $\frac{11}{?} = \frac{22}{40}$

(20) 21 22 23

5. Mr. Roberts bought T-shirts for his classroom of 27 students. If the total amount was $357.75, how much did each shirt cost?

$13.25

Spelling
Circle the correctly spelled form of each word.

1. greedly — (greedily) — greedlly
2. chillily — chillie — (chilly)
3. (batty) — battey — battie
4. (riding) — ridding — rideing
5. fortunatly — (fortunately) — fortunatelly
6. hideing — hidding — (hiding)

🖉 **Writing Practice:** Write a descriptive paragraph about your neighborhood and community.

Page 179

Equivalent Fractions
Cross out the fraction that is NOT equivalent to the first fraction. Then solve problem 5.

1. $\frac{4}{5}$ $\frac{16}{20}$ $\frac{20}{25}$ ~~$\frac{18}{30}$~~ $\frac{12}{15}$

2. $\frac{5}{6}$ $\frac{10}{12}$ $\frac{20}{24}$ $\frac{30}{36}$ ~~$\frac{16}{16}$~~

3. $\frac{2}{3}$ $\frac{4}{6}$ $\frac{10}{15}$ $\frac{16}{24}$ ~~$\frac{18}{18}$~~

4. $\frac{3}{4}$ $\frac{9}{12}$ $\frac{18}{24}$ ~~$\frac{17}{20}$~~ $\frac{24}{32}$

5. After 3 minutes into a basketball game, the score was 12 to 8. If this pattern continues, what would the score be after 12 minutes?

48 to 32

Dictionary Skills
Look at the pronunciation of each pair of words. Circle the correct pronunciation that matches the definition.

1. (con´ test)   con test´   competition or fight
2. pro´ duce   (pro duce´)   bring into existence
3. re bel´   (reb´ el)   person who rebels
4. graj´ u āt   (graj´ u it)   person who finishes school
5. (prez´ ent)   pri zent´   gift
6. ob´ jekt   (ob jekt´)   protest

✍ *Writing Practice:* If you were to create a charity to help others, how would it benefit your community and what would its purpose be?

Page 180

Equivalent Fractions
Circle the correct answer that is equivalent to the given fraction. Then, solve problem 5.

1. $\frac{4}{5}$ $\frac{10}{18}$ (⁸⁄₁₀) $\frac{12}{22}$

2. $\frac{3}{7}$ (¹⁵⁄₃₅) $\frac{5}{14}$ $\frac{6}{12}$

3. $\frac{2}{3}$ $\frac{10}{16}$ $\frac{12}{20}$ (⁸⁄₁₂)

4. $\frac{3}{4}$ $\frac{25}{30}$ (²¹⁄₂₈) $\frac{15}{18}$

5. Sharon wanted to buy a dress for her school dance. She had only $30.15, but the dress cost $59.87. How much more money does she need?

$29.72

Verbs
Write sentences using these vivid verbs.

1. sobbed: _____
2. mumbled: _____
3. moaned: _____
4. protested: _____
5. gasped: _____
6. insisted: _____

✍ *Writing Practice:* Use this writing prompt to write a short paragraph:
I began my time travels by . . .

Page 181

Comparing Fractions
For problems 1 and 2, arrange fractions from least to greatest. For problems 3 and 4, arrange fractions from greatest to least. Then solve problem 5.

1. $\frac{1}{5}$ $\frac{1}{2}$ $\frac{1}{3}$ $\frac{1}{6}$ $\frac{1}{6}, \frac{1}{5}, \frac{1}{3}, \frac{1}{2}$

2. $\frac{2}{3}$ $\frac{1}{4}$ $\frac{3}{4}$ $\frac{1}{3}$ $\frac{1}{4}, \frac{1}{3}, \frac{2}{3}, \frac{3}{4}$

3. $\frac{3}{9}$ $\frac{5}{16}$ $\frac{4}{30}$ $\frac{6}{35}$ $\frac{3}{9}, \frac{4}{16}, \frac{6}{30}, \frac{5}{35}$

4. $\frac{3}{5}$ $\frac{1}{2}$ $\frac{2}{6}$ $\frac{1}{5}$ $\frac{3}{5}, \frac{1}{2}, \frac{2}{6}, \frac{1}{5}$

5. If Bob has 4½ boxes of party favors left over from a party and gives Cindy ⅓ of them, how much do each get?

2⅓ boxes

Adverbs
Circle the underlined word which is an adverb.

1. Buddy said that math class would start (soon).
2. The pizza was delivered (promptly) at our house.
3. Our team played (well) at the tournament.
4. The turtle walked (slowly) across the street.
5. The child ran away from his mother.
6. He searched (longer) than his friends.

✍ *Writing Practice:* Why is it important to eat balanced, nutritional meals during the day?

Page 182

Simplifying Fractions
For problems 1–4, reduce the following fractions. Then solve problem 5.

1. $\frac{4}{6} = \frac{2}{3}$
2. $\frac{9}{18} = \frac{1}{2}$
3. $\frac{3}{15} = \frac{1}{5}$
4. $\frac{6}{8} = \frac{3}{4}$

5. The average speed limit on most highways is 65 miles per hour. If a car went exactly 65 mph, how far would it go in 5 hours?

325 miles

Story Comprehension
Read the story and answer the following questions.

The Kiwi

The kiwi is the national emblem of Australia. The kiwi is a bird, like the eagle of the U. S., yet the kiwi cannot fly. Years ago, the kiwi was hunted for its valuable feathers, just as the American eagle was. The kiwi is a nocturnal animal, which means it comes out at night and sleeps during the day. It is considered the strangest bird of all birds.

1. What makes the kiwi a different kind of bird? **It cannot fly.**
2. How is the kiwi like the eagle? **It's a national emblem. It's hunted for its feathers.**
3. What is a nocturnal animal? **It comes out at night. It sleeps in the day.**
4. Why do you think the kiwi is a strange bird? **It cannot fly.**

✍ *Writing Practice:* The turkey was almost named our national bird. Do you think the eagle was a better choice? Why or why not?

Page 183

Simplifying Fractions
Simplify all fractions to their lowest terms. Then solve problem 5.

1. $\frac{10}{12} = \frac{5}{6}$
2. $\frac{7}{42} = \frac{1}{6}$
3. $\frac{9}{15} = \frac{3}{5}$
4. $\frac{14}{20} = \frac{7}{10}$

5. A can of vegetable soup contains 13 ounces. How many ounces are there in 57 cans?

741

Spelling
Circle the word with the correct spelling.

1. (receive)   recieve
2. pade   (paid)
3. rember   (remember)
4. (efficient)   eficcient
5. baloon   (balloon)
6. (vacuum)   vaccuum
7. (ancient)   anceint
8. (myriad)   miriad

✍ *Writing Practice:* What is your favorite school subject? Why?

Page 184

Mixed Fractions
Change each numeral to a mixed number or an improper fraction. Reduce to lowest terms. Then solve problem 5.

1. $8\frac{2}{3} = \frac{26}{3}$
2. $3\frac{8}{7} = \frac{29}{7}$
3. $15\frac{7}{10} = \frac{157}{10}$
4. $7\frac{4}{8} = \frac{60}{8}$

5. This past year the library bought 1,675 new books at the average cost of $9.00 per book. What was the total cost of books?

$15,075.00

Dictionary Skills
Answer these questions about the dictionary entry.

cus´-tard	n. sweet milk and egg mixture; like pudding	
cus´-to-dy	n. 1. guardianship; care	2. legal restraint
cut´	v. 1. divide with sharp tool	2. wounding remark
cute´	adj. 1. attractive	2. clever

1. How many syllables does custody have? **3**
2. What part of speech is cute? **adjective**
3. Which syllable is accented in custard? **first**
4. Which definition of cut means "her words cut me like a knife"? **2**

✍ *Writing Practice:* Use this writing prompt to write a short paragraph:
The best gift I ever received was...

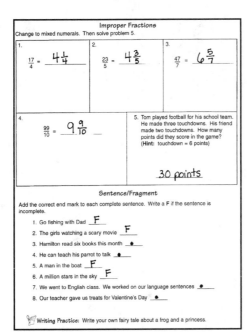

Improper Fractions

Change to mixed numerals. Then solve problem 5.

1. $\frac{17}{4} = 4\frac{1}{4}$

2. $\frac{23}{5} = 4\frac{3}{5}$

3. $\frac{47}{7} = 6\frac{5}{7}$

4. $\frac{99}{10} = 9\frac{9}{10}$

5. Tom played football for his school team. He made three touchdowns. His friend made two touchdowns. How many points did they score in the game?
(**Hint:** touchdown = 6 points)

30 points

Sentence/Fragment

Add the correct end mark to each complete sentence. Write a F if the sentence is incomplete.

1. Go fishing with Dad __F__
2. The girls watching a scary movie __F__
3. Hamilton read six books this month __.__
4. He can teach his parrot to talk __.__
5. A man in the boat __F__
6. A million stars in the sky __F__
7. We went to English class. We worked on our language sentences __.__
8. Our teacher gave us treats for Valentine's Day __.__

Writing Practice: Write your own fairy tale about a frog and a princess.

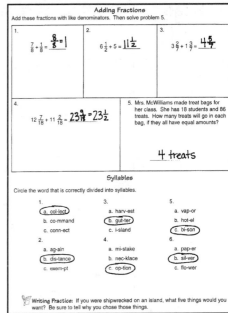

Adding Fractions

Add these fractions with like denominators. Then solve problem 5.

1. $\frac{7}{8} + \frac{1}{8} = \frac{8}{8} = 1$

2. $6\frac{1}{2} + 5 = 11\frac{1}{2}$

3. $3\frac{2}{7} + 1\frac{3}{7} = 4\frac{5}{7}$

4. $12\frac{7}{18} + 11\frac{2}{18} = 23\frac{9}{18} = 23\frac{1}{2}$

5. Mrs. McWilliams made treat bags for her class. She has 18 students and 86 treats. How many treats will go in each bag, if they all have equal amounts?

4 treats

Syllables

Circle the word that is correctly divided into syllables.

1. a. col-lect *(circled)*
   b. co-mmand
   c. conn-ect

2. a. ag-ain
   b. dis-tance *(circled)*
   c. exem-pt

3. a. harv-est
   b. gut-ter *(circled)*
   c. i-sland

4. a. mi-stake
   b. nec-klace
   c. op-tion *(circled)*

5. a. vap-or
   b. hot-el
   c. bi-son *(circled)*

6. a. pap-er
   b. sil-ver *(circled)*
   c. flo-wer

Writing Practice: If you were shipwrecked on an island, what five things would you want? Be sure to tell why you chose those things.

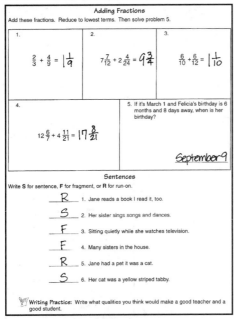

Adding Fractions

Add these fractions. Reduce to lowest terms. Then solve problem 5.

1. $\frac{2}{3} + \frac{4}{9} = 1\frac{1}{9}$

2. $7\frac{7}{12} + 2\frac{4}{24} = 9\frac{3}{4}$

3. $\frac{6}{10} + \frac{6}{12} = 1\frac{1}{10}$

4. $12\frac{6}{7} + 4\frac{11}{21} = 17\frac{8}{21}$

5. If it's March 1 and Felicia's birthday is 6 months and 8 days away, when is her birthday?

September 9

Sentences

Write **S** for sentence, **F** for fragment, or **R** for run-on.

__R__ 1. Jane reads a book I read it, too.
__S__ 2. Her sister sings songs and dances.
__F__ 3. Sitting quietly while she watches television.
__F__ 4. Many sisters in the house.
__R__ 5. Jane had a pet it was a cat.
__S__ 6. Her cat was a yellow striped tabby.

Writing Practice: Write what qualities you think would make a good teacher and a good student.

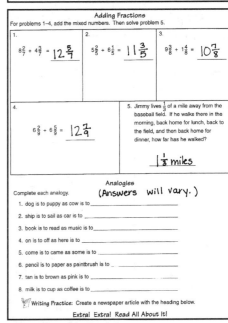

Adding Fractions

For problems 1–4, add the mixed numbers. Then solve problem 5.

1. $8\frac{2}{7} + 4\frac{3}{7} = 12\frac{5}{7}$

2. $5\frac{2}{5} + 6\frac{1}{5} = 11\frac{3}{5}$

3. $9\frac{3}{8} + 1\frac{4}{8} = 10\frac{7}{8}$

4. $6\frac{2}{9} + 6\frac{5}{9} = 12\frac{7}{9}$

5. Jimmy lives $\frac{1}{3}$ of a mile away from the baseball field. If he walks there in the morning, back home for lunch, back to the field, and then back home for dinner, how far has he walked?

$1\frac{1}{3}$ miles

Analogies

Complete each analogy. (Answers will vary.)

1. dog is to puppy as cow is to _____
2. ship is to sail as car is to _____
3. book is to read as music is to _____
4. on is to off as here is to _____
5. come is to came as some is to _____
6. pencil is to paper as paintbrush is to _____
7. tan is to brown as pink is to _____
8. milk is to cup as coffee is to _____

Writing Practice: Create a newspaper article with the heading below.

Extra! Extra! Read All About It!

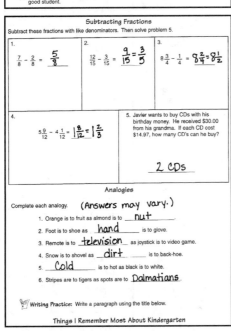

Subtracting Fractions

Subtract these fractions with like denominators. Then solve problem 5.

1. $\frac{7}{8} - \frac{2}{8} = \frac{5}{8}$

2. $\frac{12}{15} - \frac{3}{15} = \frac{9}{15} = \frac{3}{5}$

3. $8\frac{3}{4} - \frac{1}{4} = 8\frac{2}{4} = 8\frac{1}{2}$

4. $5\frac{9}{12} - 4\frac{1}{12} = 1\frac{8}{12} = 1\frac{2}{3}$

5. Javier wants to buy CDs with his birthday money. He received $30.00 from his grandma. If each CD cost $14.97, how many CD's can he buy?

2 CDs

Analogies

Complete each analogy. (Answers may vary.)

1. Orange is to fruit as almond is to __nut__
2. Foot is to shoe as __hand__ is to glove.
3. Remote is to __television__ as joystick is to video game.
4. Snow is to shovel as __dirt__ is to back-hoe.
5. __Cold__ is to hot as black is to white.
6. Stripes are to tigers as spots are to __Dalmatians__

Writing Practice: Write a paragraph using the title below.

Things I Remember Most About Kindergarten

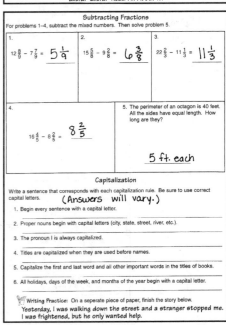

Subtracting Fractions

For problems 1–4, subtract the mixed numbers. Then solve problem 5.

1. $12\frac{8}{9} - 7\frac{7}{9} = 5\frac{1}{9}$

2. $15\frac{5}{8} - 9\frac{2}{8} = 6\frac{3}{8}$

3. $22\frac{2}{3} - 11\frac{1}{3} = 11\frac{1}{3}$

4. $16\frac{4}{5} - 8\frac{2}{5} = 8\frac{2}{5}$

5. The perimeter of an octagon is 40 feet. All the sides have equal length. How long are they?

5 ft. each

Capitalization

Write a sentence that corresponds with each capitalization rule. Be sure to use correct capital letters. (Answers will vary.)

1. Begin every sentence with a capital letter.
2. Proper nouns begin with capital letters (city, state, street, river, etc.).
3. The pronoun I is always capitalized.
4. Titles are capitalized when they are used before names.
5. Capitalize the first and last word and all other important words in the titles of books.
6. All holidays, days of the week, and months of the year begin with a capital letter.

Writing Practice: On a separate piece of paper, finish the story below.
Yesterday, I was walking down the street and a stranger stopped me. I was frightened, but he only wanted help.

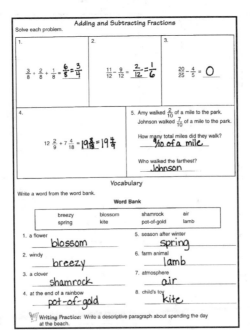

Adding and Subtracting Fractions

Solve each problem.

1. $\frac{3}{8} + \frac{2}{8} + \frac{1}{8} = \frac{6}{8} = \frac{3}{4}$

2. $\frac{11}{12} - \frac{9}{12} = \frac{2}{12} = \frac{1}{6}$

3. $\frac{20}{25} - \frac{4}{5} = 0$

4. $12\frac{2}{9} + 7\frac{4}{18} = 19\frac{4}{18} = 19\frac{4}{9}$

5. Amy walked $\frac{2}{10}$ of a mile to the park. Johnson walked $\frac{7}{10}$ of a mile to the park.

How many total miles did they walk? $\frac{9}{10}$ of a mile

Who walked the farthest? Johnson

Vocabulary

Write a word from the word bank.

Word Bank

| breezy | blossom | shamrock | air |
| spring | kite | pot-of-gold | lamb |

1. a flower — blossom
2. windy — breezy
3. a clover — shamrock
4. at the end of a rainbow — pot-of-gold
5. season after winter — spring
6. farm animal — lamb
7. atmosphere — air
8. child's toy — kite

Writing Practice: Write a descriptive paragraph about spending the day at the beach.

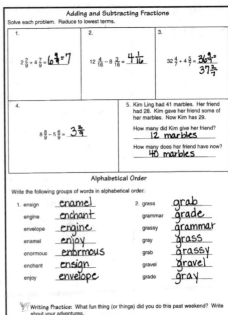

Adding and Subtracting Fractions

Solve each problem. Reduce to lowest terms.

1. $2\frac{2}{9} + 4\frac{7}{9} = 6\frac{9}{9} = 7$

2. $12\frac{4}{16} - 8\frac{3}{16} = 4\frac{1}{16}$

3. $32\frac{4}{7} + 4\frac{5}{7} = 36\frac{9}{7} = 37\frac{2}{7}$

4. $8\frac{8}{9} - 5\frac{6}{9} = 3\frac{2}{9}$

5. Kim Ling had 41 marbles. Her friend had 28. Kim gave her friend some of her marbles. Now Kim has 29.

How many did Kim give her friend? 12 marbles

How many does her friend have now? 40 marbles

Alphabetical Order

Write the following groups of words in alphabetical order.

1. ensign — enamel
   engine — enchant
   envelope — engine
   enamel — enjoy
   enormous — enormous
   enchant — ensign
   enjoy — envelope

2. grass — grab
   grammar — grade
   grassy — grammar
   gray — grass
   grab — grassy
   gravel — gravel
   grade — gray

Writing Practice: What fun thing (or things) did you do this past weekend? Write about your adventures.

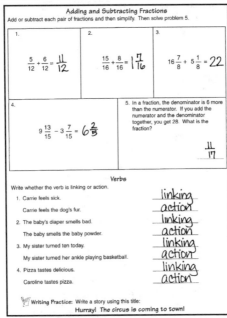

Adding and Subtracting Fractions

Add or subtract each pair of fractions and then simplify. Then solve problem 5.

1. $\frac{5}{12} + \frac{6}{12} = \frac{11}{12}$

2. $\frac{15}{16} + \frac{8}{16} = 1\frac{7}{16}$

3. $16\frac{7}{8} + 5\frac{1}{8} = 22$

4. $9\frac{13}{15} - 3\frac{7}{15} = 6\frac{2}{5}$

5. In a fraction, the denominator is 6 more than the numerator. If you add the numerator and the denominator together, you get 28. What is the fraction? $\frac{11}{17}$

Verbs

Write whether the verb is linking or action.

1. Carrie feels sick. — linking
   Carrie feels the dog's fur. — action
2. The baby's diaper smells bad. — linking
   The baby smells the baby powder. — action
3. My sister turned ten today. — linking
   My sister turned her ankle playing basketball. — action
4. Pizza tastes delicious. — linking
   Caroline tastes pizza. — action

Writing Practice: Write a story using this title: Hurray! The circus is coming to town!

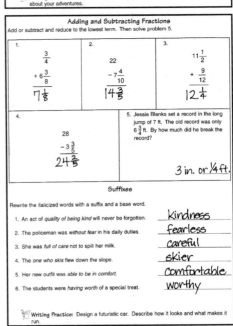

Adding and Subtracting Fractions

Add or subtract and reduce to the lowest term. Then solve problem 5.

1. $\frac{3}{4}$
   $+ 6\frac{3}{8}$
   $7\frac{1}{8}$

2. 22
   $- 7\frac{4}{10}$
   $14\frac{3}{5}$

3. $11\frac{1}{2}$
   $+ \frac{9}{12}$
   $12\frac{1}{4}$

4. 28
   $- 3\frac{3}{5}$
   $24\frac{2}{5}$

5. Jessie Blanks set a record in the long jump of 7 ft. The old record was only $6\frac{3}{4}$ ft. By how much did he break the record? 3 in. or ¼ ft.

Suffixes

Rewrite the italicized words with a suffix and a base word.

1. An act of *quality of being kind* will never be forgotten. — kindness
2. The policeman was *without fear* in his daily duties. — fearless
3. She was *full of care* not to spill her milk. — careful
4. The *one who skis* flew down the slope. — skier
5. Her new outfit was *able to be in comfort*. — comfortable
6. The students were *having worth* of a special treat. — worthy

Writing Practice: Design a futuristic car. Describe how it looks and what makes it run.

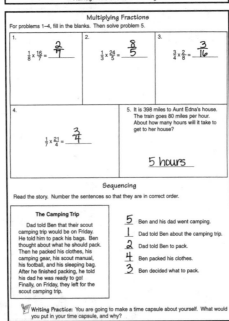

Multiplying Fractions

For problems 1–4, fill in the blanks. Then solve problem 5.

1. $\frac{1}{8} \times \frac{16}{7} = \frac{2}{7}$

2. $\frac{1}{3} \times \frac{24}{5} = \frac{8}{5}$

3. $\frac{3}{4} \times \frac{2}{8} = \frac{3}{16}$

4. $\frac{1}{7} \times \frac{21}{4} = \frac{3}{4}$

5. It is 398 miles to Aunt Edna's house. The train goes 80 miles per hour. About how many hours will it take to get to her house? 5 hours

Sequencing

Read the story. Number the sentences so that they are in correct order.

The Camping Trip

Dad told Ben that their scout camping trip would be on Friday. He told him to pack his bags. Ben thought about what he should pack. Then he packed his clothes, his camping gear, his scout manual, his football, and his sleeping bag. After he finished packing, he told his dad he was ready to go! Finally, on Friday, they left for the scout camping trip.

5 Ben and his dad went camping.
1 Dad told Ben about the camping trip.
2 Dad told Ben to pack.
4 Ben packed his clothes.
3 Ben decided what to pack.

Writing Practice: You are going to make a time capsule about yourself. What would you put in your time capsule, and why?

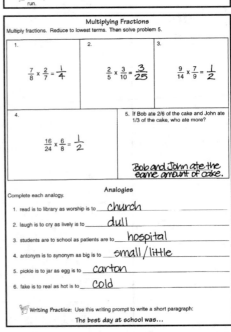

Multiplying Fractions

Multiply fractions. Reduce to lowest terms. Then solve problem 5.

1. $\frac{7}{8} \times \frac{2}{7} = \frac{1}{4}$

2. $\frac{2}{5} \times \frac{3}{10} = \frac{3}{25}$

3. $\frac{9}{14} \times \frac{7}{9} = \frac{1}{2}$

4. $\frac{16}{24} \times \frac{6}{8} = \frac{1}{2}$

5. If Bob ate 2/6 of the cake and John ate 1/3 of the cake, who ate more? Bob and John ate the same amount of cake.

Analogies

Complete each analogy.

1. read is to library as worship is to church
2. laugh is to cry as lively is to dull
3. students are to school as patients are to hospital
4. antonym is to synonym as big is to small/little
5. pickle is to jar as egg is to carton
6. fake is to real as hot is to cold

Writing Practice: Use this writing prompt to write a short paragraph: The best day at school was…

Page 197

Dividing Fractions
Divide the fractions and reduce to lowest terms. Then solve problem 5.

1. $\frac{3}{5} \div \frac{8}{9} = \frac{27}{40}$

2. $\frac{2}{7} \div \frac{4}{5} = \frac{5}{14}$

3. $\frac{7}{8} \div \frac{2}{7} = 3\frac{1}{16}$

4. $\frac{12}{14} \div \frac{3}{4} = 1\frac{1}{7}$

5. Basset School needs two 48-seat buses to take the football team to the playoffs. They will have only 6 vacant seats. How many people will be riding the bus?

90

Alphabetical Order
Write each group of words in alphabetical order.

1. prohibit, probate, proud, proclaim
   probate, proclaim, prohibit, proud
2. further, fuel, fuzz, furlough
   fuel, furlough, further, fuzz
3. commune, communicate, commotion, community
   commotion, commune, communicate, community
4. span, spatter, space, spacious
   space, spacious, span, spatter
5. receipt, realize, react, reason
   react, realize, reason, receipt
6. overlay, overlook, overhaul, overseas
   overhaul, overlay, overlook, overseas

Writing Practice: When does a rainbow appear? Why does it appear?

Page 198

Dividing Fractions
Solve each problem below.

1. $\frac{2}{3} \div \frac{12}{18} = 1$

2. $\frac{4}{5} \div \frac{6}{8} = 1\frac{1}{15}$

3. $\frac{7}{12} \div \frac{3}{4} = \frac{7}{9}$

4. $\frac{2}{5} \div \frac{9}{12} = \frac{8}{15}$

5. The temperature in Minnesota was -5° F. If it dropped 4°, what would be the new temperature?

-9° F

Main Idea
Write a category for each group of words.

1. tree
   children
   grass
   mold
   category _things that grow_

2. rose
   carnation
   marigold
   daffodil
   category _flowers_

3. peanuts
   potatoes
   treasure
   fossil
   category _things underground_

4. hairbrush
   comb
   headband
   barrette
   category _hair items_

Writing Practice: Why is it important to protect endangered animals and rain forests?

Page 199

Mixed Fractions
Write +, −, ÷, or x in each box to make each equation correct. Then solve problem 5.

1. $\frac{2}{3} \boxed{X} \frac{2}{3} = \frac{4}{9}$

2. $\frac{2}{7} \boxed{+} \frac{8}{14} = \frac{6}{7}$

3. $1\frac{4}{5} \boxed{-} \frac{3}{4} = 1\frac{1}{20}$

4. $\frac{3}{4} \boxed{X} \frac{7}{9} = \frac{7}{12}$

5. A 35 mm camera costs $72.00, but it's on sale for 20% off. How much does it cost now?

$57.60

Antonyms
Circle the antonym for the first word in each row.

1. abolish — destroy — (restore)
2. begin — start — (terminate)
3. correct — (false) — accurate
4. dingy — dull — (bright)
5. expect — (surprise) — anticipate
6. famous — celebrated — (unknown)

Writing Practice: Write about similarities and differences between doctors and lawyers.

Page 200

Percents and Fractions
For problems 1–4, write the fraction as a percentage. Then solve problem 5.

1. $\frac{1}{2} = \underline{50}$ %

2. $\frac{1}{4} = \underline{25}$ %

3. $\frac{1}{5} = \underline{20}$ %

4. $\frac{1}{10} = \underline{10}$ %

5. In a football game, a touchdown plus the extra point gets 7 points and a field goal gets 3 points. If one team's score is 15 points, how many touchdowns and field goals have they scored?

0 touchdowns 5 field goals

Synonyms
Write a synonym for each underlined word. **(Answers will vary.)**

1. You are _correct_.
2. It _arrived_ yesterday.
3. Mom sang her baby a _lullaby_.
4. Ghosts don't _scare_ me.
5. The students were _quiet_.
6. What was the _name_ of the song?
7. The _shears_ were sharp.
8. I sat on the _sofa_.

Writing Practice: Write a paragraph using the sentence starter below.
The last thing I want to do this year is . . .

Page 201

Percents and Fractions
For problems 1–4, write each percent as a fraction. Make sure to reduce each answer. Then solve problem 5.

1. $17\% = \frac{17}{100}$

2. $35\% = \frac{35}{100} = \frac{7}{20}$

3. $75\% = \frac{75}{100} = \frac{3}{4}$

4. $20\% = \frac{20}{100} = \frac{1}{5}$

5. The perimeter of a triangle is 58 meters. One side is 18 meters long, and another side is 25 meters long. How long is the third side?

15 meters

Possessives
Write the correct possessive in the blank.

1. The cat has a toy mouse. Evan played with the _cat's_ toy mouse.
2. My sisters have dolls. My _sisters'_ dolls are fun to play with.
3. Sue Ellen is on the basketball team. We saw _Sue Ellen's_ team play yesterday.
4. Her uncle has a bicycle shop. Her _uncle's_ bicycle shop is on Third Street.
5. The pencils belong to the students. The _students'_ pencils were on their desks.
6. The birds sing merrily. The _birds'_ song is sweet to hear.

Writing Practice: Write a paragraph using the sentence starter below.
"Well, it's about time you came . . ."

Page 202

Percents
Write each number as a percent. Then solve problem 5.

1. 6 out of 100
   6%

2. $\frac{43}{100}$
   43%

3. 58 to 100
   58%

4. $\frac{79}{100}$
   79%

5. Tami had $1.00. She spent 42¢. What percent of a dollar does she have left?
   58%

Analogies
Complete each analogy.

1. animal is to herd as person is to _crowd_
2. drought is to dry as rain is to _wet_
3. end is to begin as finish is to _start_
4. clean is to neat as _dirty_ is to grimy
5. adult is to thirty as _child_ is to ten
6. small is to enormous as _easy_ is to difficult

Writing Practice: Write the steps involved in baking a cake or cupcakes.

Percents
Solve each problem below.

1.	2.	3.
20% of 40	25% of 100	50% of 30
8	**25**	**15**

4.	5. If your eyes blink about 20 times per minute, how many times will you blink in an hour?
$33\frac{1}{3}$ % of 99	
33	**1,200**

Cause/Effect
Underline the word that signals a cause or effect relationship.

1. The teacher gave a retest <u>because</u> so many students were absent.

2. <u>Since</u> we had a mild winter, we will have a hot summer.

3. I didn't feel safe <u>when</u> the news said a tornado was coming.

4. <u>If</u> you work hard, you should do well on the test.

5. <u>As</u> the day went on, the rain turned to snow.

6. The bicycle wouldn't go <u>since</u> the tires were flat.

✍ **Writing Practice:** How do you feel when you accomplish a goal that you worked hard to achieve? Give a recent example of a goal that you have set and met.

Percents
Calculate the percent. Then solve problem 5.

1.	2.	3.
8% of 20	6% of 16	100% of 239
1.6	**0.96**	**239**

4.	5. Mrs. Coleman begins her first class at 8:45 A.M. If her next class starts 52 minutes later, what time does it start?
12% of 65	
7.8	**9:37 A.M.**

Dictionary Skills
Read the entry and definitions. Identify the best meaning for each underlined word.

> **hold** v. 1. have in the hand. 2. keep from moving or changing. 3. embrace.
> 4. contain. 5. remain firm or fixed. 6. cargo space (also, holding or held).

- **1** a. We had to <u>hold</u> our luggage for 1 hour.
- **6** b. It couldn't be put in the <u>holding</u> area.
- **3** c. We <u>held</u> our niece before boarding the plane.
- **5** d. Our eyes <u>held</u> each other anxiously.
- **2** e. Finally, we <u>held</u> our breath as the plane took off.
- **4** f. Our carry-on bag <u>held</u> pictures of our visit.

✍ **Writing Practice:** If you could create a new language and alphabet, what would it be like? How would it be useful for people?

Fractions/Decimals/Percents
For problems 1–4, fill in the blanks on the chart. Then solve problem 5.

1.	2.	3.
Fraction = $\frac{33}{100}$	Fraction = $\frac{54}{100}$	Fraction = $\frac{77}{100}$
Decimal = **.33**	Decimal = .54	Decimal = .77
Percent = 33%	Percent = 54%	Percent = **77%**

4.	5. A television Joe wanted cost $185.00. He noticed the store put it on sale at 25% off. How much would the television cost after the discount?
Fraction = $\frac{12}{100}$	
Decimal = **.12**	
Percent = 12%	**$138.75**

Compound Sentences
Add a connecting word and finish each sentence to make a compound sentence.

1. My best friend is nice, **Answers will vary.**

2. Our cat likes to lay on the couch, _____

3. My math teacher is strict, _____

4. Mac sings in the shower, _____

5. Harry wants to go bowling, _____

✍ **Writing Practice:** Write a story using the sentence starter below.
I went ice skating on the pond, when suddenly I heard a cracking sound . . .

Time
Write how many hours are between the times given. Then solve problem 5.

1. 2:00 P.M. and 10:00 P.M.	2. 6:00 A.M. and 1:00 P.M.	3. 1:18 A.M. and 10:18 A.M.
8 hours	**7 hours**	**21 hours**

4. 12:00 P.M. and 12:00 A.M.	5. Mehul called his friend Jim at 2:23 P.M. to come over and work on their school project. If they met at 6:30 P.M., how long would it be before they began working?
12 hours	**4 hrs. 7 min.**

Prefixes
Match the correct **en** prefix word with its definition.

- **d.** 1. get pleasure from — a. enslave
- **b.** 2. commit — b. engage
- **e.** 3. wrap — c. entrap
- **g.** 4. put name on a list — d. enjoy
- **a.** 5. make a slave of — e. enfold
- **h.** 6. on the way — f. enliven
- **f.** 7. make lively — g. enroll
- **c.** 8. catch — h. enroute

✍ **Writing Practice:** Write a paragraph using the sentence starter below.
Everyone in the room started to laugh when . . .

Time
Read the times and write A.M. or P.M.

1. 6:30 (sunrise)	2. 3:00 (day)	3. 8:30 (bedtime)
A.M.	**P.M.**	**P.M.**

4. 1:00 (night)	5. It is 8:00 A.M. If 12 hours go by, is it 8:00 A.M. or P.M.?
A.M.	**8:00 P.M.**

Dictionary Skills
Read each definition for *back*. Decide which definition best fits each sentence. Write the letter of the correct definition in each blank.

> a. part of a person opposite the face
> b. uppermost part of an animal
> c. related to the past
> d. at the rear
> e. spine

- **e.** 1. Tyra hurt her back playing volleyball.
- **d.** 2. Jerrod was told to go to the back of the line.
- **b.** 3. Michael likes to pet his dog on his back.
- **c.** 4. Shannon turned around and went back to school.
- **a.** 5. I combed the back of my hair.

✍ **Writing Practice:** What part of the school day do you like the best? Write a paragraph telling about your favorite part of school.

Time
Write how many minutes are between the given times. Then solve problem 5.

1. 6:00 A.M. and 6:25 A.M.	2. 4:25 P.M. and 5:10 P.M.	3. 2:30 A.M. and 2:56 A.M.
25 min.	**45 min.**	**26 min.**

4. 11:55 P.M. and 12:05 A.M.	5. Jan gets up at 7:20 A.M. She goes to school at 8:05 A.M. How much time does she have to get ready? **45 min.** Her class comes back from lunch at 12:00. Is this A.M. or P.M.? **P.M.**
10 min.	

Abbreviations
Choose the correct abbreviation of each state.

MA	ME	MN	MS	WA	WV
MD	MI	MO	MT	WI	WY

Maine	**ME**	Maryland	**MD**	Massachusetts	**MA**
Michigan	**MI**	Minnesota	**MN**	Mississippi	**MS**
Missouri	**MO**	Montana	**MT**	Washington	**WA**
West Virginia	**WV**	Wisconsin	**WI**	Wyoming	**WY**

✍ **Writing Practice:** Write about a superstition you believe in.

Page 209

Time

If 60 seconds (sec) equals 1 minute (min) and if 60 minutes (min) equals 1 hour (hr), calculate the times in the problems below and then solve problem 5.

1.	2.	3.
93 sec = **1** min **33** sec	76 min = **1** min **16** sec	12 hrs = **720** min

4.	5. Michelle walks 45 minutes everyday. How many total hours and minutes does she walk in one week?
41 min = **2,460** sec	**5** hrs **25** min

Proofreading

Copy each sentence correctly.

1. didn't they put on a play in november
   Didn't they put on a play in November?
2. there class saw two plays this year
   Their class saw two plays this year.
3. have you ever ben to cape canaveral
   Have you ever been to Cape Canaveral?
4. next yeare bobs aunt will work for the post office
   Next year Bob's aunt will work for the post office.
5. the olympics is fun too watch
   The Olympics is fun to watch.
6. I like the knew sport called snowboarding
   I like the new sport called "snowboarding."

Writing Practice: Describe a sporting event you would like to compete in during an upcoming Olympics. What kind of training would be involved? What kind of time and dedication would you have to give towards your training?

Page 210

Time

Calculate how much time has passed in each problem. Then solve problem 5.

1. 8:10 A.M. to 3:40 P.M.	2. 12:46 P.M. to 9:06 P.M.	3. 5:28 A.M. to 12:00 P.M.
7 hrs. 30 min.	**8 hrs. 20 min.**	**6 hrs. 32 min.**

4. 10:37 P.M. to 9:00 A.M.	5. It's 38° at 7:00 A.M. By 3:00 P.M. it is 52°. How much did the temperature rise?
10 hrs. 23 min.	**14°**

Possessives

Fill in the chart with the correct possessive nouns.

Noun	Singular Possessive	Plural Possessive
class	class's	classes'
town	town's	towns'
child	child's	children's
beach	beach's	beaches'
whale	whale's	whales'

Writing Practice: Write a letter to your local newspaper expressing your concerns and views about an issue (examples: pollution, driving safety, pet adoption, etc.) that you feel needs some attention.

Page 211

Time

Solve the problems below.

1.	2.	3.
$2\frac{1}{2}$ hours after 6 A.M. **8:30 A.M.**	3 hours 45 minutes before 7 P.M. **3:15 P.M.**	420 seconds = **7** minutes

4.	5. Find the batting average of Ty Cobb. He hit 4,191 times out of 11,429 times at bat.
35 days = **5** weeks	**0.367**

Synonyms/Antonyms

Determine whether each pair of words is a synonym (S) or an antonym (A).

S 1. grief – mourning   **A** 5. wander – halt

A 2. flood – drought   **S** 6. ugly – hideous

S 3. establish – settle   **S** 7. special – extraordinary

S 4. oval – oblong   **A** 8. thick – sparse

Writing Practice: If you could design your own school, describe how it would be different from or similar to the one you currently attend.

Page 212

Reading a Graph

Use the pictograph to answer the questions.

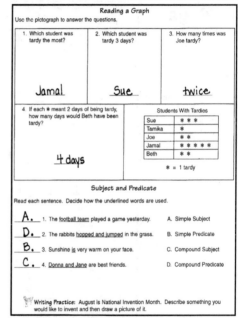

1. Which student was tardy the most?	2. Which student was tardy 3 days?	3. How many times was Joe tardy?
Jamal	**Sue**	**twice**

4. If each ✱ meant 2 days of being tardy, how many days would Beth have been tardy? **4 days**	Students With Tardies

Students With Tardies

Sue	✱ ✱ ✱
Tamika	✱
Joe	✱ ✱
Jamal	✱ ✱ ✱ ✱ ✱
Beth	✱ ✱

✱ = 1 tardy

Subject and Predicate

Read each sentence. Decide how the underlined words are used.

A. 1. The football team played a game yesterday.   A. Simple Subject

D. 2. The rabbits hopped and jumped in the grass.   B. Simple Predicate

B. 3. Sunshine is very warm on your face.   C. Compound Subject

C. 4. Donna and Jane are best friends.   D. Compound Predicate

Writing Practice: August is National Invention Month. Describe something you would like to invent and then draw a picture of it.

Page 213

Reading a Graph

Use the bar graph to answer the questions.

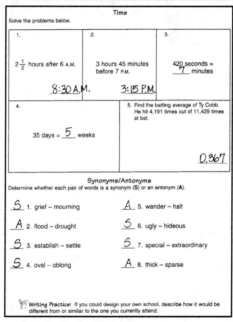

1. How many horses are on the farm? **80**	2. Are there more pigs or goats? **pigs**	Animals on the Farm
3. On the farm there are 20 of what animal? **chickens**	4. What is the total number of pigs and horses? **145**	

Possessive Nouns

Add an 's or ' to each word to show ownership.

1. The child **'s** toy was put on the shelf.

2. Please turn your papers in the teacher **'s** box.

3. Bobby found his friends **'** baseball cards outside.

4. Mrs. Saxton **'s** students went on a field trip.

5. The dog **'s** bone was buried under the tree.

Writing Practice: Write a paragraph describing a time you went to a fair. Include your favorite ride and all the things you saw.

Page 214

Reading a Graph

Study the graph and answer the questions.

1. How many chocolate ice cream cones were sold? **50 cones**	2. Which flavor of ice cream sold the most? **strawberry**	3. How many more strawberry cones were sold than vanilla cones? **20 cones**

4. How many ice cream cones were sold in all? **180 cones**	Ice Cream Cones Sold on Sunday

Ice Cream Cones Sold on Sunday

Chocolate	🍦🍦🍦🍦🍦
Vanilla	🍦🍦🍦
Strawberry	🍦🍦🍦🍦🍦🍦🍦
Sherbet	🍦

= 10 cones

Punctuation

Add a colon (:) or a semicolon (;) to each sentence.

1. Shari felt funny **;** her stomach hurt.

2. She had just been to the fair **;** it was fun.

3. She rode many rides **:** the ferris wheel, the swings, and the bumper cars.

4. Shari had eaten before the rides **;** it was a mistake.

5. Shari ate these foods **:** popcorn, a hot dog, two sodas, and cotton candy.

6. She knew her mom would come home at 5 **:** 00.

Writing Practice: Write about what you like and dislike about where you live.

Page 215

Reading a Graph
Use the bar graph to answer each question.

1. Which city is the largest in population?	2. Which city has less than 100,000 in population?	3. Where does Nashville rank (first, second, third, fourth, fifth)?
Memphis	Clarksville	second

4. Which two cities have almost the same amount in population?

Knoxville

Chattanooga

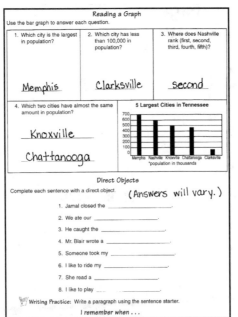

5 Largest Cities in Tennessee

Memphis Nashville Knoxville Chattanooga Clarksville
*population in thousands

Direct Objects
Complete each sentence with a direct object.   (Answers will vary.)

1. Jamal closed the _____.
2. We ate our _____.
3. He caught the _____.
4. Mr. Blair wrote a _____.
5. Someone took my _____.
6. I like to ride my _____.
7. She read a _____.
8. I like to play _____.

Writing Practice: Write a paragraph using the sentence starter.
I remember when . . .

Page 216

Reading a Graph
Answer the questions about the graph below.

1. How many fish did Robert catch?	2. How many fish were caught altogether?	3. Who caught the same number of fish?
9 fish	39 fish	J.J. and Dixie

4. How many more fish did Jalisa catch than Ashley?

12 more fish

Name	Number of Fish
Robert	☞ ☞ ☞
Ashley	☞
J. J.	☞ ☞
Jalisa	☞ ☞ ☞ ☞ ☞
Dixie	☞ ☞

☞ = 3 fish

Proofreading
Rewrite the sentences correctly.

1. scotts father said,"the month of march is finalle here
   Scott's father said, "The month of March is finally here."
2. the white house is in washington dc
   The White House is in Washington, D.C.
3. Janessa alway smiles and she seem happy
   Janessa always smiles, and she seems happy.
4. will she helps uus chek our homework?
   Will she help us check our homework?
5. my Friend is leaving next weak
   My friend is leaving next week.
6. his mother weights for him and he wants to sea her
   His mother waits for him, and he wants to see her.

Writing Practice: Write a paragraph about why you think we need our circulatory system.

Page 217

Reading a Graph
Answer the questions about the graph.

1. On which days were 3 students absent?	2. Which day had the most students absent?	3. Were more students absent on Wednesday or Thursday?
Monday Thursday	Tuesday	Thursday

4. How many more students were absent on Tuesday than Wednesday?

2 more students

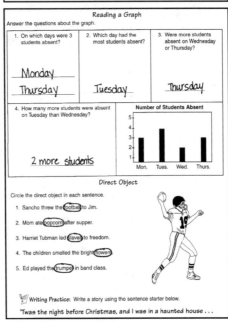

Number of Students Absent

Mon. Tues. Wed. Thurs.

Direct Object
Circle the direct object in each sentence.

1. Sancho threw the (football) to Jim.
2. Mom ate (popcorn) after supper.
3. Harriet Tubman led (slaves) to freedom.
4. The children smelled the bright (flowers).
5. Ed played the (trumpet) in band class.

Writing Practice: Write a story using the sentence starter below.
'Twas the night before Christmas, and I was in a haunted house . . .

Page 218

Reading a Graph
Use the graph to answer the following questions.

1. How old is Marques?	2. Who is oldest?	3. How much older is Greg than Marques?
3 years old	Maria	4 years

4. What is the difference in the ages of Greg and Maria?

3 years

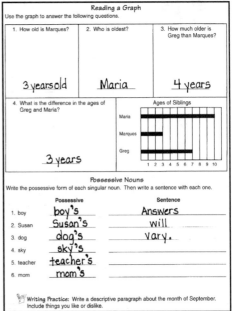

Ages of Siblings

Maria
Marques
Greg

1 2 3 4 5 6 7 8 9 10

Possessive Nouns
Write the possessive form of each singular noun. Then write a sentence with each one.

		Possessive	Sentence
1.	boy	boy's	Answers
2.	Susan	Susan's	will
3.	dog	dog's	vary.
4.	sky	sky's	
5.	teacher	teacher's	
6.	mom	mom's	

Writing Practice: Write a descriptive paragraph about the month of September. Include things you like or dislike.

Page 219

Reading a Graph
Answer the questions about the circle graph.

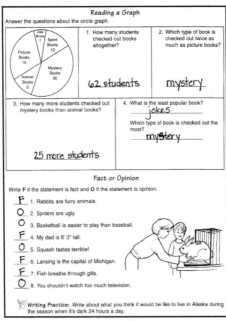

1. How many students checked out books altogether?	2. Which type of book is checked out twice as much as picture books?
62 students	mystery

3. How many more students checked out mystery books than animal books?	4. What is the least popular book? jokes Which type of book is checked out the most? mystery
25 more students	

Fact or Opinion
Write F if the statement is fact and O if the statement is opinion.

F 1. Rabbits are furry animals.
O 2. Spiders are ugly.
O 3. Basketball is easier to play than baseball.
F 4. My dad is 6' 3" tall.
O 5. Squash tastes terrible!
F 6. Lansing is the capital of Michigan.
F 7. Fish breathe through gills.
O 8. You shouldn't watch too much television.

Writing Practice: Write about what you think it would be like to live in Alaska during the season when it's dark 24 hours a day.

Page 220

Reading a Graph
Answer each question about the graph.

1. Which activity is enjoyed the most?	2. How many more people go on vacation than go to camp?	3. Which activities have the same number of people?
vacation	7 people	swim play outside

4. Which activity is enjoyed the least?

go to camp

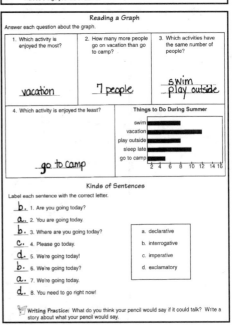

Things to Do During Summer

swim
vacation
play outside
sleep late
go to camp

2 4 6 8 10 12 14 16

Kinds of Sentences
Label each sentence with the correct letter.

b 1. Are you going today?
a 2. You are going today.
b 3. Where are you going today?
c 4. Please go today.
d 5. We're going today!
b 6. We're going today?
a 7. We're going today.
d 8. You need to go right now!

a. declarative
b. interrogative
c. imperative
d. exclamatory

Writing Practice: What do you think your pencil would say if it could talk? Write a story about what your pencil would say.

Page 221

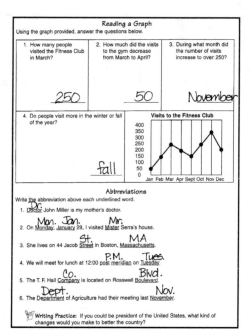

Reading a Graph
Using the graph provided, answer the questions below.

1. How many people visited the Fitness Club in March?	2. How much did the visits to the gym decrease from March to April?	3. During what month did the number of visits increase to over 250?
250	50	November

4. Do people visit more in the winter or fall of the year?	Visits to the Fitness Club
fall	(line graph: 400 350 300 250 200 150 100 50 0, Jan Feb Mar Apr Sept Oct Nov Dec)

Abbreviations
Write the abbreviation above each underlined word.

1. Dr. Doctor John Miller is my mother's doctor.
2. On Mon. Monday, Jan. January 29, I visited Mr. Mister Serra's house.
3. She lives on 44 Jacob St. Street in Boston, MA Massachusetts.
4. We will meet for lunch at 12:00 P.M. post meridian on Tues. Tuesday.
5. The T. F. Hall Co. Company is located on Rosswell Blvd. Boulevard.
6. The Dept. Department of Agriculture had their meeting last Nov. November.

🖊 **Writing Practice:** If you could be president of the United States, what kind of changes would you make to better the country?

Page 222

Reading a Graph
Answer the questions using the provided pictograph.

1. How many students ate pizza?	2. How many students ate corn dogs?	3. How many students ate fries?
30	15	40

4. How many more students ate pizza than salad?	Student's Lunch on Friday
25	(pictograph: pizza, corn dog, fries, salad) = 10 students

Cause/Effect
Underline the effect in each sentence.

1. I go to bed when I am tired.
2. The hunter stopped and shot the bear.
3. Because he wanted to sing, Hans joined the choir.
4. I got soaked walking home in the thunderstorm.
5. When Andrew organized his folder, he found his assignment.
6. The swimming pool was crowded after we arrived.

🖊 **Writing Practice:** Write a personal narrative about going on a picnic. Underline any cause/effect statements.

Page 223

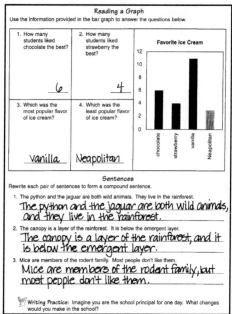

Reading a Graph
Use the information provided in the bar graph to answer the questions below.

1. How many students liked chocolate the best?	2. How many students liked strawberry the best?	Favorite Ice Cream
6	4	(bar graph: 12 down to 0; chocolate, strawberry, vanilla, Neapolitan)

3. Which was the most popular flavor of ice cream?	4. Which was the least popular flavor of ice cream?
vanilla	Neapolitan

Sentences
Rewrite each pair of sentences to form a compound sentence.

1. The python and the jaguar are both wild animals. They live in the rainforest.
   The python and the jaguar are both wild animals, and they live in the rainforest.
2. The canopy is a layer of the rainforest. It is below the emergent layer.
   The canopy is a layer of the rainforest, and it is below the emergent layer.
3. Mice are members of the rodent family. Most people don't like them.
   Mice are members of the rodent family, but most people don't like them.

🖊 **Writing Practice:** Imagine you are the school principal for one day. What changes would you make in the school?

Page 224

Reading a Table
Use the table to answer the questions.

1. How many more pencils does Charles have than Kim?	2. Who has more pencils, Rachel or Kim?	3. How many pencils does Taryn need in order to have the same amount as Phillippe?
9 pencils	Rachel	4 pencils

4. How many pencils are there in all?	Student	Amount of Pencils
	Kim	3
	Charles	12
	Rachel	7
28 pencils	Taryn	1
	Phillippe	5

Punctuation
Add quotation marks where they belong.

1. We sang "The Star Spangled Banner" at the baseball game.
2. My mom read the poem "The Raven" to me.
3. Our family saw "The Pearls of Parlay," a short story, at the theater.
4. The band aboard the ship played "Nearer My God to Thee."
5. The newspaper printed an article entitled "2000: The Millennium."

🖊 **Writing Practice:** Peace, Friendship, and Good Will Week is in October. Write a paragraph about what you think will make all of these things happen in your classroom. Then underline which ones you will work on.

Page 225

Reading a Chart
Look at the chart. Answer the questions using the information from the chart.

1. Who is older, Jesse Jackson or Muhammad Ali?	2. How many years younger is Ali than Rosa Parks?	3. How many years older is Rosa Parks than Bill Cosby?
Jesse Jackson	29 years	24 years

4. Jesse Owens was famous for running in track and field events. He was born in 1913 and died in 1980. How old was he when he died?	Black American	Born
	Bill Cosby	1937
	Rosa Parks	1913
	Shirley Chisholm	1924
67 years old	Jesse Jackson	1941
	Muhammad Ali	1942

Cause/Effect
Underline the cause in each sentence.

1. When Sally listens in class, she makes better grades.
2. We'll go outside for P.E. because the weather is nice.
3. If Betsy cleans her room, she'll be able to go to the mall.
4. April talked on the phone and ordered a pizza.
5. Jeff tried out for the lead in Romeo and Juliet and was chosen to play the part of Romeo.
6. We went to the ballgame, when my uncle came for a visit.

🖊 **Writing Practice:** Margaret Thatcher once said, "Being powerful is like being a lady. If you have to tell people you are, you aren't." What do you think she meant by that? Do you agree with her?

Page 226

Reading a Chart
Answer the questions about these mountain ranges.

Mountains in Feet		1. Which mountain has the highest peak?	2. How much higher is Aconcagua than Mount McKinley?
Mont Blanc	15,771		
Mount Kilimanjaro	19,340		
Mount McKinley	20,320		
Aconcagua	22,834		
Mount Everest	29,028	Mount Everest	2,514 feet

3. Which mountain has the lowest peak?	4. In the list above, what is the difference between the highest and lowest peaks?
Mont Blanc	13,257 feet

Handwriting
Write the names of the 13 original colonies in your best handwriting.

New Hampshire *New Hampshire* — North Carolina *North Carolina*
Delaware *Delaware* — Connecticut *Connecticut*
Massachusetts *Massachusetts* — South Carolina *South Carolina*
Maryland *Maryland* — Pennsylvania *Pennsylvania*
New York *New York* — Georgia *Georgia*
Virginia *Virginia* — New Jersey *New Jersey*
Rhode Island *Rhode Island*

🖊 **Writing Practice:** There is a poem called "The Purple Cow." Write a poem with another colored animal.

Reading a Chart
Using the information in the chart, answer the following questions below.

1. How many more dogs were owned in 2000 than 1990?	2. What was the total number of cats and dogs owned in 2000?	3. Which pet had the smallest increase?
340	1,680	bird

4. How many pets were owned in 1990? In 2000?	Pet Population		
1990: 1,296 2000: 1,869	Pet	1990	2000
	Cat	540	718
	Dog	622	962
	Bird	83	110
	Fish	51	79

Sentences
Rewrite each sentence to make more sense.

1. Under the table were her shoes.
   Her shoes were under the table.
2. For the party I had to pick her up.
   I had to pick her up for the party.
3. Across the room sat Miss Michaels.
   Miss Michaels sat across the room.
4. Near the couch was the baby's toy.
   The baby's toy was near the couch.
5. For quietly just a moment she sat.
   She sat quietly for just a moment.
6. Faster and faster came the runners.
   The runners came faster and faster.

Writing Practice: Write a paragraph about a pet you have or a pet you've always wanted.

Reading a Chart
Use the information provided in the chart to answer the questions below.

1. How many more electoral votes do Florida and North Carolina have than Georgia and Tennessee?	2. Which 2 states' total electoral votes are equal to Florida?	3. What is the total number of electoral votes in all 8 states?
15	North Carolina Tennessee	96

4. Find the average of the total electoral votes.	Electoral Votes			
	Alabama	9	Mississippi	7
	Florida	25	North Carolina	14
	Georgia	13	South Carolina	8
12	Louisiana	9	Tennessee	11

Context Clues
Look at how the underlined Australian word is used. Write what you think the word means.

1. My mom will flog our dog's puppies when they get older.   sell
2. The jackaroo worked on a ranch in Texas.   cowboy
3. Our chalkie gave us yakka to do in class.   teacher, work
4. The bloke and sheila jogged around the block.   man, woman
5. He bought new clobbers at the department store.   clothes

Writing Practice: If you could create a new holiday, what would it be and why? Be sure to describe when it would be celebrated and anything special that will happen on this day.

Reading a Chart
Use the information in the chart to answer the questions below about the different mountain ranges.

1. Which mountain is the tallest?	2. Which mountain is only 20 ft. taller than Clingman's Dome?	Mountain	Elevation
Mt. Rainier	Mt. Mitchell	Mt. Rainier	14,410 ft.
		Clingman's Dome	6,642 ft.
		Mt. Hood	6,225 ft.
3. Which mountain is the shortest?	4. Which mountain is 300 ft. shorter than Mt. Rainier?	Mt. Mitchell	6,662 ft.
		Mt. Lassen	10,446 ft.
Mt. Hood	Pike's Peak	Pike's Peak	14,110 ft.

Alphabetical Order
Write the names of these patriots in alphabetical order.

Thomas Paine
Paul Revere
Deborah Sampson
Nathan Hale
Patrick Henry
Mary Ludwig Hays
Crispus Attucks
John Paul Jones
Samuel Adams
Baron Friedrich von Steuben

Samuel Adams
Crispus Attucks
Nathan Hale
Mary Ludwig Hays
Patrick Henry
John Paul Jones
Thomas Paine
Paul Revere
Deborah Sampson
Baron Friedrich von Steuben

Writing Practice: National Grandparent's Day is in September. Write a descriptive paragraph about your grandparents.

Reading a Chart
Use the sales tax chart to determine the amount of tax on each amount below. Write the tax below the amount. Then add for the total.

1. $14.09 tax: .66 total: $14.75	2. $11.33 tax: .60 total: $11.93	Tax Chart	
		Amount	Tax
		$9.00–9.49	56¢
		$9.50–9.99	57¢
		$10.00–10.49	58¢
		$10.50–10.99	59¢
		$11.00–11.49	60¢
		$11.50–11.99	61¢
3. $9.72 tax: .57 total: $10.29	4. $12.18 tax: .62 total: $12.80	$12.00–12.49	62¢
		$12.50–12.99	63¢
		$13.00–13.49	64¢
		$13.50–13.99	65¢
		$14.00–14.49	66¢
		$14.50–14.99	67¢
		$15.00–15.49	68¢
		$15.50–15.99	69¢

Compound Words
Underline the open compound words in each sentence.

1. He ate lunch on a picnic table in the park.
2. Mom opened up a savings account for my sister and me.
3. My friend, Antonio, became the president of the sixth grade.
4. I was the flower girl in my aunt's wedding.
5. Our Girl Scout troop had fun swimming at our neighbor's swimming pool.
6. We learned about the largest mountain range in Alaska.

Writing Practice: Write a story using the following compound words: fire engine, vice president, parking lot, and open house.

Reading a Chart
Use the information in the chart to answer the questions below.

1. You have $50.00 to spend. Which two items would you buy if your change was $10.00?	2. You have $50.00 to spend. Which two items would you buy if your change was $3.00?	Item	Price
2 watches or shirt and jeans	blouse and skirt	shirt	$15.00
		shoes	$36.00
		blouse	$17.00
		necklace	$9.00
3. You have $50.00 to spend. Which two items would you buy if your change was $11.00?	4. You have $50.00 to spend. Which two items would you buy if your change was $21.00?	jeans	$25.00
		watch	$20.00
necklace and skirt or shoes and socks	necklace and watch	skirt	$30.00
		socks	$3.00

Figurative Language
Rewrite each sentence using literal language.

1. I'm dead!
   I'm exhausted!
2. It's raining cats and dogs.
   It's pouring rain.
3. We're like two ships that pass in the night.
   We never see each other.
4. She cried a bucket of tears.
   She cried and cried.
5. He's blind as a bat.
   He cannot see.
6. Stanley has a chip on his shoulder.
   Stanley felt he was wronged.

Writing Practice: The 19th Amendment to the Constitution of the United States gave women the right to vote. If you could add an amendment for children, what would it be and why?

Coordinates
Write the coordinate pair for each point on the grid.

1. What is the ordered pair for A?	2. What is the ordered pair for B?	3. What is the ordered pair for C?
(5,2)	(6,4)	(7,1)

4. What is the ordered pair for D?   (8,3)

Noun/Verb
Write N if the word is a noun. Write V if the word is a verb.

V 1. sing
N 2. song
N 3. greeting
V 4. greet
V 5. collect
N 6. collection
V 7. freeze
N 8. freezer
N 9. traveller
V 10. travel
V 11. erase
N 12. eraser
N 13. measurement
V 14. measure
V 15. see
N 16. sea

Writing Practice: Predict the first day you think it will snow. Now write a paragraph to persuade me that you can have fun in the snow.

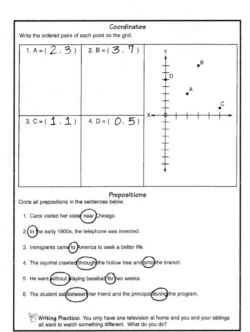

Coordinates
Write the ordered pairs of each point on the grid.

1. A = (2 , 3)   2. B = (3 , 7)
3. C = (1 , 1)   4. D = (0 , 5)

Prepositions
Circle all prepositions in the sentences below.

1. Carol visited her sister (near) Chicago.
2. (In) the early 1900s, the telephone was invented.
3. Immigrants came (to) America to seek a better life.
4. The squirrel crawled (through) the hollow tree and (onto) the branch.
5. He went (without) playing baseball (for) two weeks.
6. The student sat (between) her friend and the principal (during) the program.

🖊 *Writing Practice:* You only have one television at home and you and your siblings all want to watch something different. What do you do?

Coordinates
Use the graph and write the matching point to each set of coordinates for each problem.

1. (2, -3)   A
2. (-1, -2)   B
3. (1, 3)   C
4. (-2, 2)   D

Nouns
Write a noun for each letter in "nouns." Then write a sentence with each word.

1. N: _____
2. O: _____
3. U: _____
4. N: _____
5. S: _____

🖊 *Writing Practice:* Write a review of a restaurant that you have recently been to. Be sure to describe what sort of food is served there and where it is located.

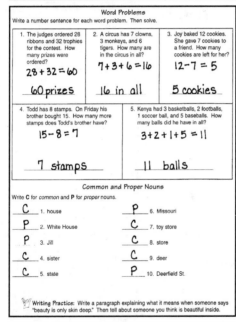

Word Problems
Write a number sentence for each word problem. Then solve.

1. The judges ordered 28 ribbons and 32 trophies for the contest. How many prizes were ordered?
$28 + 32 = 60$
60 prizes

2. A circus has 7 clowns, 3 monkeys, and 6 tigers. How many are in the circus in all?
$7 + 3 + 6 = 16$
16 in all

3. Joy baked 12 cookies. She gave 7 cookies to a friend. How many cookies are left for her?
$12 - 7 = 5$
5 cookies

4. Todd has 8 stamps. On Friday his brother bought 15. How many more stamps does Todd's brother have?
$15 - 8 = 7$
7 stamps

5. Kenya had 3 basketballs, 2 footballs, 1 soccer ball, and 5 baseballs. How many balls did he have in all?
$3 + 2 + 1 + 5 = 11$
11 balls

Common and Proper Nouns
Write C for *common* and P for *proper* nouns.

C 1. house
P 2. White House
P 3. Jill
C 4. sister
C 5. state
P 6. Missouri
C 7. toy store
C 8. store
C 9. deer
P 10. Deerfield St.

🖊 *Writing Practice:* Write a paragraph explaining what it means when someone says "beauty is only skin deep." Then tell about someone you think is beautiful inside.

Word Problems
Write a number sentence for each word problem and solve.

1. Clarence had 139 baseball cards. He gave 23 to Allen. How many cards does he have left?
$139 - 23 =$
116 cards

2. At the dollar store, I spent $6.48. I gave the cashier a 10 dollar bill. How much money should I get back?
$\$10.00 - \$6.48 =$
$3.52

3. I bought a pencil for $0.25, an eraser for $0.05, and a pack of paper for $0.75. How much did I spend in all?
$\$0.25 + \$0.05 + \$0.75 =$
$1.05

4. Josiah had a pack of notebook paper with 150 sheets. He gave four friends 6 pieces of paper each. How many sheets does he have left?
$150 - 24 =$
126 sheets

5. Ramon wants to take his 375 gumballs and put them in machines. Each machine can only hold 10 gumballs. What is the greatest number of gumball machines Ramon needs?
$375 \div 10 = 37 \text{ r } 5$
38 machines

Figurative Language
Finish each hyperbole.   (Answers will vary.)

1. It rained so hard _____
2. It was so hot _____
3. My cat is so lazy _____
4. It was so foggy _____
5. My little sister is so annoying _____
6. The room was so crowded _____

🖊 *Writing Practice:* Write a paragraph using the sentence starter below.
If there's one thing I hate, it's . . .

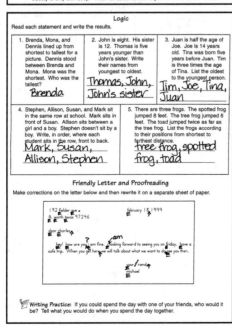

Logic
Read each statement and write the results.

1. Brenda, Mona, and Dennis lined up from shortest to tallest for a picture. Dennis stood between Brenda and Mona. Mona was the shortest. Who was the tallest?
Brenda

2. John is eight. His sister is 12. Thomas is five years younger than John's sister. Write their names from youngest to oldest.
Thomas, John, John's sister

3. Juan is half the age of Joe. Joe is 14 years old. Tina was born five years before Juan. Tim is three times the age of Tina. List the oldest to the youngest person.
Tim, Joe, Tina, Juan

4. Stephen, Allison, Susan, and Mark sit in the same row at school. Mark sits in front of Susan. Allison sits between a girl and a boy. Stephen doesn't sit by a boy. Write, in order, where each student sits in the row, front to back.
Mark, Susan, Allison, Stephen

5. There are three frogs. The spotted frog jumped 8 feet. The tree frog jumped 6 feet. The toad jumped twice as far as the tree frog. List the frogs according to their positions from shortest to farthest distance.
tree frog, spotted frog, toad

Friendly Letter and Proofreading
Make corrections on the letter below and then rewrite it on a separate sheet of paper.

192 felder ave
ft. worth texas 97246
february 18, 1999

dear charles,

hey! how are you? I am fine. I am looking forward to seeing you on friday. have a safe trip. When you get here we will talk about what we want to do while you are here.

your friend,
michael

🖊 *Writing Practice:* If you could spend the day with one of your friends, who would it be? Tell what you would do when you spend the day together.

Logic
Read each statement and write the results.

1. Jerry is taller than Jamal. Shemeka is taller than Jerry. And Ollie is shorter than Jamal. Write in order from the tallest to the shortest student.
Shemeka, Jerry, Jamal, Ollie

2. Ben sits by Joan. Kim sits by a girl, and Theron sits beside Kim. Write the order in which students are sitting next to each other.
Ben, Joan, Kim, Theron

3. Eric runs the race faster than Loren. Bob wins the race. Mara finishes in front of Eric. Write in order first through fourth place.
Bob, Mara, Eric, Loren

4. Emily jumped higher that Sharon. Karen jumped higher than Emily. Sara did not jump as high as Sharon. Write in order the highest to lowest jumper.
Karen, Emily, Sharon, Sara

5. Leo ate less pizza than Julio. Tyrone ate less pizza than Emily. Sara ate the most pizza. Write in order who ate the most pizza to who ate the least.
James, Julio, Leo, Tyrone

Alphabetical Order
Write the names of these presidents in alphabetical order.

George Washington
Abraham Lincoln
John Adams
William Harrison
Dwight Eisenhower
Ronald Reagan
Jimmy Carter
Gerald Ford
Richard Nixon
Bill Clinton

John Adams
Jimmy Carter
Bill Clinton
Dwight Eisenhower
Gerald Ford
William Harrison
Abraham Lincoln
Richard Nixon
Ronald Reagan
George Washington

🖊 *Writing Practice:* If you could visit any continent, which one would it be, and why? Write a paragraph about your adventures.

Magic Squares
All rows, both horizontal and vertical, when added up will equal the stated sum. Fill in the missing numbers in the puzzle. Then solve number 5.

1.

8	2	6
8	5	3
0	9	7

sum = 16

2.

5	9	4
6	3	9
7	6	5

sum = 18

3.

3	6	2
7	1	3
1	4	6

sum = 11

4.

6	6	7
10	5	4
3	8	8

sum = 19

5. James spent $104.90 on a coat. Tabitha spent $56.73 on a coat. How much more money did James spend than Tabitha?

$48.17

Spelling
There is a misspelled word in each sentence. Circle the misspelled word and write the correct spelling in the blank beside the sentence.

1. Have you (studied) for the test? — studied
2. It was (cloudy) yesterday than today. — cloudier
3. Are you (worryed) about the exam? — worried
4. Johnny (caried) the trash to the dumpster. — carried
5. Do you have any (hobbies)? — hobbies
6. Nashville and Knoxville are large (citys). — cities
7. Martha is the (prettiest) girl I know. — prettiest
8. I (copyed) my homework down today. — copied

Writing Practice: Write a newspaper article about your favorite team in baseball, basketball, or football.

Magic Squares
All rows, both horizontal and vertical, will equal the sum indicated when added up. Fill in the missing numbers in the squares.

1.

5	0	7
6	4	2
1	8	3

sum = 12

2.

8	2	5
1	5	9
6	8	1

sum = 15

3.

1	7	6
4	4	6
9	3	2

sum = 14

4.

9	1	3
2	8	3
2	4	7

sum = 13

5. Janet and David picked 12 berries one day, 34 the next day, and 27 the following day. How many did they pick in all?

73 berries

Plurals
Write the plural forms of each word under the correct title.

tray   berry
cowboy   fly
penny   journey
city   key
fry   buy
way   cry
turkey   lady

y + s	y to i and add es
trays	pennies
cowboys	cities
ways	fries
turkeys	berries
journeys	flies
keys	cries
buys	ladies

Writing Practice: Write a story about your pet being able to talk, so you become famous. What do you do? Tell about your adventures.

Mean
For problems 1–4, find the averages of these test scores. Then solve problem 5.

1. Billy: 85, 88, 95 — 89.3
2. Jorge: 99, 100, 81 — 93.3
3. Joanne: 89, 89, 93 — 90.3
4. Jaquarius: 90, 80, 88 — 86
5. Simon and his friend Wayne set up a lemonade stand. A cup of lemonade cost $0.25 each. They made $5.00. How many cups of lemonade did they sell? — 20 cups

Compound Words
Make a compound word by adding a beginning or an ending to the words below.
(Answers will vary.)

1. _____ground   5. him_____   9. sun_____
2. grand_____   6. _____age   10. _____ball
3. book_____   7. every_____   11. _____man
4. _____plane   8. with_____   12. home_____

Writing Practice: Imagine waking up and finding out you're 10 feet tall. Write a story about your adventures.

Median
Find the median for each set of numbers and then solve problem 5.

1. 17, 24, 34, 28, 16 — 24
2. 215, 219, 225, 200, 231 — 219
3. 48, 68, 51, 65, 55 — 55
4. $3.63, $4.74, $3.59, $4.62, $3.48 — $3.63
5. Mrs. Forrest gave a questionnaire to her math class of 12 boys and 13 girls. 7 boys and 7 girls returned their questionnaires. How many will she still need to get back from the boys? from the girls? — boys 5, girls 6

Proofreading
Rewrite each sentence correctly.

1. the temperature in the woods were below freezing and i got two cold
The temperature in the woods was below freezing, and I got too cold.
2. the story about dr. terry were interesting
The story about Dr. Terry was interesting.
3. last tuesday i go to see the movie the patriot
Last Tuesday, I went to see the movie, "The Patriot."
4. canada be on the border of the united states
Canada is on the border of the United States.
5. do you like to ate shrimp
Do you like to eat shrimp?

Writing Practice: Write a story for a newspaper with the title "Whale Survives Oil Spill."

Mode
Find the mode for each set of numbers. Then solve problem 5.

1. $20, $12, $16, $12, $30 — $12
2. 46, 39, 28, 27, 39 — 39
3. 100, 200, 100, 600, 300 — 100
4. 75, 85, 95, 65, 75 — 75
5. The 5th and 6th graders sold 98 candy bars. 12 more were sold by the 6th grade than 5th grade. How many did each grade sell? — 5th grade 43, 6th grade 55

Adverbs
Underline each adverb. Then circle where, when, or how to indicate what each adverb describes.

1. Stand there beside the tree. — (where) when how
2. Swiftly he ran toward the fence. — where when (how)
3. A man waited eagerly for his letter. — where when (how)
4. "It should arrive soon," said Mary. — where (when) how
5. The pitcher threw the ball down. — (where) when how
6. The umpire suddenly shouted for him to stop. — where when (how)

Writing Practice: What is your favorite commercial on television? Why?

Mean, Median, Mode
The students in Mr. Dahl's math class received their tests grades back. (See below for test grades.) Find the total, the mean, the median, and the mode scores.

1. Total of All Scores = 984
2. Mean = 89.45
3. Median = 89
4. Mode = 86

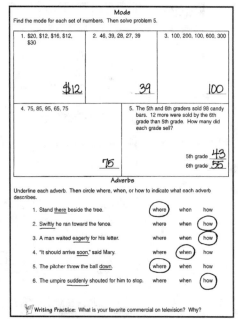

Test Scores			
Tom	97	Shelly	66
Maria	98	Howard	88
Juan	86	Lana	86
Adam	86	Eugene	93
Connie	95	Suzanne	89
Dorothy	100		

Dictionary Skills
Circle the word that would come between each set of guide words.

1. perennial   persevere
a. period
b. perspire
c. percent

2. cope   correspond
a. costume
b. coordinate
c. corps

3. gnome   govern
a. gray
b. gossip
c. gnaw

4. motorcycle   mule
a. mouth
b. motor
c. mull

5. stroke   stuff
a. stretch
b. student
c. stump

6. black   blanket
a. blackbird
b. blaze
c. blast

Writing Practice: Write a story using the sentence starter below.
I was playing outside when suddenly a UFO hovered over me. I looked up...

Mean, Median, Mode
Use the information provided on the list to answer the following questions.

1. What is the mean?	2. What is the median?	Jeff received these amounts of money for his birthday.
$17.22	$15	grandparents $40
3. What is the mode?	4. What is the total he received?	parents $30
		aunt $15
		3 brothers $10 each
$10	$155	sister $15
		best friend $20
		neighbor $5

Nouns
Write "noun" if the word names a person, place, thing, or idea. Write "verb" if it describes action, existence, or occurrence. (*Hint:* There are some words that are not nouns or verbs)

1. Rachel — noun
2. discover — verb
3. socks — noun
4. cheered — verb
5. yellow —
6. talked — verb
7. peace — noun
8. up —
9. gratitude — noun
10. her —

Writing Practice: Write a paragraph using at least five of the nouns listed above. Then circle any other nouns in your paragraph.

Mean, Median, Mode
If Tamara's math test scores are 96, 92, 83, 71, 83, and 91, calculate the answer for each problem. Then solve problem 5.

1. mean	2. median	3. mode
86	87	83
4. range		5. Mr. Garcia bought a new car. His payments for 48 months are $185.00 per month. What is the price of the car?
25		$8,800.00

Pronouns
Circle the underlined pronoun in each sentence.

1. The coach was talking to (him).
2. He said for the team to put on (their) uniforms.
3. (They) would be practicing after school tomorrow.
4. (We) had an assembly in school today.
5. (It) was about Black History month.
6. My friend said, "(I) have seen the program before."

Writing Practice: Can you cook? Do you like to cook? Write about something you can cook or something you'd like to learn to cook.

Measurement
Circle the larger unit. Then solve problem number 5.

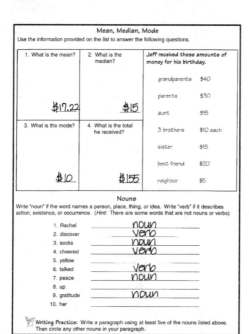

1.	2.	3.
4 in. or (4 ft.)	74 yd. or (74 mi.)	(1 yd.) or 1 in.
4.		5. Students at Gladeville Middle School collected 23 lbs. of aluminum cans, 18 lbs. of plastic bottles, and 78 lbs. of newspapers for the annual recycling drive. How many pounds of recycling material did they collect in all?
(60 ft.) or 60 in.		119 pounds

Syllables
How many syllables does each word have? Write each word under the correct heading.

library
table
magazine
paper
globe
reference
shelf
computer
book

One	Two	Three
globe	table	library
shelf	paper	magazine
book		reference
		computer

Writing Practice: Write a paragraph using the sentence starter below.

Happiness is . . .

Measurement
Write the correct measurement (in., ft., yd., or mi.). Then solve number 5.

1. the depth of a swimming pool	2. the distance to Mars	3. the width of your hand
ft.	mi.	in.
4. the material in a dress		5. D'Andre worked on his homework after school. He started at 4:15 P.M. and finished right before supper at 6:00 P.M. How long did he work on his homework?
yd.		1 hr. 45 min.

Compound Sentences
Combine the two simple sentences with a comma and a connecting word to make a compound sentence. (Answers may vary.)

1. Joellyn woke up late. She was late to school.

2. She told her teacher she was late. She had overslept.

3. Mrs. Sagraves was teaching math. She was giving directions.

4. Her teacher said to sit down quickly. She had to take off her coat.

5. She sat down. She worked very hard.

Writing Practice: Write a paragraph about a time you were late to school.

Measurement
Circle the more reasonable temperature. Then solve problem 5.

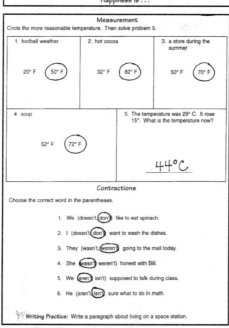

1. football weather	2. hot cocoa	3. a store during the summer
20° F (50° F)	32° F (82° F)	50° F (70° F)
4. soup		5. The temperature was 29° C. It rose 15°. What is the temperature now?
52° F (72° F)		44° C

Contractions
Choose the correct word in the parentheses.

1. We (doesn't, (don't)) like to eat spinach.
2. I (doesn't, (don't)) want to wash the dishes.
3. They (wasn't, (weren't)) going to the mall today.
4. She ((wasn't), weren't) honest with Bill.
5. We ((aren't), isn't) supposed to talk during class.
6. He (aren't, (isn't)) sure what to do in math.

Writing Practice: Write a paragraph about living on a space station.

Measurement
Write which metric measure you would use to measure the following: cm (centimeter), m (meter), or km (kilometer). Then solve problem 5.

1. the length of your pencil	2. the length of the hallway at school	3. your height
cm	m	m
4. the distance from your house to school		5. You sold Teri a pencil for $0.35. She gave you a dollar. How much change does she get back? $0.65 She receives four coins back. What type of coins does she get back? 2 quarters, 1 dime, and 1 nickel
km		

Nouns or Verbs
Some words can be a noun or a verb, depending on the way it is used. Read the sentences below and write whether the underlined word is a *noun* or a *verb*.

1. The wind blew so hard, my bicycle fell over. — noun
2. The string on my yo-yo got stuck, and I had to wind it up again. — verb
3. Kindergarten students should rest after lunch. — verb
4. The rest of the animals in the zoo went to sleep. — noun
5. Go down the street and turn left onto Front Street. — verb
6. Terry said, "It's my turn!" — noun
7. Dad's suit was dark gray. — noun
8. He said the student's homework would suit him. — verb
9. The cut on his finger was bleeding. — noun
10. Mrs. Roberts said not to cut the picture out. — verb

Writing Practice: What is your favorite fairy tale? Write your own version of it.

Page 251

Measurement

Fill in the blanks for problems 1–4. Then solve problem 5.

1.	2.	3.
1 quart is **2** pints.	There are **16** ounces in a pound.	4 quarts make **1** gallon.

4.	5. Stanley's father bought a car that weighed $\frac{1}{4}$ of a ton. How much did it weigh in pounds?
$\frac{1}{2}$ of a gallon is **2** quarts.	**500 pounds**

Syllables

Circle the words that have a long vowel sound in the first syllable.

(table) (baby) (bridle)
money apple lucky
(lady) (nature) (pizza)
window hero (pilot)
robin (fatal) nickel
flower drama (music)

Writing Practice: Some people like to be by themselves. Others don't like to be alone. Write a paragraph explaining which one you prefer.

Page 252

Measurement

Solve each problem.

1. About how long is a crayon?	2. About how much does a large bucket hold?	3. Which is used to measure milk in a glass?
(3 in) or 3 ft.	5 pt. or (5 gal.)	(cup) or pint

4. About how long is a straw?	5. What was the total distance of a race if it had 4 laps, each 1,125 meters long?
(5 cm) or 5.2 km	**4,500 meters**

Nouns, Verbs, and Adjectives

Write words that begin with the letter at the top of each chart. **(Answers will vary.)**

	m		a		l
noun		noun		noun	
verb		verb		verb	
adjective		adjective		adjective	

	s		r		w
noun		noun		noun	
verb		verb		verb	
adjective		adjective		adjective	

Writing Practice: If you could give your teacher a suggestion, what would it be?

Page 253

Measurement

Circle which method of measurement would be more appropriate. Then solve problem 5.

1. width of your math book	2. length of your classroom	3. height of your teacher
(ruler) or yardstick	ruler or (yardstick)	ruler or (yardstick)

4. length of your arm	5. Sammy gave Antonio six apples, Samantha three apples, and Kershawn five apples. If he started with 35 apples, how many does he have left?
(ruler) or yardstick	**21 apples**

Spelling

Unscramble these words having to do with Christmas.

1. aittesnoip **poinsettia**
2. bbrion **ribbon**
3. cdar **card**
4. kingcots **stocking**
5. glena **angel**
6. shigel **sleigh**
7. lloyh **holly**
8. rewaht **wreath**
9. lorac **carol**
10. repnest **present**

Writing Practice: Write a Christmas story using six of the words above.

Page 254

Measurement

For problems 1–4, fill in the blanks. Then solve problem 5.

1.	2.	3.
$\frac{2}{3}$ yd. = **2** feet	$\frac{3}{4}$ hr. = **45** minutes	$\frac{1}{2}$ doz. = **6** eggs

4.	5. A jar of candy has 592 pieces in it. Each bag of candy used to fill up the jar contained 30 pieces. How many bags were needed to fill the jar? **20 bags** How many extra pieces of candy were left over? **8 pieces**
$\frac{1}{4}$ ft. = **3** inches	

Handwriting

Write this poem in your best handwriting.

Bugs
I like bugs.
Black bugs, green bugs,
Bad bugs, mean bugs,
Any kind of bug.
A bug in a rug, a bug in the grass,
A bug on the sidewalk, a bug in a glass,
I like bugs.
Big bugs, fat bugs,
Shiny bugs, round bugs,
Lady bugs, buggy bugs,
I like bugs.
—Unknown

(title) **Students' writing will vary.**

Writing Practice: Write your own poem about an animal or insect that you like.

Page 255

Measurement

For problems 1–4, write the correct answers. Then solve problem 5.

1. At 100° C, do you take a bath or boil eggs?	2. At 0° C, do you freeze ice cream or cook hotdogs?	3. At 35° C, do you wear a bathing suit or wear a jacket?
boil eggs	**freeze ice cream**	**wear a bathing suit**

4. At 40° C, are you at the North Pole or the Sahara Desert?	5. If John was cold, and he looked at the thermometer and it said 32°, would it be Celsius or Fahrenheit?
Sahara Desert	**Fahrenheit**

Adverb/Verb

Underline the verb and circle each adverb.

1. The football player fell (down).
2. The old dog just lies (there).
3. The fire trucks drove (nearby).
4. The pool table sits (downstairs) in the den.
5. The young baby crawled (over) to me.
6. The big dogs barked (loudly).
7. The jet plane landed (today).
8. My good friend arrives (tomorrow).

Writing Practice: Write a story using the sentence starter below.

In the year 2020 . . .

Page 256

Measurement

Calculate the correct equivalent measurement for each problem and then solve problem 5.

1.	2.	3.
$\frac{1}{2}$ gal. = **2** qt.	2 pt. = **1** qt.	$\frac{1}{2}$ c. = **4** fl. oz.

4.	5. Monkeys in a zoo eat 796 bananas and 283 cans of peanuts per day. How much do they eat in 1 week? bananas **5,572** cans of peanuts **1,981**
$\frac{1}{2}$ qt. = **1** pt.	

Prefix

Replace the italicized words with a prefix and a base word.

1. The girl *wrote again* her science report. **rewrote**
2. She *read incorrectly* the instructions on the list. **misread**
3. Mom likes to drink a big glass of *not fat* milk. **nonfat**
4. Dad *planned ahead* our trip to the Grand Canyon. **preplanned**
5. The baseball game was *scheduled again*. **rescheduled**
6. I had some *opposite of comfort* after my leg broke. **discomfort**

Writing Practice: Write about the best dream that you've ever had or can remember.

Measurement
Write the unit (in., ft., yd., mi.) you would use to measure the items listed below. Then solve problem 5.

1. height of a light pole	2. length of a school bus	3. distance between east and west coast
ft.	ft.	mi.

4. length of your arm	5. Toni owed her sister 75¢. She paid her with a combination of 5 coins. What coins did she give to her sister?
in.	2 quarters, 2 dimes, 1 nickel

Synonyms
Circle the best synonym for each boldfaced word.

1. **drill** — (train) · useful · lifted
2. **drab** — stylish · (dreary) · oppressed
3. **duty** — (requirement) · doubtful · created
4. **doodle** — unsteady · enhance · (scribble)
5. **desert** — gained · cake · (abandon)
6. **dainty** — courteous · (delicate) · helpful

✍ **Writing Practice:** Write a story using this title:

The Strangest Place I've Ever Been

Measurement
Write the correct measurements. Then solve problem 5.

1.	2.	3.
16 ounces in a pound	8 fluid ounces in a cup	4 quarts in a gallon

4.	5. If you add Yolanda and Wanda's ages, you get a total of 21 years. If you multiply their ages, you get 110. What age is each girl? (Yolanda is older than Wanda.)
2 cups in a pint	Yolanda: 11 Wanda: 10

Punctuation
Write a sentence that is an example of each punctuation rule.

1. Place quotation marks before and after a person's spoken words.
2. Underline the title of a book or newspaper.
3. Place an exclamation mark at the end of an exclamatory sentence.
4. Place a comma between the city and state.
5. Place a colon between the hour and minute in time.
6. Place a period after the abbreviated title in a person's name.

✍ **Writing Practice:** You wake up one morning and find that your skin has turned purple. Write a story about it.

Measurement
Solve each problem by using the conversion chart provided.

1.	2.	3.
35 cm = 350 mm	652 m = 65,200 cm	15 g = 15,000 mg

4.	conversion chart
32,000 mg = 32 g	1 cm = 10 mm 1 m = 100 cm 1 g = 1,000 mg

Dictionary Skills
Match the correct definition of the word *course* as used in the sentences below.

c 1. Dessert is the best *course*. — a. direction
b 2. I took a *course* in Spanish. — b. lessons or classes
a 3. The ship sailed on course to Fiji. — c. part of a meal

Match the correct definition of the word *low* as used in the sentences below.

b 4. Speak in a *low* voice in the hall. — a. nearly used up
c 5. The price of the wallet was *low*. — b. soft
a 6. The battery was *low* on my CD player. — c. less than usual

✍ **Writing Practice:** Use this writing prompt to write a short paragraph:

I feel good about myself when ...

Measurement
Find the volume of each object. (Remember, V = l x w x h.) Then solve problem 5.

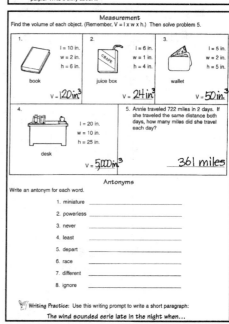

1. book	2. juice box	3. wallet
l = 10 in. w = 2 in. h = 6 in.	l = 6 in. w = 1 in. h = 4 in.	l = 5 in. w = 2 in. h = 5 in.
V = 120 in³	V = 24 in³	V = 50 in³

4. desk	5. Annie traveled 722 miles in 2 days. If she traveled the same distance both days, how many miles did she travel each day?
l = 20 in. w = 10 in. h = 25 in. V = 5,000 in³	361 miles

Antonyms
Write an antonym for each word.

1. miniature _____
2. powerless _____
3. never _____
4. least _____
5. depart _____
6. race _____
7. different _____
8. ignore _____

✍ **Writing Practice:** Use this writing prompt to write a short paragraph:

The wind sounded eerie late in the night when...

Measurement
Match the unit of measure with its equivalent. Circle the answers then solve problem 5.

1. deci	2. deka	3. kilo
a. 100	a. 100	a. 100
(b. 0.1)	b. 0.1	b. 0.1
c. 1,000	c. 1,000	(c. 1,000)
d. 10	(d. 10)	d. 10

4. hecto	5. Ten campers signed up for 1 week of camp. The total amount paid was $2,025.00. How much did each camper have to pay?
(a. 100) c. 1,000 b. 0.1 d. 10	$202.50

Word Usage
Use the code to find out famous authors.

code	z	y	x	w	v	u	t	s	r	q	p	o	n
letter	a	b	c	d	e	f	g	h	i	j	k	l	m
code	m	l	k	j	i	h	g	f	e	d	c	b	a
letter	n	o	p	q	r	s	t	u	v	w	x	y	z

1. pjmrthyfit — *Konigsburg*
2. xovzjb — *Cleary*
3. wzso — *Dahl*
4. ijldormt — *Rowling*
5. nvbvih — *Meyers*
6. hgrmv — *Stine*

✍ **Writing Practice:** Write a fan letter to your favorite author.

Measurement
Solve each equation and give each answer in centimeters. Then solve problem 5.

1.	2.	3.
2 m + 32 cm = 232 cm	30 cm + 80 mm = 38 cm	24 mm + 3.6 cm = 6 cm

4.	5. How many squares are in this figure?
5 m + 16 cm = 516 cm	14

Nouns/Word Usage
Fill in the blanks with a word to make each sentence complete.

1. Clark wrote his _____ and told about his trip to _____.
2. Mary Sue and _____ went to visit _____ in _____.
3. John, my _____, asked if he could give me a _____.
4. In _____, there is a special holiday called _____.
5. My sister lives on _____, right next door to _____.
6. My _____ gave me homework in _____.

✍ **Writing Practice:** What is the best way to travel—by bus, car, train, plane, etc.? Why?

Page 263

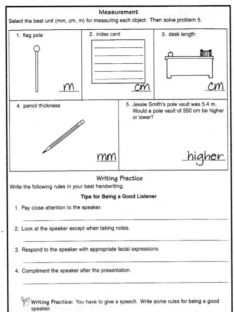

Measurement

Select the best unit (mm, cm, m) for measuring each object. Then solve problem 5.

1. flag pole — m

2. index card — cm

3. desk length — cm

4. pencil thickness — mm

5. Jessie Smith's pole vault was 5.4 m. Would a pole vault of 550 cm be higher or lower? — higher

Writing Practice

Write the following rules in your best handwriting.

Tips for Being a Good Listener

1. Pay close attention to the speaker.

2. Look at the speaker except when taking notes.

3. Respond to the speaker with appropriate facial expressions.

4. Compliment the speaker after the presentation.

Writing Practice: You have to give a speech. Write some rules for being a good speaker.

Page 264

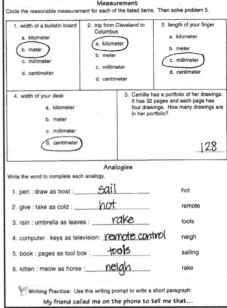

Measurement

Circle the reasonable measurement for each of the listed items. Then solve problem 5.

1. width of a bulletin board
   a. kilometer
   b. meter ⟵ (circled)
   c. millimeter
   d. centimeter

2. trip from Cleveland to Columbus
   a. kilometer ⟵ (circled)
   b. meter
   c. millimeter
   d. centimeter

3. length of your finger
   a. kilometer
   b. meter
   c. millimeter ⟵ (circled)
   d. centimeter

4. width of your desk
   a. kilometer
   b. meter
   c. millimeter
   d. centimeter ⟵ (circled)

5. Camille has a portfolio of her drawings. It has 32 pages and each page has four drawings. How many drawings are in her portfolio? — 128

Analogies

Write the word to complete each analogy.

1. pen : draw as boat : __sail__   hot

2. give : take as cold : __hot__   remote

3. rain : umbrella as leaves : __rake__   tools

4. computer : keys as television : __remote control__   neigh

5. book : pages as tool box : __tools__   salling

6. kitten : meow as horse : __neigh__   rake

Writing Practice: Use this writing prompt to write a short paragraph:

My friend called me on the phone to tell me that...

Page 265

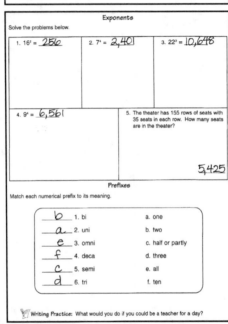

Exponents

Solve the problems below.

1. $16^2 = 256$

2. $7^4 = 2,401$

3. $22^3 = 10,648$

4. $9^4 = 6,561$

5. The theater has 155 rows of seats with 35 seats in each row. How many seats are in the theater? — 5,425

Prefixes

Match each numerical prefix to its meaning.

b 1. bi   a. one
a 2. uni   b. two
e 3. omni   c. half or partly
f 4. deca   d. three
c 5. semi   e. all
d 6. tri   f. ten

Writing Practice: What would you do if you could be a teacher for a day?

Page 266

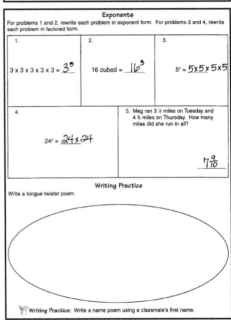

Exponents

For problems 1 and 2, rewrite each problem in exponent form. For problems 3 and 4, rewrite each problem in factored form.

1. $3 \times 3 \times 3 \times 3 \times 3 = 3^5$

2. 16 cubed = 16^3

3. $5^4 = 5 \times 5 \times 5 \times 5$

4. $24^2 = 24 \times 24$

5. Meg ran 3½ miles on Tuesday and 4¼ miles on Thursday. How many miles did she run in all? — $7\frac{9}{10}$

Writing Practice

Write a tongue twister poem.

Writing Practice: Write a name poem using a classmate's first name.

Page 267

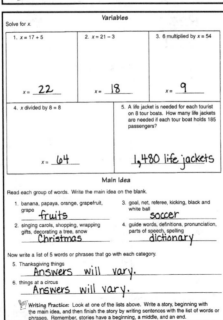

Variables

Solve for x.

1. $x = 17 + 5$ $x = 22$

2. $x = 21 - 3$ $x = 18$

3. 6 multiplied by $x = 54$ $x = 9$

4. x divided by $8 = 8$ $x = 64$

5. A life jacket is needed for each tourist on 8 tour boats. How many life jackets are needed if each tour boat holds 185 passengers? — 1,480 life jackets

Main Idea

Read each group of words. Write the main idea on the blank.

1. banana, papaya, orange, grapefruit, grape — fruits

2. singing carols, shopping, wrapping gifts, decorating a tree, snow — Christmas

3. goal, net, referee, kicking, black and white ball — soccer

4. guide words, definitions, pronunciation, parts of speech, spelling — dictionary

Now write a list of 5 words or phrases that go with each category.

5. Thanksgiving things — Answers will vary.

6. things at a circus — Answers will vary.

Writing Practice: Look at one of the lists above. Write a story, beginning with the main idea, and then finish the story by writing sentences with the list of words or phrases. Remember, stories have a beginning, a middle, and an end.

Page 268

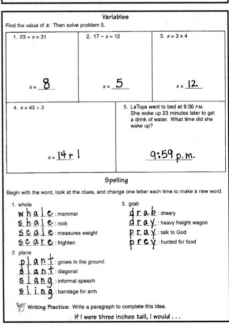

Variables

Find the value of x. Then solve problem 5.

1. $23 + x = 31$ $x = 8$

2. $17 - x = 12$ $x = 5$

3. $x = 3 \times 4$ $x = 12$

4. $x = 43 \div 3$ $x = 14 \, r \, 1$

5. LaToya went to bed at 9:36 P.M. She woke up 23 minutes later to get a drink of water. What time did she wake up? — 9:59 p.m.

Spelling

Begin with the word, look at the clues, and change one letter each time to make a new word.

1. whole
   w h a l e : mammal
   s h a l e : rock
   s c a l e : measures weight
   s c a r e : frighten

2. plane
   p l a n t : grows in the ground
   s l a n t : diagonal
   s l a n g : informal speech
   s l i n g : bandage for arm

3. grab
   d r a b : dreary
   d r a y : heavy freight wagon
   p r a y : talk to God
   p r e y : hunted for food

Writing Practice: Write a paragraph to complete this idea.

If I were three inches tall, I would . . .

Page 269

Variables
Fill in the blanks. Then solve problem 5.

1. If $6 + a = 10$, then $a =$ __4__	2. If $20 - b = 15$, then $b =$ __5__	3. If $4 \times c = 40$, then $c =$ __10__
4. If $50 \div d = 25$, then $d =$ __2__	5. Your neighbor Mr. Jones is paying you to walk his dog Tubbs. If he gives you $0.50 a day, how many days will it take to earn $10.00? __20 days__	

Verbs
Complete each sentence by adding appropriate verbs. **(Answers will vary.)**

1. The rabbits _____ and _____ in the forest.

2. The squirrels _____ and _____ up the tree.

3. The snake _____ and _____ along the ground.

4. The lions _____ and _____ in their cages.

5. The baby birds _____ and _____ in their nests.

Writing Practice: Do you have a favorite poster on the wall in your room at home? Do you collect things? Write a descriptive paragraph describing your room.

Page 270

Variables
For problems 1–4, fill in the blanks. Then solve problem 5.

1. If $10 + e = 32$, then $e =$ __22__	2. If $21 - f = 10$, then $f =$ __11__	3. If $6 \times g = 48$, then $g =$ __8__
4. If $99 \div h = 11$, then $h =$ __9__	5. The perimeter of a square is 20 inches. How long is each side? __5 inches__	

Commas
Write a sentence that corresponds with each comma rule. Be sure to use the comma correctly. **(Answers will vary.)**

1. Use a comma to separate items in a list.

2. Use a comma to set off direct quotes.

3. Use a comma to separate the names of cities and states.

4. Use a comma to set off a direct address.

5. Use a comma and a connecting word to connect two clauses.

Writing Practice: There are over 250,000 kinds of flowers. Flowers are given to people sometimes to help them feel better. Write a story about either getting flowers or giving flowers and how it made you feel.

Page 271

Variables
For problems 1–4, find the variable. Then solve problem 5.

1. $56 + 6 = x + 13$ $x =$ __49__	2. $25 + 7 = 20 + y$ $y =$ __12__	3. $66 - 6 = 72 - x$ $x =$ __12__
4. $87 - 8 = y - 9$ $y =$ __88__	5. Samuel paid for a new jacket. The jacket cost $24.98. His change was $15.02. How much money did he give the clerk? __$40.00__	

Synonyms
Write a synonym for each word. **(Answers will vary.)**

1. scarce _____   5. identical _____

2. alarm _____   6. jersey _____

3. joyful _____   7. mammoth _____

4. startle _____   8. valuable _____

Writing Practice: Write a story using the sentence starter.
I was home by myself when I heard a noise in the attic . . .

Page 272

Variables
Find the value of each expression. Then solve problem 5.

1. $x - 12 = 88$ $x =$ __100__	2. $7 \times z = 49$ $z =$ __7__	3. $144 \div y = 12$ $y =$ __12__
4. $n + 120 = 241$ $n =$ __121__	5. On the way to Mrs. Ward's classroom, the new student will pass five rooms. Mrs. Proctor's room is next to Mrs. Baker's room. Mrs. Morgan's room is between Mrs. Proctor's and Mrs. Prince's room. Mrs. Prince's room is not next to Mrs. Ward's room. Which classroom is beside Mrs. Ward's room? __Mrs. Baker's__	

Nouns
Write the following nouns under the correct heading. Use capitalization where needed.

- playground
- book
- elm street
- athlete
- detroit
- caddie woodlawn
- aunt
- england

Common Nouns	Proper Nouns
playground book athlete aunt	Elm Street Detroit Caddie Woodlawn England

Writing Practice: Write a short story about your class at school. Underline each common noun and circle each proper noun.

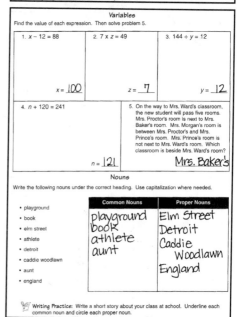

Page 273

Variables
Solve each problem below.

1. If $a = 3$ and $b = \frac{1}{2}$, then $3a + b = ?$ $9\frac{1}{2}$	2. If $a = 2.3$ and $b = 4$, then $2a + 2b = ?$ 12.6	3. $x - 1\frac{1}{2} = 6\frac{3}{4}$ $x = ?$ $8\frac{1}{4}$
4. $6m = 24$ $m =$ __4__	5. Leo and Larry work at 2 different theaters. Leo's theater employs 12 people, and Larry's theater employs 2/3 as many as Leo's. How many people does Larry's theater employ? __8__	

Subjects
Write simple or compound once you identify the type of subject used in each sentence.

simple 1. Pauline went to the mall and bought a sweater.

compound 2. Sandy and Jason found a stray dog.

simple 3. They nursed the dog back to health.

compound 4. Mom and Dad played Scrabble® with us.

simple 5. The children ran and played on the playground.

simple 6. We all like to eat pizza.

Writing Practice: Describe a fun day at the beach.

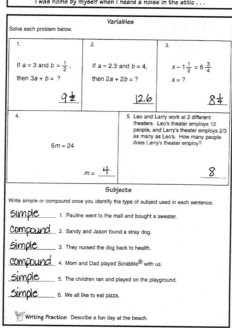

Page 274

Variables
Solve each problem below.

1. $y + 19 = 42$ $y =$ __23__	2. $26 - b = 14$ $b =$ __12__	3. $23 + x = 50$ $x =$ __27__
4. $\frac{24}{n} = 6$ $n =$ __4__	5. The decorating committee bought crepe paper for the school party. If the total cost was $15.87, how many rolls did they buy at 69¢ each? __23__	

Spelling
Choose the correctly spelled word.

1. ⟨laid⟩   layed   layied

2. hankerchief   ⟨handkerchief⟩   handerchief

3. ⟨forty⟩   fourty   fourtly

4. daugter   dauther   ⟨daughter⟩

5. farer   ⟨farther⟩   farthor

6. ⟨running⟩   runing   runnying

Writing Practice: Use this writing prompt to write a short paragraph:
Things I like in a friend...

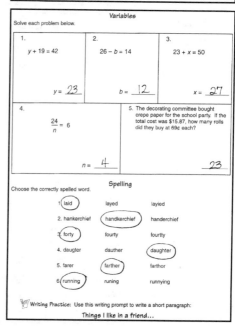

Page 275

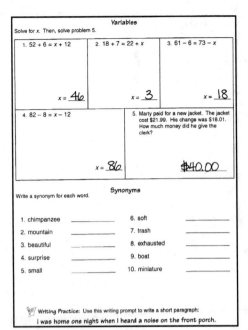

Variables

Solve for *x*. Then, solve problem 5.

1. $52 + 6 = x + 12$	2. $18 + 7 = 22 + x$	3. $61 - 6 = 73 - x$
$x = 46$	$x = 3$	$x = 18$

4. $82 - 8 = x - 12$	5. Marty paid for a new jacket. The jacket cost $21.99. His change was $18.01. How much money did he give the clerk?
$x = 86$	$40.00

Synonyms

Write a synonym for each word.

1. chimpanzee _____
2. mountain _____
3. beautiful _____
4. surprise _____
5. small _____

6. soft _____
7. trash _____
8. exhausted _____
9. boat _____
10. miniature _____

Writing Practice: Use this writing prompt to write a short paragraph:
I was home one night when I heard a noise on the front porch.

Page 276

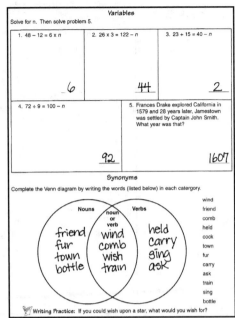

Variables

Solve for n. Then solve problem 5.

1. $48 - 12 = 6 \times n$	2. $26 \times 3 = 122 - n$	3. $23 + 15 = 40 - n$
6	44	2

4. $72 \div 9 = 100 - n$	5. Frances Drake explored California in 1579 and 28 years later, Jamestown was settled by Captain John Smith. What year was that?
92	1607

Synonyms

Complete the Venn diagram by writing the words (listed below) in each catergory.

Nouns — friend, fur, town, bottle
noun or verb — wind, comb, wish, train
Verbs — held, carry, sing, ask

wind
friend
comb
held
cook
town
fur
carry
ask
train
sing
bottle

Writing Practice: If you could wish upon a star, what would you wish for?

Page 277

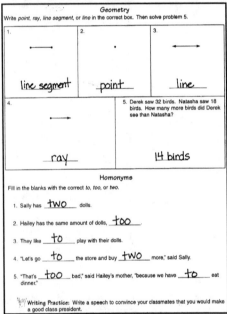

Geometry

Write *point, ray, line segment,* or *line* in the correct box. Then solve problem 5.

1.	2.	3.
line segment	point	line

4.	5. Derek saw 32 birds. Natasha saw 18 birds. How many more birds did Derek see than Natasha?
ray	14 birds

Homonyms

Fill in the blanks with the correct *to, too,* or *two*.

1. Sally has **two** dolls.
2. Hailey has the same amount of dolls, **too**.
3. They like **to** play with their dolls.
4. "Let's go **to** the store and buy **two** more," said Sally.
5. "That's **too** bad," said Hailey's mother, "because we have **to** eat dinner."

Writing Practice: Write a speech to convince your classmates that you would make a good class president.

Page 278

Geometry

Fill in the blanks with the correct answer.

A, B, C

1. In angle ABC, the vertex is **B**	2. In angle ABC, one side of the angle is **AB or BC**
3. Angle ABC is an **acute** angle.	4. Angle ABC is made up of two **rays**

Handwriting

Write the following quote from William Durant, the founder of General Motors, in your best handwriting.

"Forget mistakes. Forget failures. Forget everything except what you're going to do today. Today is your lucky day."

"Forget mistakes. Forget failures. Forget everything except what you're going to do today. Today is your lucky day."

Writing Practice: Write a paragraph explaining what the quote you just wrote means to you.

Page 279

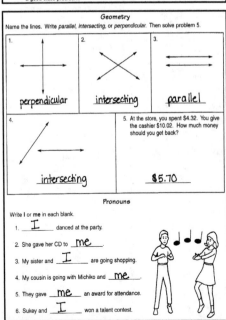

Geometry

Name the lines. Write *parallel, intersecting,* or *perpendicular*. Then solve problem 5.

1.	2.	3.
perpendicular	intersecting	parallel

4.	5. At the store, you spent $4.32. You give the cashier $10.02. How much money should you get back?
intersecting	$5.70

Pronouns

Write I or me in each blank.

1. **I** danced at the party.
2. She gave her CD to **me**.
3. My sister and **I** are going shopping.
4. My cousin is going with Michiko and **me**.
5. They gave **me** an award for attendance.
6. Sukey and **I** won a talent contest.

Page 280

Geometry

Write what type of angle—*right, acute,* or *obtuse*—is being used. Then solve problem 5.

1.	2.	3.
acute	right	acute

4.	5. Mrs. Brown wanted to buy a washer and a dryer that cost $923.00 together. If the washer cost $498.00, how much is the dryer?
obtuse	$425.00

Adjectives

Write the correct adjective in each blank. Choose between *this, that, these,* and *those*.

(Answers will vary.)

1. We like _____ new clothes best.
2. Do you have any of _____ blue gel pens?
3. Surely _____ kind of safety program is best.
4. _____ math problem is very hard.
5. I wore _____ old shoes to school.
6. We saw _____ movies last summer.
7. _____ kind of book interests me.
8. Al likes _____ cars.

Writing Practice: National Book Week is in November. Tell about a book you have read recently. What did you like about it? What did you dislike about it? Then illustrate a scene in the book.

Geometry
Identify each type of triangle (right, scalene, equilateral, obtuse). Then solve problem 5.

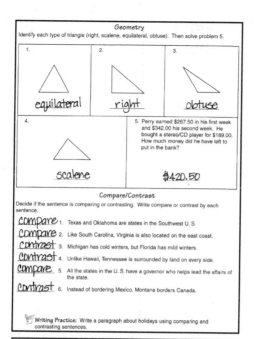

1. equilateral
2. right
3. obtuse
4. scalene
5. Perry earned $267.50 in his first week and $342.00 his second week. He bought a stereo/CD player for $189.00. How much money did he have left to put in the bank?

$420.50

Compare/Contrast
Decide if the sentence is comparing or contrasting. Write compare or contrast by each sentence.

1. compare — Texas and Oklahoma are states in the Southwest U. S.
2. compare — Like South Carolina, Virginia is also located on the east coast.
3. contrast — Michigan has cold winters, but Florida has mild winters.
4. contrast — Unlike Hawaii, Tennessee is surrounded by land on every side.
5. compare — All the states in the U. S. have a governor who helps lead the affairs of the state.
6. contrast — Instead of bordering Mexico, Montana borders Canada.

Writing Practice: Write a paragraph about holidays using comparing and contrasting sentences.

Geometry
Fill in the missing answer and draw a picture of the shape. Then solve problem 5.

1. A pentagon has **5** sides.
2. A hexagon has **6** sides.
3. An octagon has **8** sides.
4. Kelly, DeWayne, Jerika, and Edgar went to a masquerade party. They were dressed as a lion, tiger, bear, and cougar, but not in that order. Jerika was not the cougar, and Edgar's costume did not have a long tail. Kelly was either the tiger or the bear. What were each person's costume?

Kelly = tiger
DeWayne = cougar
Jerika = lion
Edgar = bear

Consonant Blends
Add two different blends (scr, spl, shr, spr, str, thr) to each word ending to make two new words.

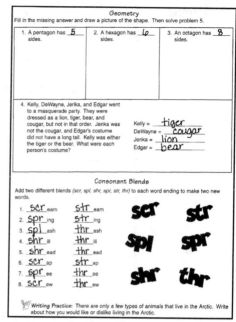

1. scr eam / str eam
2. spr ing / str ing
3. spl ash / thr ash
4. shr ill / thr ill
5. shr ead / thr ead
6. scr ap / str ap
7. spr ee / thr ee
8. scr ew / thr ew

Writing Practice: There are only a few types of animals that live in the Arctic. Write about how you would like or dislike living in the Arctic.

Geometry
Determine whether the figure is plane or solid and then solve problem 5.

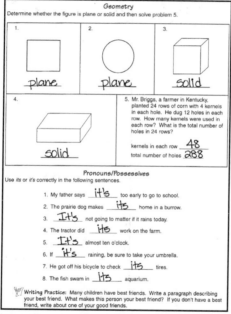

1. plane
2. plane
3. solid
4. solid
5. Mr. Briggs, a farmer in Kentucky, planted 24 rows of corn with 4 kernels in each hole. He dug 12 holes in each row. How many kernels were used in each row? What is the total number of holes in 24 rows?

kernels in each row **48**
total number of holes **288**

Pronouns/Possessives
Use its or it's correctly in the following sentences.

1. My father says ___it's___ too early to go to school.
2. The prairie dog makes ___its___ home in a burrow.
3. ___It's___ not going to matter if it rains today.
4. The tractor did ___its___ work on the farm.
5. ___It's___ almost ten o'clock.
6. If ___it's___ raining, be sure to take your umbrella.
7. He got off his bicycle to check ___its___ tires.
8. The fish swam in ___its___ aquarium.

Writing Practice: Many children have best friends. Write a paragraph describing your best friend. What makes this person your best friend? If you don't have a best friend, write about one of your good friends.

Geometry
Label each figure with its geometric name—rectangular prism, pyramid, sphere, cone, or cylinder.

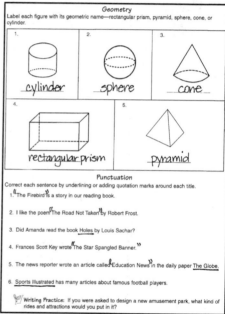

1. cylinder
2. sphere
3. cone
4. rectangular prism
5. pyramid

Punctuation
Correct each sentence by underlining or adding quotation marks around each title.

1. "The Firebird" is a story in our reading book.
2. I like the poem "The Road Not Taken" by Robert Frost.
3. Did Amanda read the book Holes by Louis Sachar?
4. Frances Scott Key wrote "The Star Spangled Banner."
5. The news reporter wrote an article called "Education News" in the daily paper The Globe.
6. Sports Illustrated has many articles about famous football players.

Writing Practice: If you were asked to design a new amusement park, what kind of rides and attractions would you put in it?

Geometry
Determine if the pair of figures is congruent or similar and then solve problem 5.

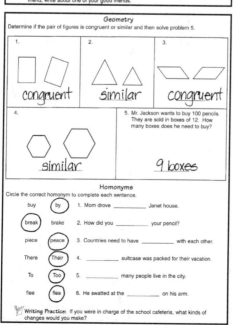

1. congruent
2. similar
3. congruent
4. similar
5. Mr. Jackson wants to buy 100 pencils. They are sold in boxes of 12. How many boxes does he need to buy?

9 boxes

Homonyms
Circle the correct homonym to complete each sentence.

buy / (by) — 1. Mom drove ___ Janet house.
(break) / brake — 2. How did you ___ your pencil?
piece / (peace) — 3. Countries need to have ___ with each other.
There / (Their) — 4. ___ suitcase was packed for their vacation.
To / (Too) — 5. ___ many people live in the city.
flee / (flea) — 6. He swatted at the ___ on his arm.

Writing Practice: If you were in charge of the school cafeteria, what kinds of changes would you make?

Geometry
Circle each pair of congruent figures. Then solve problem 5.

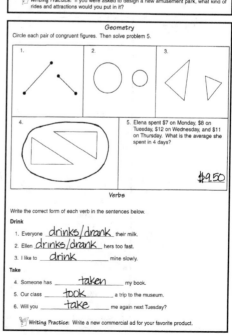

5. Elena spent $7 on Monday, $8 on Tuesday, $12 on Wednesday, and $11 on Thursday. What is the average she spent in 4 days?

$9.50

Verbs
Write the correct form of each verb in the sentences below.

Drink
1. Everyone drinks/drank their milk.
2. Ellen drinks/drank hers too fast.
3. I like to drink mine slowly.

Take
4. Someone has taken my book.
5. Our class took a trip to the museum.
6. Will you take me again next Tuesday?

Writing Practice: Write a new commercial ad for your favorite product.

Geometry
Determine if each figure has a line of symmetry. Write symmetrical or not symmetrical for each problem. Then solve problem 5.

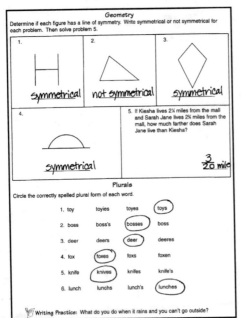

1. symmetrical
2. not symmetrical
3. symmetrical
4. symmetrical
5. If Kiesha lives 2¼ miles from the mall and Sarah Jane lives 2⅖ miles from the mall, how much farther does Sarah Jane live than Kiesha?

$\frac{3}{20}$ mile

Plurals
Circle the correctly spelled plural form of each word.

1. toy — toyies — toyes — (toys)
2. boss — boss's — (bosses) — boss
3. deer — deers — (deer) — deeres
4. fox — (foxes) — foxs — foxen
5. knife — (knives) — knifes — knife's
6. lunch — lunchs — lunch's — (lunches)

✍ **Writing Practice:** What do you do when it rains and you can't go outside?

Geometry
Write S if the figure is symmetrical or N if it is not symmetrical. Then solve problem 5.

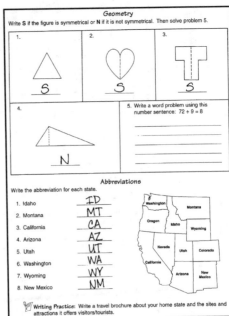

1. S
2. S
3. S
4. N
5. Write a word problem using this number sentence: 72 ÷ 9 = 8

Abbreviations
Write the abbreviation for each state.

1. Idaho — ID
2. Montana — MT
3. California — CA
4. Arizona — AZ
5. Utah — UT
6. Washington — WA
7. Wyoming — WY
8. New Mexico — NM

✍ **Writing Practice:** Write a travel brochure about your home state and the sites and attractions it offers visitors/tourists.

Geometry
Match the correct term for each pair of shapes.

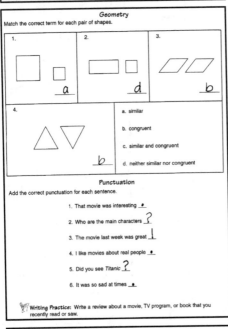

1. a
2. d
3. b
4. b

a. similar
b. congruent
c. similar and congruent
d. neither similar nor congruent

Punctuation
Add the correct punctuation for each sentence.

1. That movie was interesting **.**
2. Who are the main characters **?**
3. The movie last week was great **!**
4. I like movies about real people **.**
5. Did you see *Titanic* **?**
6. It was so sad at times **.**

✍ **Writing Practice:** Write a review about a movie, TV program, or book that you recently read or saw.

Geometry
Use the diagram to solve the problems.

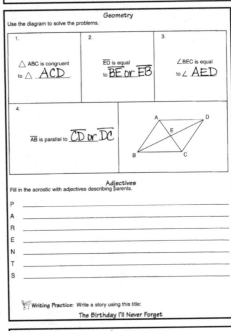

1. △ABC is congruent to △ ACD
2. $\overline{ED}$ is equal to $\overline{BE}$ or $\overline{EB}$
3. ∠BEC is equal to ∠ AED
4. $\overline{AB}$ is parallel to $\overline{CD}$ or $\overline{DC}$

Adjectives
Fill in the acrostic with adjectives describing parents.

P ____
A ____
R ____
E ____
N ____
T ____
S ____

✍ **Writing Practice:** Write a story using this title:
The Birthday I'll Never Forget

Geometry
Match each name with the correct symbol.

1. line AB — b
2. ray AB — a
3. line segment AB — c
4. vertex AB — d

a. $\overrightarrow{AB}$
b. $\overleftrightarrow{AB}$
c. $\overline{AB}$
d. ∠AB

Homonyms
Circle the correct homonym in each sentence.

1. Charlton was the first actor to come (forth/ fourth) on stage.
2. "The weather (vain, (vane)) looks like a rooster," said Meryl.
3. Sarah is (dying, (dyeing)) her dress green.
4. Margaret had a (miner/ (minor)) part in the school play.
5. The ((principal)/ principle) of the school made the morning announcements.
6. We (new/ (knew)) right away that we didn't belong in the meeting.

✍ **Writing Practice:** Write a persuasive paragraph to convince someone to recycle.

Geometry
Estimate the degrees of each angle and then solve problem 5.

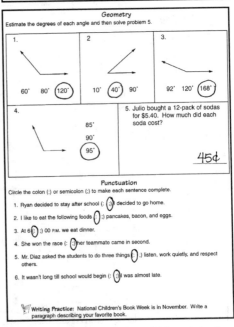

1. 60° — 80° — (120°)
2. 10° — (40°) — 90°
3. 92° — 120° — (168°)
4. 85° — 90° — (95°)
5. Julio bought a 12-pack of sodas for $5.40. How much did each soda cost?

45¢

Punctuation
Circle the colon (:) or semicolon (;) to make each sentence complete.

1. Ryan decided to stay after school (: (;)) I decided to go home.
2. I like to eat the following foods (:) ;) pancakes, bacon, and eggs.
3. At 6(:) ;) 00 P.M. we eat dinner.
4. She won the race (: (;)) her teammate came in second.
5. Mr. Diaz asked the students to do three things (:) ;) listen, work quietly, and respect others.
6. It wasn't long till school would begin (: (;)) I was almost late.

✍ **Writing Practice:** National Children's Book Week is in November. Write a paragraph describing your favorite book.

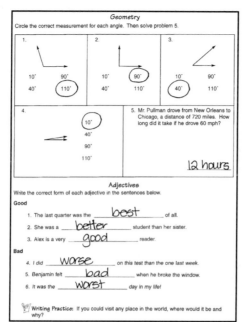

Geometry

Circle the correct measurement for each angle. Then solve problem 5.

1. 10° / (90°) / 40° / 110°

2. 10° / (90°) / 40° / 110°

3. 10° / 90° / (40°) / 110°

4. (10°) / 40° / 90° / 110°

5. Mr. Pullman drove from New Orleans to Chicago, a distance of 720 miles. How long did it take if he drove 60 mph?

12 hours

Adjectives

Write the correct form of each adjective in the sentences below.

Good

1. The last quarter was the ___best___ of all.
2. She was a ___better___ student than her sister.
3. Alex is a very ___good___ reader.

Bad

4. I did ___worse___ on this test than the one last week.
5. Benjamin felt ___bad___ when he broke the window.
6. It was the ___worst___ day in my life!

Writing Practice: If you could visit any place in the world, where would it be and why?

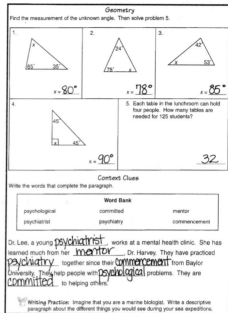

Geometry

Find the measurement of the unknown angle. Then solve problem 5.

1. 65° / 35° / x = 80°

2. 24° / 78° / x = 78°

3. 42° / 53° / x = 85°

4. 45° / 45° / x = 90°

5. Each table in the lunchroom can hold four people. How many tables are needed for 125 students?

32

Context Clues

Write the words that complete the paragraph.

Word Bank		
psychological	committed	mentor
psychiatrist	psychiatry	commencement

Dr. Lee, a young psychiatrist, works at a mental health clinic. She has learned much from her mentor, Dr. Harvey. They have practiced psychiatry together since their commencement from Baylor University. They help people with psychological problems. They are committed to helping others.

Writing Practice: Imagine that you are a marine biologist. Write a descriptive paragraph about the different things you would see during your sea expeditions.

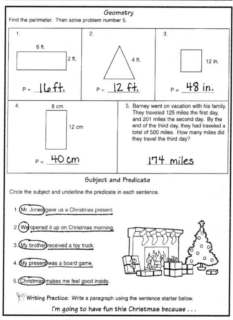

Geometry

Find the perimeter. Then solve problem number 5.

1. 6 ft / 2 ft / P = 16 ft.

2. 4 ft. / P = 12 ft.

3. 12 in. / P = 48 in.

4. 8 cm / 12 cm / P = 40 cm

5. Barney went on vacation with his family. They traveled 125 miles the first day, and 201 miles the second day. By the end of the third day, they had traveled a total of 500 miles. How many miles did they travel the third day?

174 miles

Subject and Predicate

Circle the subject and underline the predicate in each sentence.

1. (Mr. Jones) gave us a Christmas present.
2. (We) opened it up on Christmas morning.
3. (My brother) received a toy truck.
4. (My present) was a board game.
5. (Christmas) makes me feel good inside.

Writing Practice: Write a paragraph using the sentence starter below.

I'm going to have fun this Christmas because . . .

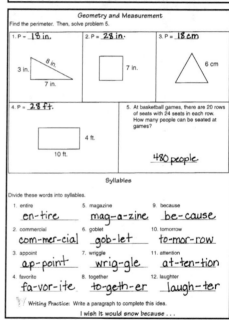

Geometry and Measurement

Find the perimeter. Then, solve problem 5.

1. P = 18 in. / 3 in. / 8 in. / 7 in.

2. P = 28 in. / 7 in.

3. P = 18 cm / 6 cm

4. P = 28 ft. / 4 ft. / 10 ft.

5. At basketball games, there are 20 rows of seats with 24 seats in each row. How many people can be seated at games?

480 people

Syllables

Divide these words into syllables.

1. entire — en-tire
2. commercial — com-mer-cial
3. appoint — ap-point
4. favorite — fa-vor-ite
5. magazine — mag-a-zine
6. goblet — gob-let
7. wriggle — wrig-gle
8. together — to-geth-er
9. because — be-cause
10. tomorrow — to-mor-row
11. attention — at-ten-tion
12. laughter — laugh-ter

Writing Practice: Write a paragraph to complete this idea.

I wish it would snow because . . .

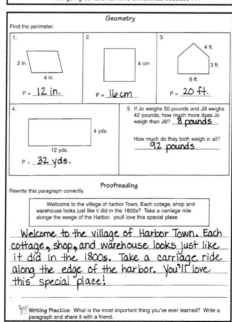

Geometry

Find the perimeter.

1. 2 in. / 4 in. / P = 12 in.

2. 4 cm / P = 16 cm

3. 4 ft / 3 ft / 6 ft. / P = 20 ft.

4. 4 yds. / 12 yds. / P = 32 yds.

5. If Jo weighs 50 pounds and Jill weighs 42 pounds, how much more does Jo weigh than Jill? 8 pounds

How much do they both weigh in all? 92 pounds

Proofreading

Rewrite this paragraph correctly.

Wellcome to the village of harbor Town, Each cotage, shop and warehouse looks just like it did in the 1800s? Take a carriage ride alonge the eeege of the Harbor. youll love this special plase

Welcome to the village of Harbor Town. Each cottage, shop, and warehouse looks just like it did in the 1800s. Take a carriage ride along the edge of the harbor. You'll love this special place!

Writing Practice: What is the most important thing you've ever learned? Write a paragraph and share it with a friend.

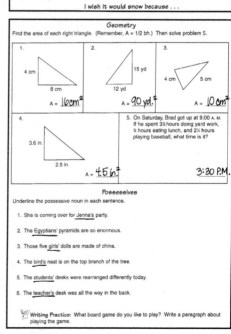

Geometry

Find the area of each right triangle. (Remember, A = 1/2 bh.) Then solve problem 5.

1. 4 cm / 8 cm / A = 16 cm²

2. 15 yd / 12 yd / A = 90 yd.²

3. 4 cm / 5 cm / A = 10 cm²

4. 3.6 in. / 2.5 in. / A = 4.5 in.²

5. On Saturday, Brad got up at 9:00 A.M. If he spent 3½ hours doing yard work, ¾ hours eating lunch, and 2¼ hours playing baseball, what time is it?

3:30 P.M.

Possessives

Underline the possessive noun in each sentence.

1. She is coming over for Jenna's party.
2. The Egyptians' pyramids are so enormous.
3. Those five girls' dolls are made of china.
4. The bird's nest is on the top branch of the tree.
5. The students' desks were rearranged differently today.
6. The teacher's desk was all the way in the back.

Writing Practice: What board game do you like to play? Write a paragraph about playing the game.

Page 299

Geometry
Find the area of each figure. (Remember, A = l x w.) Then solve problem 5.

1.
l = 12 cm
w = 32 cm
A = 384 cm²

2.
l = 18 in
w = 16.5 in
A = 297 in.²

3.
l = 4 ft.
w = 4 ft.
A = 16 ft.²

4.
l = 25 in.
w = 5 in.
A = 125 in.²

5. Marcos bought a pair of jeans at the department store for $19.99. He has to pay a 6% sales tax. What is the tax? What is his total cost?

tax: $1.20
total: $21.19

Dictionary Skills
Match the correct definition of the word *mine* that goes with each sentence.

d 1. My friend's father mined coal in Kentucky.   a. *pron.* my own

c 2. During World War II, there were many minefields in Europe.   b. *n.* excavation for coal and mineral

a 3. The pen he has is really mine.   c. *n.* buried or floating bomb

b 4. Would you like to work in a diamond mine?   d. *v.* dig for a coal or mineral

e 5. The coal miner has a dangerous job.   e. *v.* one who works in a mine

Writing Practice: Become a detective and write a mystery.

Page 300

Geometry
Find the area. Then solve problem 5.

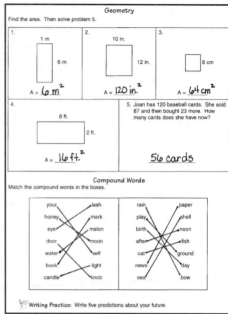

1.
1 m
6 m
A = 6 m²

2.
10 in.
12 in.
A = 120 in.²

3.
8 cm
A = 64 cm²

4.
8 ft.
2 ft.
A = 16 ft.²

5. Joan has 120 baseball cards. She sold 87 and then bought 23 more. How many cards does she have now?

56 cards

Compound Words
Match the compound words in the boxes.

your — lash
honey — mark
eye — melon
door — moon
water — self
book — light
candle — knob

rain — paper
play — shell
birth — noon
after — fish
cat — ground
news — day
sea — bow

Writing Practice: Write five predictions about your future.

Page 301

Geometry
Find the circumference of each figure. (Remember C = dπ or 2rπ. Use 3.14 for π.) Then solve for problem 5.

1.
12 cm
C = 37.68 cm

2.
6.1 cm
C = 19.154 cm

3.
8 mm
C = 50.24 cm

4.
2.5 cm
C = 15.7 cm

5. Mindy got 9 out of every 10 problems correct. If the test had 50 questions, how many problems did she answer correctly?

45

Synonyms
Circle the synonym for the first word in each row.

1. zest — clean — (enjoyment)
2. yearn — (crave) — shudder
3. potent — (value) — demerit
4. valid — powerless — (strong)
5. unfit — like — (unsuitable)
6. tremble — (shake) — calm

Writing Practice: What route do you take to get from your house to school every day? Write a set of directions.

Page 302

Geometry
Solve the problems below.

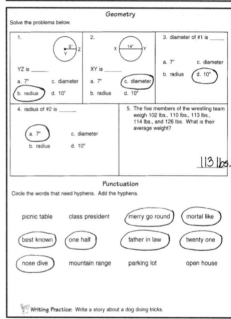

1.
5"
Y Z
YZ is _____
a. 7"   c. diameter
(b. radius)   d. 10"

2.
14"
X Y
XY is _____
a. 7"   (c. diameter)
b. radius   d. 10"

3. diameter of #1 is _____
a. 7"   c. diameter
b. radius   (d. 10")

4. radius of #2 is _____
(a. 7")   c. diameter
b. radius   d. 10"

5. The five members of the wrestling team weigh 102 lbs., 110 lbs., 113 lbs., 114 lbs., and 126 lbs. What is their average weight?

113 lbs.

Punctuation
Circle the words that need hyphens. Add the hyphens.

picnic table   class president   (merry go round)   (mortal like)
(best known)   (one half)   (father in law)   (twenty one)
(nose dive)   mountain range   parking lot   open house

Writing Practice: Write a story about a dog doing tricks.

Page 303

Geometry
Calculate the volume for each problem. (Remember, V = l x w x h.) Then solve problem 5.

1.
5 in. long
2 in. wide
7 in. high
V = 70 in.³

2.
10 cm long
4 cm wide
15 cm high
V = 600 cm³

3.
31 ft. long
6 ft. wide
20 ft. high
V = 3,720 ft.³

4.
12 yd. long
13 yd. wide
14 yd. high
V = 2,184 yd.³

5. Eddie earns $5.37 an hour after school. He worked 17 hours last week. How much did he earn?

$91.29

Main Idea
Choose the sentence that would go in a paragraph with the main idea.

1. Yellowstone National Park is a place of beautiful scenery.
a. We camped outside in the park.
(b.) The trees were tall and green.

2. There were some interesting animals at the zoo.
(a.) The bengal tiger roared loudly.
b. I enjoyed walking through the zoo.

3. The Christmas Parade had colorful floats.
a. It was so cold that we watched it on television.
(b.) The best float had Santa Claus sitting on top.

4. Yahtzee® is a fun game to play.
(a.) You roll the dice to get points.
b. I beat my brother three times.

Writing Practice: Write a persuasive paragraph explaining why you need a computer in your bedroom.

Page 304

Geometry
Calculate the volume for each problem. (Remember, V = l x w x h)

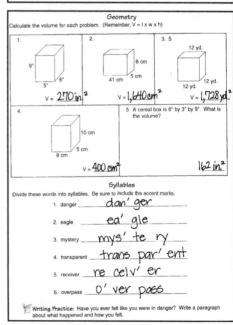

1.
9"
5" 6"
V = 270 in.²

2.
8 cm
41 cm 5 cm
V = 1,640 cm²

3. S
12 yd.
12 yd. 12 yd.
V = 1,728 yd.²

4.
10 cm
8 cm 5 cm
V = 400 cm²

5. A cereal box is 6" by 3" by 9". What is the volume?

162 in.²

Syllables
Divide these words into syllables. Be sure to include the accent marks.

1. danger   dan' ger
2. eagle   ea' gle
3. mystery   mys' te ry
4. transparent   trans par' ent
5. receiver   re ceiv' er
6. overpass   o' ver pass

Writing Practice: Have you ever felt like you were in danger? Write a paragraph about what happened and how you felt.

Award

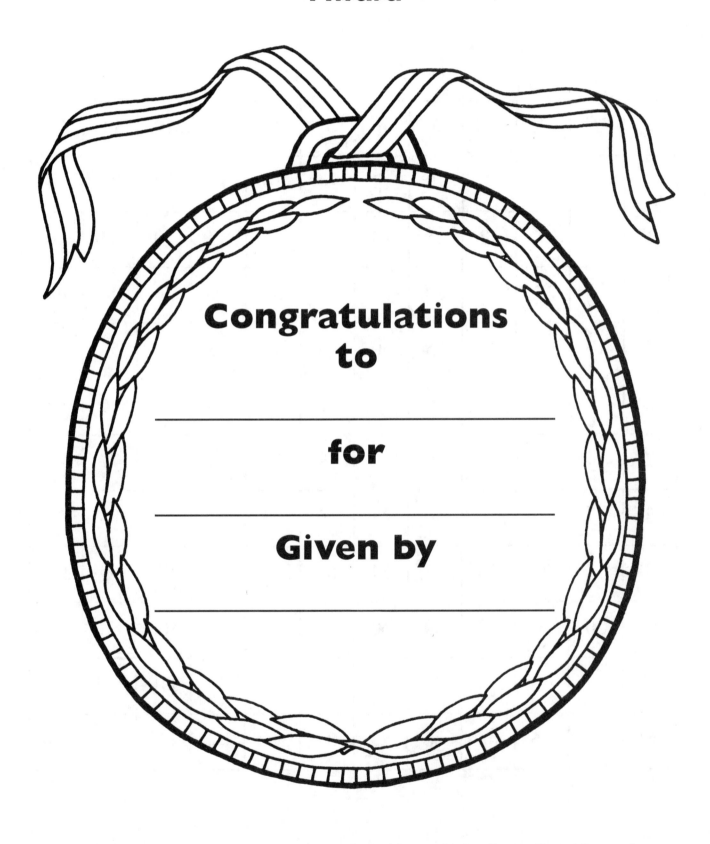

Congratulations to

_____

for

_____

Given by

_____

Multiplication Chart

1	2	3	4	5	6	7	8	9	10	11	12
2	4	6	8	10	12	14	16	18	20	22	24
3	6	9	12	15	18	21	24	27	30	33	36
4	8	12	16	20	24	28	32	36	40	44	48
5	10	15	20	25	30	35	40	45	50	55	60
6	12	18	24	30	36	42	48	54	60	66	72
7	14	21	28	35	42	49	56	63	70	77	84
8	16	24	32	40	48	56	64	72	80	88	96
9	18	27	36	45	54	63	72	81	90	99	108
10	20	30	40	50	60	70	80	90	100	110	120
11	22	33	44	55	66	77	88	99	110	121	132
12	24	36	48	60	72	84	96	108	120	132	144

Protractor and Geometric Formulas

Protractor

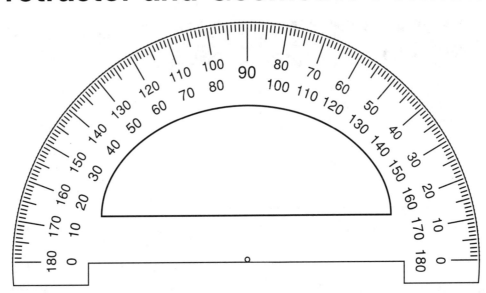

Geometric Formulas

	Area	
Figure	**Formula**	**Using the Formula**
Square	$A = s^2$	Square one side or multiply the length of one side by another.
Rectangle	$A = lw$	Multiply a length by a width.
Parallelogram	$A = \dfrac{bh}{2}$	Find the product of the length of the base and the height.
Triangle	$A = \dfrac{bh}{2}$	After multiplying the length of the base by the height, divide the product by 2.
Trapezoid	$A = \dfrac{(b_1 + b_2)h}{2}$	First, add the lengths of the parallel bases. Then, multiply the sum by the height and divide this product by 2.
Circle	$A = \pi r^2$	Find the square of the radius and multiply that number by 3.14 or 22/7 ($\pi \approx 3.14$ or 22/7). Note: If given a diameter, divide the diameter by 2 to find the radius.

Metric Conversion Chart

	Metric	Customary
Length	1 centimeter (cm) = 10 millimeters (mm) 1 meter (m) = 100 centimeters (cm) 1 kilometer (km) = 1,000 meters (m)	1 foot (ft.) = 12 inches (in.) 1 yard (yd.) = 3 feet (ft.) 1 mile (mi.) = 5,280 feet (ft.) 1 mile (mi.) = 1,760 yards (yd.)
Volume	1 liter (L) = 1,000 milliliters (mL)	1 cup (c.) = 8 ounces (oz.) 1 pint (pt.) = 2 cups (c.) 1 quart (qt.) = 2 pints (pt.) 1 gallon (gal.) = 128 ounces (oz.) 1 gallon (gal.) = 4 quarts (qt.)
Weight	1 gram (g) = 1,000 milligrams (mg) 1 kilogram (kg) = 1,000 grams (g)	1 pound (lb.) = 16 ounces (oz.) 1 ton = 2,000 pounds (lb.)

	*Changing Customary to Metric	*Changing Metric to Customary Length
Length	1 inch = 2.54 centimeters 1 foot = 30 centimeters 1 yard = 0.91 meters 1 mile = 1.6 kilometers	1 centimeter = 0.4 inches 1 meter = 1.09 yards 1 kilometer = 0.62 miles
Volume	1 cup = 240 milliliters 1 pint = 0.47 liters 1 quart = 0.95 liters 1 gallon = 3.79 liters	1 liter = 1.06 quarts 1 liter = 0.26 gallons
Weight	1 ounce = 28.4 grams 1 pound = 0.45 kilograms	1 gram = 0.035 ounces 1 kilogram = 2.21 pounds

* Approximations

My Writing Journal

Writing Journal